OIL PAPER FAMILY

OIL PAPER FAMILY

BY MELANIE KIM

NEW DEGREE PRESS

OIL PAPER FAMILY

ISBN   978-1-63730-804-2   *Paperback*
              978-1-63730-863-9   *Kindle Ebook*
              978-1-63730-984-1   *Ebook*

To my family

TABLE OF CONTENTS

NOTE FROM THE AUTHOR

———

I have always been curious about my grandfather's story. I could see it in the scribbled questions I asked him in fourth grade, the way my notes went off into the margins and the words blended together because I was writing too fast. I was excited to hear these stories, little tidbits of a past that was mine but was also not.

I can't remember exactly what sparked the journey toward this book, but I do remember the picture of my grandfather's mother in his office. Among pictures of award ceremonies, his children, and his grandchildren, she was always smiling.

She looked so much like my grandfather. The same wide jaw, the same ears, the same lined forehead. There were so many stories in her face and so many unspoken words. I wanted to know more.

I spent a year and a half interviewing my grandfather. Spring and summer of my junior year of high school slipped into fall and winter and spring of my senior year. My grandfather and I spent countless hours together in his office, a room with a little alcove window and boxes upon boxes of dusty papers. It was almost always afternoon, and the dust motes floated down around his head as we sipped water and ate sliced watermelon and talked. Over the course of the three or so years after, I began to piece together the stories my grandfather told me, weaving them into a cohesive narrative and into this book you are holding now.

To me, my grandfather had always been just my grandfather—kind-hearted, deeply intelligent, quick to smile, and always ready with his shirt pocket full of his favorite blue pens. But in that cluttered office, I began to see the story of his life unfold. The more we talked, the more I was struck by the fact that he could smile and laugh; the fact that he even sat in front of me was a miracle.

That's something I hope you, the reader, will not miss either. I hope you ask questions and take the time to listen to the stories of a loved one. I hope you get to hold their hand when they're crying, when they laugh, when they tell you something they've never told anyone else. I hope you get to see that beautifully intimate moment when they are talking about the person whom they love best in the entire world.

My grandfather's story is a part of mine. Though I never lived through what he did, his past is not removed from mine. His blood courses through my veins, and his past is just a thread in the richer tapestry of the history of my heritage. It's a history that is not just Korean but also is a story of humanity and resilience and strength.

As a third-generation Korean American who has set foot in Korea only once in my life, I truly knew nothing about my heritage. I didn't speak the language beyond the New Year's blessing or a few choice food dishes. I knew very little about Korean culture or history beyond the brief mentions of the Korean War in class or the guilty pleasure of late-night

K-dramas. It certainly made the entire book writing process more difficult, and I worried often about its effect on this entire project. However, at the same time, because I knew so little about this topic, I approached it at first as many readers might, with wide-eyed curiosity and a thirst for knowledge and truth. I had the opportunity to center around the particular experience of my grandfather with the background of such key historical moments as the Japanese occupation of Korea, the March First Movement, the Korean War, and Communist rule. In this journey of combing through books and primary sources and old footage, I've developed a deeper connection to my heritage and to my grandfather.

Maybe I started writing this book for myself. I always wanted to be an author. But to say that was all would reduce the vast canvas of this story. To say that would rob my grandfather of the vulnerability and the realism and the emotion of his story.

I wrote this book because of how my grandfather looked while he was telling me the stories of his life. Immense pain and sorrow, guilt and joy were etched into the lines of his face. Much of his story was told as he tumbled over words, repeating stories and misremembering and re-remembering. Telling circuitously, not telling, and telling too much. A human voice illustrating the blank landscape of history in my head, populating it with faces of family members and friends, with dramatic events and color and life. When he held my hand and told me about his siblings and his mother, when I saw so much passion and life and resilience…how could I *not* write this book?

So, I hope my grandfather's story will be more than just a brief read. I hope for other Korean Americans like me and for anyone interested in underrepresented history, this guides you to ask your loved ones about their stories, too. I hope it explores the broader themes of humanity and war and family love. I hope you can see my grandfather as he is: a man who lived through decades of conflict and war and emerged flawed, but resilient and strong.

A man who I am so proud to call my grandfather.

***

All the events I have written about are true; only the names have been changed to protect people's identities.

CHAPTER ONE

It was 1921, and Sang Chul's newly wed bride, Yang Sil, was fourteen.

They were a quiet procession slipping into the fog of an early morning, avoiding the stares of neighbors and officials. Yang Sil sat in the swaying wedding litter, an enclosed wooden box raised by poles on the shoulders of her husband and one of his brothers. Her heart thumped rapidly. If they were caught, would they be shot on the spot? It was all too clear they were fleeing into the mountains. Would they be arrested?

She could hear her father-in-law walking ahead, occasionally turning to breathe a word of warning about a loose rock, a low-hanging branch. They stopped at the sound of footsteps crunching over leaves. Yang Sil could see nothing from inside the litter, and she froze, hardly daring to breathe, lest the crinkling fabric of her dress give them away.

She had heard horrible stories about those who disappeared into the prisons. Brutal beatings that made faces unrecognizable beneath blood and bruises. Whippings that left the buttocks flayed almost like the thin strips of raw beef her mother bought at the market. What more would they do to her, a young woman? And what about these men who carried her into the mountains? Would they leave her and run if they heard the shouts of Japanese soldiers? Would they be willing to sacrifice their lives just to save hers?

It was just a pair of deer.

As they climbed deeper into the forest, the singing rumble of cicadas overwhelmed them.

Yang Sil could not keep back the flood of her thoughts. There had been no time for a full wedding ceremony, no time to decorate the litter with colored tassels and paintings of pairs of birds and fish to express wishes for the couple's harmony. Barely any time to say goodbye to her family and hurriedly fold away a few clothing items into a little sack.

A little wet puddle of tears grew on her skirt, and Yang Sil's palms were full of crescent moon indentations from clenching her fists.

Just a few months ago, she had promised her parents she would be brave. She had promised herself she would never cry. Just a few months ago, she had peered around the corner of a doorframe and listened to her father-in-law-to-be, Kim Chul Soo, talk about how he feared reprisal from the Japanese government. Though the Japanese government officials had shed their military uniforms and violence, threats by the Japanese officials had lessened, and vernacular newspapers had reopened, he still feared. It was 1920, and there had been ten years of Japanese occupation in Korea. If Chul Soo had learned anything, it was that the Japanese would not see him as an equal. It was that behind the written edicts and spoken words of a "cultural rule" and relaxation, he saw the hardness in the eyes of the Japanese colonizers. It was that these heavy feet did not belong on the soil of his ancestors, that these mouths that had spit insults and these hands that had wrung blood and tears from his nation could never be trusted. He planned to slip away into a mountain village in Koksan, in the Northern HwangHaeDo province. Tucked away among the jagged ridges and thick forests of oak, Kim Chul Soo hoped to continue his practice of the Chondogyo religion without any interference from the Japanese.

Practically everyone knew the history of Chondogyo, which had been created by Suun Choe Je-U in 1860 under the name of Donghak, Eastern Learning. People recalled differently whether there were a hundred thousand members or over three million by the early 1900s. Regardless, Donghak (termed Chondogyo only in 1905) was characterized by its involvement in social movements. Followers of the religion fought for freedom of worship, the end of governmental corruption, and the elimination of foreign influences. They led popular uprisings in 1871, again in 1892, and 1894. With this came persecution: first by the Korean government and later by the Japanese government. Suun Choe Je-U was beheaded in 1864. Pain and persecution extended to the other leaders of Chondogyo and thousands of protestors. In 1919, thirty-three individuals signed a Korean Declaration of Independence from Japan, fifteen of whom were members of Chondogyo. It was from the violence that followed in the wake of this movement that Chul Soo fled.

Chul Soo's four sons had demanded to follow him, feverish in their anti-Japanese sentiment. It was impossible for them to continue to live as they were: second-class citizens in their own nation. They agreed they would spread out in all four directions in the mountains, each with their families and a few sacks of seeds. This way, even if one of them were caught, the others would be free to continue living safely. They would never know where the others lived. Maybe in a year, ten years, fifty years, they could finally emerge into a new and safer world. That was their hope, and Yang Sil was swept up into it.

Yang Sil allowed herself a few more tears of self-pity as she sat in the gently rocking litter. The unfamiliar voices of her husband and his brother were rough to her ears. She clutched her skirt. To marry a man she had never met, this she accepted. Her parents and her husband's parents had planned this union nearly from her birth. But to leave her entire family behind, to go into the wilderness with this strange wide-jawed man, to live as his wife in a home not yet built…how could she bear such a burden?

Sang Chul's brother began teasing the groom with the *sillangdarugi* that was usually a whole family affair, though primarily of the male relatives, to embarrass the newlywed couple. Yang Sil cringed away from the crass remarks, surely spoken more loudly for her benefit. The bridal clothing was scratchy. The men stopped for a drink of water and the jolting of the litter dropped tears into her lap. *Umma*, she wanted to call. *Mom. Is this what it means to love someone? That when you leave, your heart aches like this. This dull and terrible ache deep in my chest.* She shook her head and clenched her fists. *Yang Sil, you promised you wouldn't cry.*

When they resumed their journey, Yang Sil could feel the climb becoming steeper. Holding her knees tight against her chest, she held back her instinct to squeak when she felt the litter tip. The hum of cicadas was suffocatingly loud as the sun rose.

They had been traveling for a few hours when Yang Sil heard her father-in-law gently calling, "*Aga*, child, come on out for *shi*."

She had felt the press of her bladder for at least an hour, but she had been embarrassed to ask to urinate in the presence of three men. She was thankful for her father-in-law. Her mother had warned Yang Sil that her father-in-law would be remote and distant, but Chul Soo treated her kindly, and his stern eyes were not nearly so hard and angry as she would have expected for a man so fiercely against the Japanese. The word *shi*, too, was familiar and comfortable. She remembered cold nights with her younger siblings, holding their hands to walk to the toilet outside. Crouching beside them and murmuring, *shi*.

Yang Sil was grateful, too, that her father-in-law, and not her husband, had come with her to hold up her skirts as she relieved herself. She did not have to fear the tigers either, not next to this man with his fierce eyes and quiet strength.

Yang Sil clambered back into the litter, rubbing the cramped muscles in her legs. They traveled for several more hours in this way, after which Sang Chul's brother bid his farewells.

***

Over the course of the year, Sang Chul and Yang Sil worked hard to open up a clearing and build a small hut. Sang Chul wrestled with the remaining stumps for hours, while Yang Sil steadily cut away at the grass and weeds. They had brought a few sacks of seeds with them, and they planted these and watered them with buckets of water from a nearby stream. They had only each other to talk to, but Sang Chul had very little to say and spent most of his time sitting in the doorway of the house staring out in stony silence. In the humid summer downpours of rain, the receding heat of fall, and then the blisteringly cold winter, a backbreaking year passed.

A month after Yang Sil turned fifteen, Sang Chul disappeared from the home without warning or explanation.

Yang Sil waited a week, then two. The wailing sound of animals calling out in the night became the anthem of her heart. Alone.

Surely, he would have left some word if he had intended to make a long journey. Maybe he was visiting one of his brothers? Maybe his father?

After a month, Yang Sil no longer waited at night for the sound of returning footsteps nor did she look up when the trees rustled as she worked in the field. Rather than curse Sang Chul's name, she worked steadily onward, tending the crops, preparing food, mending her worn clothing, patching leaks in the thatched roof, and fighting back the ever-encroaching shrubs and weeds. The long and difficult hours in the field left little time for thought.

Nighttime, however, was a different matter. At nighttime, the forest breathed, and she felt its resistance to her presence, her footsteps, her destruction of its trees, her fight to keep open the small clearing, to resist the swallow of nature. Rubbing her blistered fingers and sore arms, she thought about her father and mother and siblings, picturing their faces in front of her. Other times, she thought about Sang Chul, the man she hardly knew.

The man who had abandoned her.

She thought about the betrothal process that had started even before she was born. She imagined her parents and Sang Chul's parents sitting together on some warm summer evening, drinking rice wine together in the courtyard of one of their houses, saying, *If we ever have a daughter, and you a son, they shall be married.*

When she was ten, the long process of the customary *uihon* began: discussing her and Sang Chul's age, their surnames, ancestral origins, family status, and traditions. Sang Chul's family's proposal, and her own family's acceptance, of it. The fortune teller who had predicted the future of their life as a couple and read Sang Chul's horoscopic data. Later, the decision of Yang Sil's family on the date of the wedding.

She remembered the little thrill of excitement when Sang Chul's friend had delivered the traditional wooden chest of silks and a *yejangji*, letter of appreciation. How beautiful the red and blue silks had seemed against the white and gray clothing with which she was accustomed! She had looked forward to the ceremony, the gifts, the clothing, the food, the smiling faces of all her family members and friends watching her approach true adulthood.

But the rest of the traditional marriage practices had been cut out in a frenzied rush to flee into the mountains. It was a marriage with just the prayer of her father-in-law over the two newlyweds. She had never even met Sang Chul until the day of the ceremony. There was nothing familiar about his rough manner, well-built body, or crooked smile.

Sang Chul. Why did you abandon me?

Now at nights, the mat next to her was empty. Sang Chul's farming tools stood still in a corner of the room. Yang Sil cooked too much food in the beginning, expecting him to come through the door when the sun set or when it rose again. The rice stuck in the pot, and she had to scrape it out and eat it herself rather than let it go to waste. Had he always eaten this much food? There was only one bowl to wash now. One pair of chopsticks. One set of socks to darn. One. One. One. Pounded into her head again and again. *You are alone.*

Yang Sil visited her father-in-law's home with some frequency, which was only a little distance from Sang Chul's plot of land. Sometimes she wondered if it had been intentional so he could help care for her, a young wife new to bearing all the burdens of a home on her shoulders. Other times she wondered if he perhaps knew Sang Chul's character and had predicted his disappearance.

The few others who had hidden away in the mountainside nearby were followers of Chondogyo, scattered within a few miles of their leader, Chul Soo. He was well-respected for his purity and godliness.

Sometimes when Yang Sil visited him, Chul Soo sat in the doorway of his home, and they looked out together across the small, cultivated field and the thick border of trees. Chul Soo's voice rose gently over the sound of rustling leaves as he explained Chondogyo and his belief in the oneness of man with God.

Occasionally, Yang Sil's visits to her father-in-law coincided with the daily Chondogyo ceremonies. She heard the *jumun*, incantations seeking oneness with God. A bowl of clear water on a table represented spiritual purity, and worshippers sat nearby to meditate on its significance. The prayer, *kido*, occurred during all ceremonies. The people sat in silent meditative prayer known as the *simgo*, or heart's address.

On one occasion, Chul Soo entered a forty-day fast. Every day, he knelt by the mountain spring, his long beard drooping to his knees, and filled a brass bowl with clear water. After praying and silently meditating over the water, he lifted it to his lips and drained it. When the forty days had passed, he emerged from his solitude, and the people around him bowed deeply: "How holy is he! He is like God!"

Laughingly, as Yang Sil would often tell her family later, "If God saved your grandfather, then I am God, because every day I added honey to his water!"

***

Shortly after Yang Sil turned sixteen, it came time to sell the year's harvest at the market. It was her father's birthday as well, and Yang Sil asked for her father-in-law's permission to visit her parents. Chul Soo agreed. He did not make eye contact with her, and she sensed pity in his stern and quiet goodbye.

Yang Sil had already made up her mind that she would not return to that lonely hut in the mountains. As she clambered down the mountain with the large bundle of her harvest strapped to her back in a rough straw sack, she was already convinced she would live with her parents, even if it was for the rest of her life. She would never go back to that terrible mountain. Sang Chul was not her husband anymore. She would just live at home. Home...home was where she belonged.

With a pocketful of crumpled money from the market, Yang Sil ran toward her home, desperate to run into her parents' arms and tell them of her struggles in the past year, her tears, her victories. She ran through the gate to the courtyard. Her father would be sitting on the warm floor, eyes closed in a blissful moment of quiet rest. Her mother would be in the kitchen, stoking the fire to heat the floor and begin cooking the evening meal. It would be so good just to see their faces again, to hear their voices. She threw open the front door. They would say, "Daughter, you came? We—"

Yang Sil froze.

Sang Chul was staring at her, a cup of warm tea in his hand.

CHAPTER TWO

———

The empty water bucket clattered on the kitchen floor as Yang Sil scrambled for its handle. Her hands trembled and she balled them into fists around the handle. *Breathe, Yang Sil.* She lifted the bucket on top of her head with both hands, and without a word, she shoved past Sang Chul and ran from the house in the direction of the neighborhood well.

Sang Chul was on his feet immediately, and Yang Sil could hear his heavy footsteps quickening as he caught up to her. He breathed heavily as he pulled her arm and forced her to face him. The bucket fell to the ground. "Why did you run away? You didn't even say hello."

She ignored him, bending to pick up the fallen bucket.

"Yang Sil!" He jerked her arm. The bucket tumbled in the dirt again. "Why did you run away?"

She yanked her arm out of his grasp and glared up at him. "Why are you in my parents' home? And who do you think you are to talk to me like that? You are nobody to me. You left me in the mountains. Did you forget that? You ran away…you left me without telling me anything. Not even a single word!" Her voice rose a pitch and angry tears glistened in her eyes.

"Do you know how hard I had to work? Do you know how lonely I was on that farm for a whole year by myself?" She turned away from him. "I'm not going to talk to you anymore. I won't see you. You ran away, you coward." She snatched up the bucket.

Heads were turning to watch them, village busybodies and young girls whispering on their way to the well.

"What did you say? Coward?" Sang Chul's voice was incredulous. "Coward?" He stood huffing angrily with his hands behind his head, shifting from foot to foot. "How could you say...I... *Aish...* " He drew close and spoke in a hushed tone, though there was a sharp bite behind his words. "So? Would you like to go back and live there? You fool, you don't want to live there; you don't want to go back. *I* can't live there; *I* can't go back there either."

Yang Sil started walking away. Fool? How dare he call her a fool!

Sang Chul followed her. "I've rented out a room, a single room. I knew that someday you would come back to your parents. You ask them! I've been at their home faithfully working, waiting for you to return. Finally, you came." He sped up his pace to match hers, straining to meet her eyes. "You should not go back."

Yang Sil didn't say anything but continued to the well, where she filled the bucket. Sang Chul watched her, noting the wiry muscle of her arms, her tanned complexion, her glaring eyes.

They walked back together in silence on opposite sides of the road. Yang Sil leaned away from him, balancing the bucket on her head.

After Yang Sil greeted her parents, they were enthusiastic in telling her about her husband's efforts to rent a home for her in Pyongyang.

"Your husband, he carried this much dirt on his back. Like this, like this." Her father hunched down and mimed carrying a heavy load on his back with a strained face. "So much dirt from the countryside, and he carried it to Pyongyang to sell for the floors of homes."

Her husband? He was away for an entire year, and suddenly he was her husband again? Yang Sil struggled to keep a blank expression on her face.

Sang Chul leaped in, too. "When I earned some money, I bought a handcart, and then later an ox to pull the cart. I saved it all to buy a home for us." He spoke more gently now. "Would you like to go with me there?"

Yang Sil stared at the smiling and nodding faces of her mother and father. What would she do if she didn't go with this man? Would she stay forever in her parents' home? She could only bring shame on them, a disobedient daughter who had broken off her marriage, a burden on the household. And this man…his husband of hers. He had done the unforgivable and yet…he hadn't truly abandoned her. He promised her a home. It was true he had never apologized, but she already expected very little from him. What choice did she really have?

Yang Sil nodded. "I'll go with you."

Within a year, Yang Sil's first child was born. Yang Sil was overjoyed with the birth of a son with a little pouting mouth and wildly flailing limbs. *Strong like his father*, she joked, when a little fist met her face while he was feeding.

Cheotjjae was to be only the first of seven children born over a twenty-one-year period. For twenty-one years, Yang Sil would breastfeed her little suckling children. For twenty-one years, she would sleep on a thin cotton mat on the floor, waking to the sound of their mewling cries. For twenty-one years she would wake in a damp bed, sighing as her children wet the bed through the pieces of cotton she used as diapers.

When Cheotjjae had turned three and Yang Sil's milk had finally run dry, Yang Sil became pregnant with her second son. Soon after Duljjae was born, Yang Sil's elder brother traveled the twenty miles to Pyongyang from his town. He appeared at her home smiling, holding a basket of apples from his farm.

"Congratulations, Dongsaeng!" Yang Sil knew what her brother was going to say before he even opened his mouth. "You know my wife and I have no children…" He clasped his hands together and smiled widely. "You already have such a strong and beautiful son, Cheotjjae. Now you have been blessed with a second son! We would take good care of Duljjae and raise him as our own."

Sang Chul agreed immediately. "Of course, brother-in-law." Sang Chul was building up a tidy sum of savings, but it would help his family of four if one small body were cared for elsewhere. After all, it was not unusual for those with several children to give to those relatives without.

Yang Sil, however, was hesitant. This tiny child in her arms was her son, her dear Duljjae. Her body had fought for his birth, and he was such a small child, too. Small and sickly and weak. And so, she said to her brother, "Oppa, my Duljjae is not healthy. See how small and thin he is? He will not grow up to be strong like his brother. I cannot give you a weak child, but my next son…when I have him, I will give him to you."

Young Bok was born in 1929, three years later, and again, Yang Sil's brother appeared at the doorstep with a basket of fruit. "Dongsaeng." He was beaming. This son was healthy; he had heard word from Sang Chul already.

Yang Sil looked down at her infant son and stroked back wispy strands of hair. "Oppa, I cannot give my Young Bok to you."

Her brother let his arms fall limply to his sides.

"I had a *tae mong,* a conception dream," Yang Sil continued. She broke her gaze upon Young Bok and met her brother's eyes. "Because of my son, the whole village gathered around me and lifted me up, praising me as a queen and giving me blessings and glory. This son will be a precious one. I cannot give him up. I'm sorry, Oppa."

Her brother hardly let her finish her sentence. "I don't need your children. One is too sickly," he gestured roughly, "and the other is too good and precious. I don't want any of your children." He bowed quickly and with scarcely a pause, he walked out the gate, still clutching the basket of apples.

Yang Sil told this story to Young Bok frequently, stroking his head affectionately. "My Setjjae, third child, you were too precious."

CHAPTER THREE

———

One cool fall day, a tall stranger stood hesitating at the gateway of the Kims' home. He shaded his eyes from the sun and stood swinging his arms slowly back and forth for some time before he noticed Young Bok, a toddler, playing in the dirt of the courtyard. Then he smiled, grasped his knapsack strap a little more tightly, and crossed into the courtyard. Yang Sil peered out of the kitchen at the sound of footsteps. Sang Chul did too, but when he saw the bowing figure of the young man, he immediately disappeared into the home without a greeting. Yang Sil, however, emerged to gently press the stranger's hand and invite him into the home. Sang Chul reappeared after a few moments, laughing, though his eyes shone a bit too brightly. "Cheotjjae, Duljjae, Setjjae, this is your *sachon*, your cousin."

The man was young, and he had a quick and easy smile. Young Bok immediately liked him. When he scooped Young Bok up onto his back, Young Bok smelled sweat and dirt and the sweet, earthy fragrance of oak trees.

That afternoon, the whole family spent a few hours walking through the shops of Pyongyang. Cheotjjae and

Duljjae clutched their cousin's hands while Young Bok clung happily to his cousin's broad back. Sang Chul kept one hand resting on his nephew's shoulder as though he were afraid he might vanish.

"Who's your dad, Sachon?" Young Bok piped.

"My Appa is… He's your Appa's older brother."

"Where do you live, Sachon?" Young Bok peered up at his cousin's face.

A little hushed, he said, "In the Koksan. Far, far away in those big, tall mountains over there. But quiet; that's a secret, baby."

Young Bok nodded, covering his mouth with both hands. "A secret," he whispered. He was quickly distracted by a beautiful figure with sparkling eyes in a shop window. "The people are so pretty! Why don't they move?"

They all laughed now. "It's a mannequin, baby. Not a real person."

***

After this visit, Young Bok never saw his cousin again. Young Bok's memory of his cousin's face and name faded away with time. He could not love or miss his other relatives because he had never seen them. He did not know their names or faces, and Sang Chul never talked about them. Never.

Even in 1945, when the Japanese fled Korea, scattering like crumpled, dry leaves into the winds of surrender, Young Bok's grandfather, uncles, aunts, and cousins did not leave the deep mountains of Koksan. Were they unable to hear the news that the occupation was over? Were they dead? These questions went unanswered.

Yet, despite his silence, Sang Chul dusted a little photograph of his father, Kim Chul Soo, every day, and he stared at it often with a silent shame and longing. Young Bok wondered if he ever thought about searching for his family. But then again, even if he scoured the entire mountain range and found them, could he have faced them? Guilt was like a great gong ringing the song of betrayal over and over again in Sang Chul's head. Even as time passed, he could still hear it ringing on and on every day, and it left him angry, with tightened shoulders and gritted teeth. *Traitor. Coward. You abandoned your family. You. Are. A. Coward.* Young Bok wondered if this was why his father hated the Japanese so much, why he called them *jjokbari* all the time. It was a penance of sorts. Though he had abandoned his family, he would not abandon the resistance they fought for.

Though Young Bok had never met his grandfather, he had memorized the man's face through that single photograph. It gave him shivers, the way Kim Chul Soo's eyes followed him as he moved about the house. He was unsmiling, tendrils of white hair sprouting from his head, upper lip, and chin. Young Bok imagined them stroking the ground, growing gray from dust, tangled by wind, but then being stubbornly reprimanded by the grimacing man: "This hair is God-given, so I do not cut it." Sometimes Young Bok squinted at the photograph, holding up his fingers to cover certain parts of the face. Yes, he could see his father's nose there, maybe his own eyebrows, his elder brother's jawline. Breaking this man down into small pieces of inherited features somehow softened the hard-set sternness of his face.

Sang Chul's eyes grew stormy whenever Chul Soo was mentioned, and he became dangerously quiet. Yang Sil tried to fill the silence with stories, gathering her children around and willingly setting aside the work she had on hand. Yang Sil was a good storyteller. Her voice was smooth and did not trip over the flow of a sentence or the rhythm of a passage. When Sang Chul fell into these moods, it was Yang Sil who told her children stories of their grandfather and began to draw them into the history of their family and their nation. Always, she returned to the March First Movement. It had been an unprecedented moment when it felt as though all of Korea had finally united against the colonialism of Japan and the heavy yoke of imperialism.

On March 3, 1919, the Japanese had decided that there would be a funeral for our emperor Gojong, began Yang Sil. *The Japanese called him a "Japanese prince" when he was truly **our** emperor, the last one who ruled us. A king of the Choseon dynasty and an Emperor of the Korean Empire. There were rumors that he had been poisoned by the Japanese. The people were angry. Caught like fish in a stream too shallow, they finally strove for deeper, stronger waters.*

For the first time in nine years, a large number of Koreans would be able to gather in a public place. They wrote a Proclamation of Independence, and everyone talked about it. Pamphlets told about a meeting where the Declaration would be read throughout the country. They said that we could finally be free from the Japanese, that if we just gathered together peacefully and respectfully that the Japanese would have to listen to our demands.

When he lost himself in the rhythmic passage of his mother's words, Young Bok could envision the past before him clearly, like the pictures in a finely illustrated book.

School boys slipped copies of the Declaration of Independence under the gates of houses. Some of them smeared, ink still wet from the churning of the mimeographs. Thousands of copies of this document spread throughout the country: powerful and rousing words that ignited the trampled spirit of Koreans.

Son Byong-hi, a Korean independence activist, said, "It is not that we can regain independence right away with our street demonstrations, shouting 'Manse!' (Long live Korea!), but I will take a part in the demonstration to awaken the spirit of independence in the hearts of our brethren" ("3.1운동 대한민국임시정부 100주년 기념사업위원회").

The Paris Peace Conference was still in session, and leaders of the Korean national independence movement judged this as the ideal moment to inform the world of the Korean people's determination to seek independence. Surely peaceful, organized mass protests would gain the Korean people a hearing at Versailles. Surely President Wilson, the champion of democracy who had recently released the Fourteen Points, would hear the Korean people's cries for self-determination and grant Korea its freedom.

There were printed leaflets with slogans, posters, manifestos of the planned demonstrations, guidelines for the objectives of the protests, and written warnings and threats calling for public officials to resign and for the Japanese to leave the country. An underground newspaper, *Joseon Dongnip Shinmun* (*The Independent*), was circulated throughout Kyungsung, present-day Seoul, to inform Koreans how the street demonstrations would be carried out.

On the afternoon of March 1, 1919, the schools of Kyungsung emptied into the streets. They had heard from student leaders that the signers of the Declaration of Independence had planned a reading of the Declaration in the Pagoda Park that afternoon. By two o'clock, nearly five thousand people gathered in the park, milling about expectantly. None of the signers appeared. The crowd was in danger of dispersing until a man in traditional white Korean clothing scrambled up a small platform and waved a crumpled copy of the Declaration of Independence. In a loud voice, he read the entire Declaration. The crowd answered in a roar of voices and a student leader raised a walking stick in the air. "Long live Korean Independence," he shouted, and the crowd erupted, "Korean Independence *Manse!*" They surged out the front gate of Pagoda Park. Throughout the city, cheers for Korean Independence spread. Korean flags waved high for the first time in years, and students passed out copies of the declaration. Workers, shop owners, men, women, and children joined the demonstrating students in the streets. They split up throughout the city: to the gate of Toksu Palace where Emperor Gojong's body rested, to the American Consulate, the Kyungsung Post Office, the Army Infantry Headquarters, the Government-General Building.

In Sonchon, Anju, Chinampo, Wonsan, Kaesong, Wiju, and Pyongyang, cities across the entire nation, similar demonstrations occurred.

In Pyongyang, at least three thousand people crowded together on March 1. They listened to a memorial for the late emperor, a benediction, and some passages from the Bible. The rumbling of a crowd trembled to a halt as another man in white rose to the podium. Chung Il Sun, a member of the Fourth Church in Pyongyang. The man's voice shook with emotion, and the crowd felt his anticipation and leaned in close. "It is the happiest and proudest day of my life and though I may die tomorrow, I cannot help but read it," said Chung Ilsun (Korean Independence Outbreak Collection). His voice steadied and rang strong and clear over the heads of the thousands gathered. "We proclaim herewith, Korea an independent state and her people free. We announce it to the nations of the world, and so make known the great truth of the equality of all humanity..." (Korean Independence Outbreak Collection).

It was a powerful Declaration of Independence drafted by thirty-three men from several backgrounds: Christianity, Chondoism, Buddhism, academia. A roaring cheer rose from the people, joyful shouts, the rustle of a thousand arms raised in excitement. Armloads of small Korean flags were passed out to the crowd, and as a large Korean flag flared out from the wall behind the podium, the crowd roared, "Korean Independence *Manse! Manse!*"

"Flags! Our Taegeukgi, our national flag." And Young Bok was brought back to his mother's voice and to the courtyard of their home.

Sang Chul would interrupt here sometimes to sketch out the flag on the dirt floor of the courtyard. "The center is the yin and yang, the opposites of light and dark, good and evil," Sang Chul said. "And these lines, these represent heaven. This is earth. Fire and then water." Neither Cheotjjae, Duljjae, nor Young Bok had ever seen the real Korean flag. This phantom version of it, contraband and covertly drawn in the dirt, was the extent of their knowledge.

"I helped my mother make one. There were other students, too, who made them," said Sang Chul. "We sang *Aegukga*, our national anthem. It had been banned since 1910 when Japan annexed Korea."

"The flags were everywhere." Yang Sil nodded. "Do you know how beautiful it was to see them waving like that? To look out at the crowds of people and realize we were not ashamed, that we were united as Koreans. To hear the song of our country and to feel everyone around us singing, too..."

Yang Sil resumed her story: *When a company of policemen, some Japanese and some Korean, marched through the assembly and demanded quiet, the crowd grew hushed, tense in anticipation. The police pulled flags from the hands of all the gathered people. Some schoolboys refused to let go, playing a dangerous game of tug-of-rope until the leaders on the podium asked them to give up the flags.*

Young Bok slipped back into the rhythm of his mother's words.

After speaking with the police, the leaders told the people to disperse. No movement. A half hour passed, and this time the chief of police tried. Again, no movement. Eventually, the police filed out and the crowd followed soon after, fusing with the masses of people already in the streets. It seemed as though the whole town was present, shouting wildly. All shop windows and doors were closed, and people pressed into the already crowded streets.

But that was where Yang Sil always stopped speaking. She could never tell more, only shook her head and sighed deeply. It was at this time when she would stand up again and return to cooking or weaving cloth or tending to her silkworms.

Sometimes, Sang Chul would pick up from here, his face tight with rage. His eyes grew small, fists tightly clenched at his sides. Here, he would lean forward, close to his sons' faces, and hold the gaze of each of them: Cheotjjae, then Duljjae, then Young Bok. And then dangerously, vehemently, he would begin to speak in growling low tones.

Twenty-nine of the thirty-three leaders of the movement gathered at Taehwagwan Restaurant in Kyungsung for the reading of the Declaration of Independence. They were supposed to go to the Pagoda Park for the reading, but they were afraid that there would be violence between the gathered students and the Japanese police. So, they met at this restaurant, where they told the owner to call the administration office of the Japanese Government-General of Korea and to tell them that the national representatives of Korea were having a party to celebrate the Independence of Korea. They drank a somber toast together, passed out copies of the Declaration, and cheered Korean Independence Manse! They knew what was ahead. Pain, torture, death…but they didn't resist when the military police arrived. As they were about to be led away, one man stood with a smile, "One last Manse!" Here with a wild glint in his eyes, Sang Chul would stand and punch his hand toward the sky. *"Manse!"*

"Just like that." Sang Chul nudged his sons to stand, to shout out the word. They all did, feeling out the word and mimicking the stance and facial expression of their father.

One last "Manse," Sang Chul continued. *And then the police shoved them into automobiles and took them to jail. The leaders of the movement were arrested, but other appointed leaders would take their place. They would fill all the jail cells until the Japanese would have to stop their arrests. Your grandfather, Kim Chul Soo, was one of these leaders of the Chondogyo movement who rose up during the arrests.*

Through March and April, the protests continued throughout the nation. Huge crowds of people gathered in the streets: students, nurses, farm women, lawyers, pastors. They had no weapons but roared for hours at a time, *"Manse! Manse!"*

The stories of occurrences around the nation began to spread. A crowd had gathered in Pyongyang and shouted, "*Manse!*" before a group of police officers. The policemen turned a hose on the people. Some Korean policemen were ordered to aid with the hose, but they threw off their uniforms to help the people. The crowd threw stones until every window in the police office had been shattered.

A crowd had been watching a company of soldiers drilling on a college campus. The soldiers suddenly charged at the people. Most of the crowd ran, still cheering, "*Manse! Manse!*" between panting breaths. The soldiers took chase and beat whomever they overtook. The strikes of their rifle butts filled the square with the sickening crunch of bone and screams of pain. One man fell and was beaten again and again with the butt of the gun until the sidewalk was splattered with the blood from his head. Nearly senseless, he was hauled away between two soldiers. A Japanese man in plainclothes started to kick a Korean man walking by the protest. Soldiers rushed to join the beating. This continued until dinner time, when people returned to their homes and the streets were quiet again. Many had been dragged off to the police station, and stragglers carried away the remaining wounded and dead.

It took six days of demonstrating before the first word of the movement was published in the local papers.

Horsemen struck down protestors with bamboo rods, and the butts of guns rained sickening blows indiscriminately on the young and old.

A twenty-two-year-old man was seized as he passed a crowd shouting, "*Manse!*" He was rammed in the side, butted with a gun. Pleading for mercy, he fell to his knees. Every word he spoke brought another sickening blow to his face. A friend tried to plead for him, saying he had been on his way to the hospital and had nothing to do with the protests.

A church's wooden gate was destroyed, and the heavy wood pieces were used to beat a man senseless.

Two women in a protest were knocked into a ditch with strikes from the butts of rifles. They were shot where they lay.

In front of a Prefect's office, Japanese firemen drove iron hooks from their long poles into the shoulders of a man, and dragged him along in the dirt.

Girls found shouting *"Manse!"* were hung by their hair from telegraph poles and beaten severely with kicks and blows from the butts of rifles.

Schoolboys were chased and tied up, whimpering with fear as they were beaten again and again.

All across the country, Japanese soldiers charged into crowds of people with clubs, pickaxe handles, iron bars, rifles, bayonets, and hard pieces of wood. Onlookers and protestors alike were beaten. Sometimes they held stones as weapons, but most were unarmed.

In MaIngSan of the South Pyongyang Province, Japanese soldiers arrived and arrested the leader of the Chondogyo movement in the area. The people followed the soldiers to the station, demanding his release. Though the soldiers beat them back, followers pushed on. They flooded the courtyard of the station, and once it was full, the Japanese soldiers shut the gate and locked it. Soldiers lined the edges of the courtyard and shot and shot and shot until the courtyard was littered with dead bodies and groaning wounded. Fifty-six were murdered that day. Survivors were run through again and again with bayonets until dead. Three men managed to escape, and the soldiers spent several days in pursuit, searching all neighboring villages.

In Sinchang, some fifty miles from Seoul, soldiers broke the bell at a Methodist church and attacked the pregnant wife of a pastor when she approached them.

In WasuRi of the GangWon Province, a crowd of protestors shouted "*Manse!*" in front of a police station. A senior police-man opened fire, killing one man and wounding another. The people beat the chief to death and set fire to the police station. A week later, soldiers and police launched an attack on the town, setting fire to the houses and shooting and beating the escaping people.

In Suchon of the Jeollanam Province, soldiers walked the narrow streets at daybreak with matches and set fire to for-ty-two homes. The thatched roofs rose up in terrific flames, and the people leapt from their sleep in panic. When they tried to put out the fire, soldiers beat them, shot them, or ran them through with bayonets.

In JeamRi of Hwaesong, soldiers ordered all adult male Christians and members of Chondogyo to assemble in the Church for a lecture. Twenty-three men went. The doors were locked, and soldiers fired at the men through the paper win-dows. When all were killed or wounded, the soldiers set fire to the building. The thatch and wooden building burned quickly. Any men who tried to escape were shot or bayoneted. Two women tried to rescue their husbands and were killed. The soldiers set fire to the entire village and the scent of burning human flesh consumed the town.

In the jails, demonstrators were told that they had been arrested based on violations of the law of the Preservation of Public Peace. Sometimes they were beaten nearly thirty times with rods on their buttocks, leaving the flesh a near pulp. Frequently, the beating was transferred over to Korean policemen, who often gave even harsher blows. If an individual squirmed or protested, they were beaten on the head or other parts of their bodies.

Shopkeepers closed their stores in solidarity with the Independence Movement and refused to open until Korean protestors were released from prisons. By April 1, the authorities issued an order that all shops were to be opened. Business was to return to normal. Soldiers forced shopkeepers to open at bayonet point. At many shops, soldiers sat on rickety stools, holding loaded rifles on their laps. In some districts, as soon as the police opened one shop, the one previously opened would close its doors again. The police took to placing soldiers at regular intervals along the main street. Even when opened, the shopkeepers made no attempts to sell anything, just staring out at passersby or at the protesting crowds. They took measures to see that Koreans got what they wanted, business conducted under cover of night or by direct deliveries to homes.

By the time the movement died down at the end of 1919, over two million Koreans had participated in more than 1,500 demonstrations across the country. Seven hundred and fifteen homes, forty-seven churches, and two school buildings had been destroyed by fire. Angry demonstrators had destroyed forty-seven local offices, thirty-one police stations, and seventy-one other facilities. Seven thousand and five hundred people had been killed by the Japanese police and soldiers. Nearly sixteen thousand were wounded, and of the forty-six thousand arrested, ten thousand were imprisoned.

Yu KwanSun, a seventeen-year-old schoolgirl who was imprisoned and later died from torture injuries, wrote, "Even if my fingernails are torn out, my nose and ears are ripped apart, and my legs and arms are crushed, this physical pain does not compare to the pain of losing my nation… My only remorse is not being able to do more than dedicating my life to my country" (Shin and Moon, 2019).

"The Japanese, those *Jjokbari*," Sang Chul spit into the dirt. *Jjokbari*, people of cloven hooves, referred to the Japanese flip flops and split-toed socks. "They crushed our voices and killed our people. But, my sons, there is a provisional Korean government in Shanghai. Even now while we are silenced, they are hard at work for our independence."

Here all three boys looked up, eyes glistening with excitement. Sang Chul continued, "Its leaders are Syngman Rhee, Ahn Chang Ho, and Kim Ku. They are working for our independence, fighting for the right of Koreans to be Korean again, to love our culture and our language. They will free us. I know they will."

CHAPTER FOUR

By 1935, Sang Chul had saved up enough money to afford a plot of land in SaInJang, present-day Pyongsong, about twenty miles from the northern city of Pyongyang. The house he bought was in SaChangRi, a small twenty-house village a couple miles away from SaInJang. The family moved into the second home from the edge of the village, right next to Yang Sil's elder brother, who had grudgingly forgiven his sister.

Their home was built in the traditional Korean style: two rows of straw-roofed buildings with a center courtyard. The first row of buildings included housing for an ox, a room for silkworms, and storage space for beans and grains. The entrance was large enough for an ox and a wagon to pass through. In the second row of buildings, Yang Sil stocked the kitchen with iron cauldrons for boiling water, rice, and soup. Bordering the kitchen was a large communal room where the family slept, ate, and spent their time together. They dug a toilet pit outside in a little shed.

SaChangRi bordered JoongDukSan, a thickly wooded mountain fragrant with pines, spruce, fir, and oak. Spring was pleasant. Frothy bunches of pale pink azaleas clothed the mountain with their nodding faces, whispering in the breezy wind. The cicadas squealed *daaadmdaaadmdaaa* throughout the day, and Young Bok and other village children chased them, screaming, *"Maemi maemi maem maem maem."* They played tag and hide-and-seek on the mountainside. Sometimes they brought along toys their fathers or elder brothers had made for them. Other times, they crouched together and with clumsy fingers, designed their own toys from twigs and scraps of cloth. They plucked horned beetles from their slow-moving crawl along the branches of the oak trees and watched them fight each other in hand-drawn circles in the dirt.

The yearly cycle of farm life gave little time for reprieve. Sang Chul led a plodding ox to plow neat furrows in the springtime fields. Young Bok remembered well that smell of new, damp soil, the kind that made him want to plunge his fingers into the dirt and wriggle them around. Planting was usually a whole village affair, and in March or early April, Yang Sil, Sang Chul, and the villagers worked together to spread rice seeds in a bed of wet earth. They sang a sowing song to pass the time and give rhythm to their slow, shifting movement down each row.

By June, the rice seedlings grew thickly to the height of the shin and were plucked and bound into small bundles to be transported to more irrigated paddies. The barley crops of last fall were harvested from the irrigated paddies to make way for the rice seedlings. In these damp terraces, Yang Sil and Sang Chul spent backbreaking hours with their pants rolled up to their knees, pressing each seedling several inches into the soft mud. They sang the *mojjigi* with smooth voices rising and falling, *Let's remove the young rice plants, let's remove.* And there were other songs that told one to *straighten up your back* and *dance to loosen the body*. The neighbors came to help, and as the children grew older, they learned to plant as well.

Young Bok hated the rice paddies most of all. When he waded into the water to weed, leeches clung to his legs and feet. With little shouts of disgust, he slapped the sucking worms and then ripped them off. Red droplets of blood dripped and blended with the muddy water on his legs, until his legs were striped like a sick tiger. As soon as he began bleeding, more leeches gathered to cling to his legs.

Summer brought heavy torrential rains, and the village river swelled muddy and fat, like an overfed snake. After rainfall, dragonflies settled on the ground and trees to dry their wings, a fluttering myriad quilt among the slopping puddles of new fallen rain. Laughing, the children would swirl a stick in freshly made spider webs and chase the dragonflies. Sometimes they tied a piece of string around a female dragonfly and ran, singing a rhyming song until a male dragonfly seeking a mate fell for the trap. In the patches of dry weather, the stream water cleared, and the village children spent hours swimming and splashing in the shallows.

In the background, Yang Sil labored in the fields. She carried her fourth son in a cloth sling tied tightly to her back. Netjjae, born in 1932, was not yet old enough to be left with his brothers to play. Though her back ached and her weary legs shook, Yang Sil worked endless hours in the fields. In these summer months, she worked alone; Sang Chul never helped with the weeding. At first, Young Bok had assumed this was the case in every family, but when he surveyed other humid fields, men and women bent in the fields together.

When the rice plants reached her waist and the rainy season had passed, Yang Sil knew it was time to drain the fields.

Her hands grew rough as she wrestled away weeds with a splintering hoe, and she sang the laborious and lonely song of the dry-field weeding. Slow and haunting, her voice soared and faded into the humid expanse of the field. Her husband languished in the shade of his stilted shack.

The shack was built over a small man-made stream for the irrigation of the crops, and it was here that Sang Chul spent much of his time sleeping or playing chess on a rough board. It could comfortably fit four people, and Cheotjjae and Duljjae often followed their father's example, lazing away the hot and humid months in the cool shade of this makeshift building.

In the shade beneath the shack, Sang Chul stored *chame*, a sweet yellow and orange striped melon, to soak in the cool stream water. Sometimes on his way home from school, Young Bok waded into the water to pick a small *chame* to eat. The *chame* was cool and sweet, and sitting in the shade of a tree, the sweat finally cooled on his forehead. Sometimes the melon stuck in his throat as he watched his mother stooped in the sun with a baby on her back. Often, he joined her in the fields.

In the fall, Young Bok went to the mountainside to collect pine nuts and chestnuts. The changing leaves rustled pleasantly overhead, and the light was golden beneath the trees' shade. Bronzy acorns tumbled from oak trees and Young Bok collected this windfall to take to his mother. Yang Sil ground the acorns into a powder and then made *dotori-muk*, an acorn jelly. This, she seasoned with soy sauce and sesame oil.

By September, the fields turned a deep gold, and the plants bent nearly double from the weight of their ripe heads of grain. In early October, the harvest began, and Sang Chul finally rejoined his wife in the fields.

It was painful work, a sharp sickle in hand to slice down each rice plant one by one as close to the ground as possible. The whole village gathered again for the harvesting; it made the work go faster. Once the rice was harvested, the grains were bound into stacked bundles, which would later be loaded onto an oxen's back or carried by hand to the threshing field. After the rice dried and was threshed, the grains were polished at various types of mills, often through pounding by hand. In time with the pounding, a leader guided lively songs, improvising a soaring solo while the chorus replied in a refrain of unvarying nonsense syllables. The rhythm continued unfalteringly until the rice kernels were freed from impurities and ready for the rice pot.

Young Bok loved coming home in the fall afternoons, when the weather was just cold enough to appreciate the warmth of the *ondol,* heated flooring. He loved the yellow-brown warmth of the earthen walls, the smoky wood smell from the cooking fire seeping through the floor and fingering clothing and hair and nose. The smell of musty mats and bedding. The spicy tang of kimchi and odor of dried fish and boiling rice. The soft voice of his mother singing an old folk tune or tapping a rhythm with her hands and feet as she cooked.

When the days slipped into winter, a cold bone-piercing wind whistled throughout the village. Snow fell up to waist height, and even with the heated floors, Young Bok was never completely warm. Cold air leaked through the windows and the cracks in the floor until his fingers and toes were painfully numb.

He and other village children spent hours climbing up the mountain with homemade sleds and zipping down, screaming with glee. The branches of trees reached up to snag his skin and clothing, and he always returned home slightly bloody and ragged.

Every Sunday, Young Bok traveled alone to the neighboring town of three hundred homes for the Presbyterian church service. He loved the singing—beautiful lyric hymns that thrilled his heart, so unlike the monotone or heavy tunes sung by workers in the rice paddies or fields. Deep inside, this was also his subtle way of emphasizing his anti-Japanese sentiments. But mostly, Young Bok went to church because he prized the attendance award that he could receive at the end of the year. That and the Christmas gift. Every year, Young Bok arrived at the church door on Christmas Day, smiling and expectant, face pinched with the cold. He waited for the gifts of sharp new pencils, notebooks with clean, creamy pages, and new packs of crayons.

The winters meant that the farming season was over, but Yang Sil was busy weaving straw mats and bags from rice husks, darning clothes, and finishing other upkeep needs.

Yang Sil wove stories, too, on the long winter nights. Stories she was too tired to tell during the backbreaking farming season.

There once was a boy named Han Seok Bong who went far, far away from his small village to a large town to study for many years.

One day, when the sky was red like gochujang paste and the tired sun sank down, down, down, the boy walked along the mountain path back to his home. His mother ran out to meet him. She was so happy to see her son that her smile was bigger than a slice of chame melon. She took him inside but asked him only one question: "Why did you come back home?"

The son was ashamed and bowed his head, "I am homesick, Uhmuhni. I want to be at home."

The mother blew out the wick of her oil lamp. In the complete darkness, she told her son, "For one minute, I will cut my rice cake into pieces." She held a foot-long cylinder of garatteok. "While I am cutting, you will write with brush and ink on this paper."

After a minute passed, the mother relit the lamp. In front of her, there were fifty pieces of perfect and equal slices of tteok. But when the mother looked at her son's paper, she could not even read the brush writing.

She looked at her son, and he bowed in shame before her. "You have not trained enough, my son. Until then, do not come home."

Han Seok Bong became a famous calligrapher in the mid-Joseon era. He even wrote the Thousand Character Classic! The lesson is that you must work your hardest to be the best that you can. Do not give up before you master a skill. You must try to reach the best possible.

CHAPTER FIVE

———

The pungent odor of motherwort seeped into Young Bok's dreams, and as he began to stir awake, he could hear gentle rustling and his mother humming softly as she untied bundles of drying herbs from the ceiling rafters. For weeks, Yang Sil had scoured the mountainside for motherwort and mugwort in preparation for Dano, the fifth day of the fifth lunar month, a day believed to be filled with abundant yang energy. The day had finally come, and she was moving the now-dried bundles of herbs to the gate of the house to ward off evil spirits.

"Good morning, Umma," Young Bok whispered. His brothers stirred awake as he got to his feet.

"Good morning, Setjjae." Yang Sil's hair was newly washed, and she wore a hair pin carved from a root of *changpo*, Korean iris, engraved with the word *fortune* in Chinese characters. She handed Young Bok a necklace to wear filled with *changpo* leaves, a charm against evil.

The entire family left home early that morning for the hour walk to the nearby town where the Dano festivities would take place. On the way, brightly colored paper talismans seemed to wave good morning to Young Bok from the doorways and kitchen windows where they hung. Many were from nearby temples, full of prayers for luck and good fortune in the coming season.

A huge circle of watchers was already gathered in the center of the town. The cloying fragrance of *changpo*, sweat, and palpable excitement nearly stifled Young Bok. But it also made his heart pound fast. He felt like running, jumping, and yelling all at once.

Young Bok caught brief glimpses of his father in the cracks between broad shoulders and fluttering clothing. He pushed forward, slipping beneath someone's elbow, around the stomachs of middle-aged men, past squealing children clinging to their mothers' skirts, until he squatted in front of the crowd of people. Dust was gritty in his mouth, and the shouting and laughter from the crowd was a swell of roaring noise.

Sang Chul had already entered the *Ssireum*, wrestling, competition, and he stood in the center of the dirt patch, bare-chested, as the *satba*, cloth belt, was adjusted. He eyed his opponent, a man of similar muscular build. Both men slipped their hands into the loops on the cloth belt of the other, squatting, shuffling into place. Sang Chul's jaw set, and Young Bok saw the wild look in his eyes that was the same as when he hit a large root while tilling the land.

A sharp command and then the men were swiveling, a quick blur of muscle and gleaming skin. The other man's leg was rising, pushing against the back of Sang Chul's leg in an effort to bring him crashing to the ground. Sang Chul pivoted, and the man's leg slipped down. They held position, both shaking with the effort before they spun again very slowly, heads against each other's shoulders, muscles bulging as they pushed steadily against one another. Sang Chul grunted with effort. He jutted his arm underneath the other man's armpit, and in one smooth movement, still gripping the other man with both arms, vaulted his torso backward, right shoulder and arm flying backward, back arched into an upside-down U. The other man fell flailing to the ground.

Voices roared around Young Bok, and he leapt to his feet shouting.

Sang Chul's next opponent was a wiry man with greasy hair. Young Bok watched as the other man extended his back leg, trying to gain traction in the dirt. Sang Chul squatted deeper, and then they were whipping around to the right. A full circle. Sang Chul heaved up the other man by the *satba*, and the man's legs kicked wildly like a frog's. Dirt sprayed. Sang Chul heaved forward and slammed down on top of the other man with a deep grunt. They lay there for a moment, a heap of sprawling limbs, before staggering to their feet.

The *Ssireum* competition continued for most of the day, with the crowd of people surrounding the ring ebbing and flowing, a sea of white-clothed people shouting and laughing.

Young Bok drifted away sometime in the afternoon to watch the *geune ttwigi*, swinging. The swing was a wooden plank hung from a tree by straw ropes and colored cloth. Young women lifted dainty feet to kick a bell hanging from a high tree branch. Young Bok was mesmerized by the brilliant reds and blues of their flowing skirts and the bright ribbons fluttering from the ends of their silky long hair. Delicate sprigs of flowers were braided and twisted into their hair, and the scent of the *changpo* whirled around Young Bok.

When the sun had sunk low, Young Bok ran back to the *Ssireum* ring, catching only the last roar of excitement as the winner of the competition finished the final match. When the congratulatory shouts and pushing bodies had finally cleared, Young Bok beamed when he found his father in the center of the ring, bowing to the passing people.

"Congratulations, Appa!" Young Bok and his brothers gathered around their father. Sang Chul flashed a rare, crooked smile.

Another year, another prize ox, as his strong father won the glory of being the strongest man in the whole province.

Young Bok saw the admiration in his brothers' eyes, the way they gazed at their father's muscles, sticky with sweat and dirt. They stood trying to emulate his posture: widely spaced legs, squared shoulders, and fists lightly clenched at his sides.

The walk home, chattering and beaming up at their father, felt short. Sang Chul had slipped a rough straw rope over the ox's head and was discussing with Yang Sil about whether they ought to keep the ox for tilling the fields in the spring. Otherwise, he would butcher the ox and share the meat with the town in a celebration of his victory and the holiday.

Cheotjjae, Duljjae, and Young Bok fell behind often, imitating the squatting posture of the starting position for *Ssireum* and recreating the swinging moves they'd seen.

Young Bok was joyful that Cheotjjae was playing with him. Just a couple days ago, Young Bok had trailed after Cheotjjae, tugging at his arm, "Hyung, older brother, let me play with you just this once. Please, Hyung."

Cheotjjae had huffed impatiently. "I never play with little kids. Go away." At twelve, he was already developing broad shoulders and a gruff temperament like his father. His push had sent six-year-old Young Bok stumbling away.

By the time Young Bok had returned to the courtyard of his home, his face was a streaming mess of tears and mucus. He had wailed as he shuffled along, wiping his eyes with his sleeve.

Duljjae was sitting by the courtyard gate, watching the clouds slip by overhead. He had stood up to meet Young Bok and took him gently by his shoulder. "He won't play with me either…but I'll play with you!" Young Bok had smiled. They always played quiet games, sitting, or talking together because his second elder brother was small and a little weak from his sickness as an infant.

But today was Dano and Cheotjjae was playing with him! Young Bok and Cheotjjae were sticky with sweat, grunting and laughing as they wrestled one another, shifting in a circle. Cheotjjae tripped over Young Bok's leg and with a yell, they both tumbled into the dirt.

Dusting off his arms, Cheotjjae said, "I'm going to be just like Appa. I'm going to be strong and win an ox, too."

CHAPTER SIX

———

Sang Chul insisted the entire family eat meals together. There were four each day, centered around the farming schedule: a big meal for breakfast, lunch, a large meal for dinner at five o'clock, and then a light supper at eight o'clock. Young Bok and Cheotjjae shared a tray on the floor, Duljjae and Netjjae another one, and Sang Chul had a separate tray. Yang Sil and the baby sat at a low round table, the only permanent fixture in the room.

The Kim family owned land, and what land they could not work, they rented out to a handful of tenants. In comparison to most of their neighbors, the Kim family ate well. Sometimes for dinner, Yang Sil made *tteok*, rice cakes, by pounding rice flour in a mortar and adding water and honey before steaming all of it in an earthenware bowl. Other times, she made *juk*, rice porridge, with *kimchi*, corn, or sweet potatoes. On summer nights, Yang Sil and Sang Chul worked in the fields until darkness had fallen and Yang Sil would boil corn, sweet potato, or *juk* for a quick supper before bed. These meals were quiet—the little ones' heads already nodding and Sang Chul and Yang Sil bent with exhaustion.

Whenever Yang Sil's brother made a dish of anything special, he brought some over to Yang Sil's home. Yang Sil would send a plate of their own food back with him. It was always Sang Chul who ate these special dishes first, and when he was finished, the children pounced on the leftovers. There was usually only enough for a mouthful each, and none left for Yang Sil.

Young Bok's favorite meal was *naengmyun*, a noodle dish in a cold broth, with pheasant meat. For this dish, Yang Sil ground buckwheat into powder, which her three sons then kneaded into noodle shapes before dropping them into boiling water.

Sang Chul hunted wild pheasants for *naengmyun* with a falcon and a German Shepherd. Young Bok rarely went with his father, though Cheotjjae often did. The times when Young Bok did go, he crouched in the underbrush with his mouth half open, watching the entire process with intense concentration. After hours of training his animals, Sang Chul used very few words and movements. With a single jerk of his hand, he sent the German Shepherd to scare the pheasant out of the underbrush. The pheasant rose squawking, and as Sang Chul signaled, the falcon flew out to meet it. In a rush of wings, it clutched the pheasant in its talons. They tumbled down toward the ground, always with the falcon on top. The falcon immediately ate out the eyes of the pheasant and Sang Chul had to send out his German Shepherd to retrieve the pheasant quickly, or else the entire head would be gone. Young Bok never saw a pheasant with an intact eye.

Once a month, Sang Chul bought a leg or a quarter of a cow from the market in the next town over. He squatted in the courtyard with a sharp knife, splattering blood as he sliced apart the meat. It looked as though an uneven rainstorm had passed by the dark dirt. Sang Chul kept a pound of meat separate to roll in sesame oil. This, Sang Chul served to the family raw, as an appetizer before dinner. Young Bok hated the consistency of the flesh with its iron blood still warm from the sun, as though the cow had just been living.

At supper, Sang Chul grilled the rest of the meat over hot charcoal, and the whole family sat tightly together, chewing contentedly with greasy mouths and fingers. On these nights, Young Bok's stomach was full, and he slept easily.

Whatever meat was left over, Yang Sil marinated with soy sauce and set it aside for school lunches.

Yang Sil often stretched the family's rice supply by adding millet or red beans to the white rice to make *jobap* and *patbap*, but Cheotjjae demanded white rice at every meal.

"If there is not enough rice, just give me a small amount with only white rice," he would repeat, a hard glint in his eyes inviting a challenge.

Yang Sil never said anything as she stood over the heavy iron cauldron where the rice boiled. Just lifted the heavy cover from it and spooned out a portion into a little bowl for her son. Even when everyone else was eating *tteok* or *juk,* Cheotjjae insisted on having white rice.

Young Bok and Duljjae would eye each other as they carried the trays of food from the kitchen. *Spoiled,* they would mouth, smirking as they avoided Cheotjjae's glaring eyes.

Occasionally, Young Bok would bite down hard on a small stone in the rice. As if attuned to the sounds of chewing, Cheotjjae's head would swivel up from shoveling the rice into his mouth. "What's the matter?"

Too many times, Young Bok had spit out a stone, and Cheotjjae had set down his chopsticks and spoon. Two words, and the room would grow silent: "Dirty food." No amount of cajoling or demanding could force Cheotjjae to start eating again. Young Bok hated this, hated seeing food his mother had worked so hard to prepare going to waste. He had seen the way that Yang Sil carefully sifted the sand from the rice with the woven bamboo *jori*, and stones and grit with the *inambak*, rice washing bowl. So, what if a few stones had slipped through? She worked hard, and Young Bok felt it was the least he could do to swallow a few stones, if only to spare her the complaints of her eldest son.

So Young Bok had learned to swallow the stones down, avoiding Cheotjjae's narrowed eyes and pointing chopsticks.

Sometimes, Cheotjjae would insist. "I heard some noise. You must have a stone."

Young Bok's eyes would widen as he opened his mouth as far as it would open. Empty. "No, nothing. See!"

***

One afternoon, after an especially long game of chase with his friends, Young Bok returned home to find his whole family already seated around the meal trays.

Young Bok was sure he was scarcely five minutes late to dinner, but he avoided eye contact and ate quickly. He was the first to finish, and leaving his utensils, he stood up very quickly, about to dash out of the room.

Sang Chul looked up from his rice bowl and uttered one word: "Stay."

After all the family had finished eating and the clacking of plates and trays and chopsticks receded into the kitchen, Sang Chul looked Young Bok sternly in the eyes and asked, "Why were you late?"

Young Bok bowed his head, "Sorry I was late. I was playing, Abeoji."

There was still a hardness about his father's face, rigidity in the set of his mouth and tightness in his shoulders. "This is our only time to eat together," Sang Chul said. "You violated it! This is our rule. It is your responsibility to come."

Young Bok's siblings scattered out of the kitchen and the room at the sound of their father's raised voice.

In the center of the room, Yang Sil had left the large stone slab she used for ironing clothes. Sang Chul pointed to it and shouted, "Lift it!"

Yang Sil grabbed Young Bok's arm and shook it gently. "Apologize, Setjjae."

Young Bok pulled his arm away. He looked down at the stone slab. "I do it in school all the time," he said. "I can lift it." He heaved it up then, muscles straining in his skinny arms and legs, veins standing out in his neck, and face burning red.

"Not enough!" his father shouted. "Lift it over your head!"

"I can do it," Young Bok grunted defiantly.

From the corner of the room, Sang Chul took a slender stick about finger width and began smacking Young Bok's legs. Young Bok cried out with each stinging blow, more from the shock at being hit than the pain. Finally, with a shout that was half scream and half sob, Young Bok dropped the stone.

It split asunder crookedly with a thundering crash, denting the clay and *hanji*, oil paper floor.

Now Sang Chul was truly angry. Yelling, he landed stinging blows all over Young Bok's cowering body. Harder and harder they came, and a wild look strangled his features.

Finally, Yang Sil intervened, pulling Young Bok away. He clung to her back, hiding his teary face. Yang Sil looked her husband straight in the eyes. "Yobo, honey, that's enough. Stop."

She loosened Young Bok's grip and stared down at him, speaking harshly, "*Pabo*, fool! Don't try to do that again. You should have apologized instead of lifting the stone. You did wrong. Beg for forgiveness from your father." Her eyes were teary but flashing with a deep anger.

Sobbing, Young Bok fell to his knees. His apology shuddered out.

He was never late to a meal again.

***

Usually the family cleaned up quickly after the meal was over, ready to go to bed with the fading light. But summer nights were warm, and sometimes Sang Chul liked to rest his feet on the sunbaked dirt of the courtyard and tell his sons a story.

On one night in particular, Cheotjjae, Duljjae, Setjjae, and Netjjae stared up at their father.

Sang Chul stared back at them, sucking at a piece of corn stuck between his front teeth before speaking. "Your grandfather could move the giant oaks just by punching them."

"How big? How big?" they clamored.

Sang Chul laughed. "At least three men wide, maybe four. A huge tree with roots as wide as an ox."

They had heard this story a million times, but it never grew old. "Harabeoji, grandfather, was the only son, wasn't he? Just like his father and great-grandfather and great-great grandfather."

"Yes. He was the treasured son of his Appa and Umma. But he was all alone. Not like you four, my Cheotjjae, Duljjae, Setjjae, and Netjjae." Sang Chul smiled at each of his four sons. "But in those days—"

"When was it, Appa. When was it?"

"When your grandfather was young. In 1860, maybe 1861. The law was far, far away from small villages in the countryside. He had to protect himself. And the only way he could do this was to make himself strong."

"So, he punched the tree?"

"*Aish.* Let me tell the story!" Sang Chul glared for a moment before returning to his story. "He boxed the huge oak tree in the center of town until his knuckles bled. He wore away a bald patch on the bark of the trunk and even the dust near his feet grew weary and drifted away. Blood fell from his hands like rain."

"For how long? How long did he punch the tree?"

"Many, many months. And the people of the town watched him and watched him."

"Some of them laughed like this," Sang Chul laughed a deep-throated, drawn-out laugh. "Some of them thought he was crazy." He clucked his tongue, shook his head like the elderly, humping his back and holding an imaginary cane.

"Some of them believed he could. And one day, the tree creaked and groaned and—*BAM*—it moved at least an ox's length to the right."

"Appa, Appa! Last time you said it moved a man's length."

"No, no, he said ox. He said ox," the siblings argued among themselves.

Sang Chul was no longer listening, looking off toward the mountainside afire with blooming pink azaleas. "And then the Japanese came with their guns and strength was no longer a protection. Your grandfather was humiliated for his strength; they made him ashamed. Ashamed…"

Sang Chul was quiet for a long time, and Cheotjjae and Duljjae and Young Bok eyed each other, mouthing questions silently.

"Your grandfather became a refugee and went to the Koksan…" Abruptly, Sang Chul was serious again and back to his no-nonsense-obey-me sternness. "Clean up now."

CHAPTER SEVEN

————

When Young Bok turned six, all his playmates and friends began attending the Japanese elementary school, a two-mile walk away in the neighboring two-hundred-house village.

Young Bok begged to go, too. "Please, Abeoji. Please!"

Sang Chul refused to send him.

In all his life, Young Bok never heard his father refer to the Japanese by anything except for *Jjokbari*, a derogatory word referring to the Japanese flip-flops. "These filthy *Jjokbari*," muttering when he returned from the market. "Don't speak those *Jjokbari* words in this house!" when Young Bok slipped into speaking Japanese.

Instead of Japanese elementary school, Young Bok attended *sodang*, a traditional Korean school, where he memorized the well-established course of study: the Thousand Character Classic (*CheonJaMun*), Three Character Classic, and Hundred Family Surnames.

Every lengthy afternoon, yellowy pages of text yawned in front of Young Bok. The teacher drifted off in the front of the classroom in the warm afternoon heat, and a fly landed on his limp hand. There was only studying to do; no breaks for exercise or play time. The few other children there were quiet, spending much of their time in a stupor staring at the page, or rubbing away sleep from their eyes with hands smudged with black ink.

Every morning, Young Bok's father had him repeat the Thousand Character Classic before leaving the house for *sodang*. The thousand Chinese characters, *hanja*, were grouped into four-line rhyming stanzas, and Young Bok had learned a song to better memorize all of them. *"Hanulcheon ttaji kamulhyeon nuruhwang...* The sky above is black, and the earth below is yellow..." He rocked back and forth in rhythm, eyes watching his father's face for signs of affirmation or disapproval. Most of the time, Sang Chul sat with his eyelids shut, arms crossed, nodding very slowly.

Young Bok learned how to write and read all of the characters in the Thousand Character Classic. Then he moved on to the Three Character Classic, which was written in a rhythmic structure of three Chinese characters in two lines.

Phrases like: *"Learn while young, and when grown up apply what you have learned; influencing the sovereign above; benefiting the people below."*

And *"The Three Bonds are the obligation between sovereign and subject, the love between father and child, the harmony between husband and wife."*

Confucian doctrine and Chinese history echoed through Young Bok's head even when he slept. Sometimes he woke still mouthing stanzas in the Three Character Classic.

He moved on to the Hundred Family Surnames, a rhyming poem in lines of eight characters that listed over four hundred Chinese surnames.

When he had finished his third book and nearly a year had passed, Young Bok approached his father again. "Abeoji, you ran away from the mountains. You *chose* the Japanese! So please, Abeoji, please let me go to school!"

Sang Chul's mouth puckered up, looking down at his seven-year-old son. Young Bok cringed, waiting for his father's angry words. Had he crossed the line?

Sang Chul frowned and muttered, half under his breath, "Why do you need more education? Isn't *sodang* enough?" Usually, children started *sodang* when they were seven or eight and studied at their own pace for the next four to five years. It was what Cheotjjae and Duljjae had done, and they had never asked for more education.

Yang Sil coughed lightly from the kitchen. Slowly, Sang Chul nodded his head.

Young Bok beamed and bowed multiple times to thank his father. Though he was a year older than his classmates, it made no difference to him. He was going to school!

***

School began in mid-April and ended in mid-March, giving time for students to help their parents sow the rice fields. Young Bok attended Shajin Kokumin Gakko, Shajin Public National School, in Pyongsong. The elementary school was a series of low rectangular buildings spaced a few feet apart with red tiled roofs and long rows of windows. Behind the school was the gentle swell of two sloping hills, wooded with trees and small bushes.

Some days, Young Bok and his friends walked the hour to school. Other days, especially with snow or rain, they clung to the back of a truck, rocking back and forth in the *pak-pak-pak* of sooty smoke.

Every morning, Young Bok passed the two concrete pillars marking the entrance to the school and the paneled shrine built in the center of the school courtyard. Painted with praises of the Emperor, flags were plastered across the top rim. Inside was an Imperial Portrait of the Japanese Emperor and a Divine Box, supposedly containing the spirit of *Amaterasu-oomikami*, the founder of the Japanese Empire.

At 9 a.m., the principal would stand before the students on a little raised platform, and belt out, "Turn to the East. Bow to the Emperor."

The principal was a slim man who wore a tiny dab of facial hair above his uncertain mouth. His shaved head gleamed in the sun, and sometimes his thick-lensed round glasses glared in the light like two staring suns. He had retired from the Japanese military a few years ago and kept the stiff movements and discipline of it with him.

The students completed the *toho yohai*, bowing to the imperial palace. They bowed at forty-five-degree angles and stayed this way for a whole minute in respectful silence. Afterward, they recited the Oath of Imperial Subjects:

> *"We are subjects of the imperial land;*
> *We repay sovereign and country with loyalty.*
> *We, subjects of the imperial land,*
> *Will cooperate in mutual faith and affection,*
> *And make stronger thereby the corpus of the state.*
> *We, subjects of the imperial land,*

Will cultivate our powers of discipline and sacrifice,
And enhance the imperial way" (Hatada, 1969).

There was a total of six pledges, things like *Long live the emperor* and *Long live Japan*. Young Bok hated these pledges. It was "slavery education" and "brainwashing," as he called it. How could he believe the Japanese emperor was a god to be worshipped?

The students then bowed to the shrine.

They sang the *kimigayo*, the Japanese national anthem. Voices slowly following the refrain, children's voices somber in the still courtyard:

"Kimigayo wa
Chiyo ni yachiyo ni
Sazare-ishi no
Iwao to narite
Koke no musu made."

"May your reign
Continue for a thousand, eight thousand generations,
Until the tiny pebbles
Grow into massive boulders
Lush with moss" (Caprio, 2009).

Though Young Bok hated these rituals, he loved the learning and the few days of celebration.

In the dry season between late summer and early fall, students and their families gathered on the elementary school grounds for a sports day to celebrate the entire school year.

Young Bok fondly remembered dancing around the field with several other classmates, watching as parents and siblings and relatives began to filter in. He had been waiting for this day for months, discussing last year's highlights with his classmates, comparing strength, and voting on who they thought was most likely to win. The slight hum of activity rose to a deafening bustle, as almost two thousand people gathered.

All the students, a total of about 480 across all six years, were required to participate in at least one game. Most students ran: the one hundred-meter, one-thousand-meter, or five-person relay teams. There was tug of war, *Ssireum*, soccer, tennis, softball, and volleyball. Young Bok never won anything, but still, he thoroughly enjoyed himself. Most of all, he loved watching the "horseback riding," where three students hoisted another student onto their shoulders with a flag tied to the back of his shirt. Several teams of four did the same, and what followed was a wild stampede of six-footed beasts sprinting across the field trying to catch the flag of the other teams.

Enterprising merchants seized the opportunity, crying out their wares and packing the grounds with their blankets and carts of goods. Young Bok and his family always feasted on this day, mostly with food from home, but buying an occasional treat from the vendors.

Young Bok loved looking at all the smiling faces, all the families gathered, laughing and sweaty. For a moment, he could let go of the heavy burden of remembering his family's past and his father's resentment of the Japanese. He could be just a student and a son and a brother playing beneath a warm summer sun.

CHAPTER EIGHT

———

Yang Sil waited twelve years for her first daughter. She had four sons who she loved dearly: Cheotjjae and Duljjae and Setjjae and Netjjae. But it was a daughter who was a treasure to the mother in Korean culture, an assistant to help with housework and cooking. Yang Sil's two eldest sons refused to have anything to do with "women's jobs." They never offered to help forage food from the forests or care for their younger siblings. Young Bok, however, was different. He was willing to do whatever he could to help his mother, and he proudly called himself a "mama's boy." Perhaps it was for this that Yang Sil always called Young Bok her precious Setjjae. Young Bok knew his brothers were jealous, but they had their father and the standards of traditional men to uphold.

Young Bok slipped easily into the role that a daughter might have filled. He collected wild vegetables and fruits from the mountains and forests: *namul,* wild onions, *tale,* mountain wild berries, and chestnuts.

At first, the other foraging girls cast side glances at him, nudging one another. Their gossiping voices traveled far in the damp quiet of the forests: "Why is he doing a girl's job? What is he doing here?" Young Bok ignored them, slipping between the trees into the darker parts of the forest where the vegetables were more flavorful, plentiful, and larger. After some time, the girls began to follow him, silent, then giggling nervously, then eventually letting him slip easily into their chit chatter.

Young Bok also liked to fish near the edge of the little stream where water swirled among the roots of bushes growing into the stream. He rolled up his pants to knee level, dropping his rough straw net into the river and standing very still. The water dripped from his bare arms, creating tiny ripples in the clear water as the fish glided around in front of him.

He brought home crawfish, shrimp, and small fish. They were precious additions to each meal, as meat was scarce. Young Bok loved when his mother smiled, a look in her eyes which said, *I am proud of you, my Setjjae.*

On one occasion, Young Bok felt his net tug violently and with a shout of triumph, he fought to close off and lift the net, convinced he had caught the largest fish of his career.

As he lifted the net toward his face to take a closer look, two eyes glared up at him from a tight ribbon-spring of writhing muscle. Young Bok screamed and tossed the net onto the bank. He sprinted across the fields toward the house, his heart about to tear through the skin of his chest.

He met his older brother, Cheotjjae, in the courtyard. Young Bok pushed back his hair, plastered with water and cold sweat, and panted. "There was a snake there!"

"Where? Where?" Cheotjjae grasped Young Bok's arm. There was a smile creeping into his mouth and eyes.

"In my fish net."

"What'd you do?"

"I left it there and ran away."

"Let's go, Setjjae." They sprinted out together, Young Bok keeping a wary distance behind his brother.

By the stream, they found the net. Young Bok backed away, covering his eyes.

Cheotjjae strode over, snatched up the net and shook it, water droplets spraying to the ground. "Empty, Setjjae. Are you sure you saw a—"

"I saw it. I saw it!"

"Setjjae…" Cheotjjae snaked a wet finger up Young Bok's back.

Young Bok screamed.

Several months later, in the fall, chestnuts fell plump and ripe in the mountainside. Overhead, the trees painted the sky with crimson and orange swatches. Young Bok wandered beneath them, humming a song as he gathered smooth chestnuts and dropped them into a sack. Deep in the forest, he suddenly stumbled upon a little Buddhist shrine. A huge snake several meters long curved its body around the shrine. Its belly crunched over the leaves, its tongue lazily slithering. Young Bok screamed.

Young Bok's mind immediately flashed to what he had heard an old village man say. A man with crooked teeth, he had leaned in confidentially to the others squatting in the shade beneath the village tree and said, "There is a guardian for the temple. It comes out if any animals come near. If anybody tries to destroy the temple, then BAHNG *jugeosseo*, you're dead! If you leave it alone, the guardian won't touch you." The other old men and women who gathered to talk beneath the tree nodded along.

Recalling these words, Young Bok inched slowly away from the shrine. Without blinking, he kept his eyes on the snake until he was far away enough to turn and sprint away.

After this, even the little harmless snakes in the garden were enough to make Young Bok throw aside his tools and run screaming for the house.

***

Finally, in 1935, when Young Bok was six, Daseotjjae, the first daughter of the family, was born. Young Bok loved her dearly. Even decades later, he still repeats, "I loved her," with great tenderness and a soft wetness in his eyes.

Every day after school, Young Bok raced home, sprinting down the hard dirt road with his backpack smacking his back in a *tuk-tuk-tuk* rhythm. At home, he threw down his backpack and books. In the distance, he could see his mother and father laboring in the fields. As he ran closer, he could see their mouths moving, singing the songs of planting or weeding. He watched the sinewy strength in their arms as they wrestled with the earth. Drops of sweat clung glistening to their foreheads, necks, and upper lips. Yang Sil always smiled wearily at Young Bok when he approached, pressing the back of her hand to her forehead to wipe away sweat. She paused in her labor to unwrap Daseotjjae from her back and used a thick swatch of cloth to wrap the baby tightly around Young Bok's back. Yang Sil smiled her thanks, and then Young Bok was off again, dashing toward the open fields to play with his friends.

Sometimes he glanced back to watch the two figures return to their work, where they would stay until dark had fallen.

Young Bok's brothers scorned the way he gathered the vegetables, fished, and carried the babies. "We are following the way of true men," they would always say. Sometimes Cheotjjae jabbed a strong finger into Young Bok's chest and pushed him. "Are you a girl?"

It was a similar refrain among Young Bok's friends. "Why're you carrying her with you? Are you a girl?"

"Let's look at the boji print," they catcalled, pulling up the back of his shirt and laughing as they pointed at the V-shaped indent on his back from his sister's pelvis.

At first, Young Bok was ashamed, hanging his blushing head and unable to meet their eyes. As time passed, he began to see the red mark on his back as a medal of honor. He was proud to help his mom. He was proud to make her happy, to see her smile even when she was tired in the fields. When his friends tried to reach for his shirt, he pulled it up first, yelling, "You want to see it? It's my badge of honor."

It became an accepted fact of life: where Young Bok went, his sister did too. Whether he squatted in the dirt to play cards, kicked around a soccer ball made of rags, or played tag or hide and seek in the fields and forests, Daseotjjae was with him.

Until he turned twelve, Young Bok cared for his younger siblings: Daseotjjae and then Yeoseotjjae, born in 1938. When Daseotjjae turned six, she took over the responsibility.

CHAPTER NINE

One morning, Young Bok struggled to wake up and change into his school uniform. Yang Sil pressed a hand to his hot forehead and said, "Setjjae, you should stay home today and sleep."

She tried to convince her seven-year-old son, bending to unfold one of the sleeping mats from the neatly stacked pile in the corner of the room. Young Bok refused, shaking his head again and again. He *would* go to school. He hadn't worked so hard to reach the top of his class and become the class president just for measles to get in the way of his education. He would *go.*

In the end, Sang Chul sighed deeply. Shaking his head, he waved his hand for Young Bok to leave.

Young Bok stumbled along the dirt road toward the elementary school, while his friends talked brightly, laughing and pushing each other. They kept their distance from Young Bok, though they glanced back once in a while. They mouthed words at each other, and in their widened eyes, he saw them asking him one question over and over: *Why don't you just go home?* Measles was nearly a rite of passage for every first or second grader. Everyone was familiar with the uncomfortable heat and rash that came with it; it was expected that they stay home to recover. *So why wouldn't he?*

It was all Young Bok could do to focus on the road. One foot in front of the other. A pause for a hacking cough, a breath leaning on his knees with his head down. He could feel the prickling itch of a rash on his forehead and sprinkled bumps across his body.

When Young Bok finally passed through the classroom door, he wiped a sleeve over the snot from his nose, panting from the effort of walking.

His teacher Maisoba Hachisangero hardly glanced at his face before waving him away. "Go home."

Tears filled Young Bok's eyes. He bowed his head slightly, watching his shoes, aware of his all-too-interested classmates. He squared his jaw. "No, I don't want to be absent."

The blackboard squeaked as Maisoba drew a swift stroke with a broken piece of chalk, continuing with his lesson. "You are not absent. You are retiring early because of the measles. You were in attendance, but now you must go home. Go rest now."

Young Bok hesitated. He stood very still, eyes a silent plea.

Maisoba kept writing but cast a brief look in Young Bok's direction, ambiguously placid. "Go home."

Young Bok turned back for the hour-long walk home.

Within a week, the measles had passed, and Young Bok was back at school as usual.

***

In class, on a rough wooden bench that hurt his behind when he sat still for too long, Young Bok learned Japanese language, Japanese history, math, and geography. Maisoba Hachisangero, Young Bok's teacher, was always hovering behind with a *bokken*, wooden sword, in his hand or slipped into his belt. He often stood behind the two tall, gangly teenage boys in Young Bok's first grade class. While they could easily outpace other students in races, their schoolwork was sloppy and Maisoba was not a patient man.

Once a week, there was music class. Gathered around an organ, Young Bok and the other students learned songs to praise Japan and its beauty, songs like *saita sakura*, an ode to the cherry blossom. "I was tone deaf," Young Bok recalled. Young Bok's eyes often wandered to the walls during these times, drifting over the portrait of His Imperial Majesty and the faded parchment papers written with inky Japanese characters.

War was already marching on in 1937, a conflict between the Japanese and Chinese that would last for eight years: the Second Sino-Japanese War.

On December 13, just across the Yellow Sea, a little over a thousand kilometers away from Pyongsong, the 66th battalion of fifty thousand Japanese soldiers surrounded the city of Nanking. After weeks of fierce battle, ninety thousand Chinese troops had retreated to the city, joining about half a million civilians. The Japanese soldiers promised the tired and ragged Chinese soldiers fair treatment if they surrendered.

They surrendered in droves.

What followed was a six-week-long massacre. Surrendered Chinese soldiers, now prisoners of war, were divided into groups of one to two hundred men and led off to be slaughtered in secret. Nearly 150,000 died this way. Japanese soldiers invaded the unprotected city, shooting people randomly in the street and storming homes to "look" for Chinese soldiers who had not yet surrendered. The blood of thousands of innocent civilians turned the banks of the Yangtze River red.

Japanese and foreign journalists were horrified by these events, documenting the atrocities that they had witnessed in graphic detail. Their writing made its way into the Japanese newspapers.

In Korea, Young Bok never saw a newspaper article about the events of these weeks.

And then there were the undiscussed events, those that would be denied for decades after. In that ill-fated city of Nanking, between twenty thousand to eighty thousand women were brutally raped. Many were mutilated or killed.

Afterward, to avoid international backlash, the Japanese high command planned a system of military prostitution. This way they could still reward their soldiers for fighting their battles but reduce the rape of local women. The provision of "comfort women" fell heavily on the Japanese colony of Korea, where a majority of the 80,000 to 200,000 comfort women were kidnapped or coerced into service between 1938 and 1945.

In 1938, the Japanese government released documents to the public detailing the further assimilation of Koreans into Japanese nationhood. It was well timed. Japan needed the willing cooperation of their Korean colony and a total mobilization of all of the empire's resources so that they might win the war. Though there were very few practical approaches to bridge the actual divide between the Japanese and Korean people, the total mobilization was effectively multi-pronged: there would be an expansion of education facilities, with an emphasis on Japanese language training, more health facilities in preparation for wartime casualties, and an adjustment of everyday life activities.

Young Bok heard little news about the war, but he knew that he was to walk rather than use public transport, eat simple food, and save water by wearing colorful clothing that could be washed less frequently than traditional white clothing. At home, Sang Chul grumbled and swore, "Those filthy Japanese!"

In February 1938, "Laws Concerning Army Special Volunteers" permitted acceptance of Koreans into the Japanese military. By 1943, this became compulsory enlistment. Korean anti-Communist associations sprouted up everywhere to combat Chinese communism. Anti-Communist "spiritual" discussions became mandatory in the workplace and in schools. These "patriotic groups" promoted support for the war, worship at Shinto shrines, and recitation of the oath of loyalty to the emperor. Leftists, nationalists, and intellectual Koreans with "impure ideas" were given the "opportunity" to join groups to "reform their thoughts." The reality was interrogation or jail.

As the undeclared war between China and Japan raged on, more and more Korean rice plumped out sacks on the railway lines to feed Japanese and conscripted Korean soldiers. At school, students were forbidden to eat plain white rice. Japanese officials insisted that they add millet or red bean, or else risk punishment.

***

Maisoba paced around the room during the lunch hour, peering at the students' different rice and side dishes. His *bokken*, wooden stick, trailed across the desks, a shuddering *thump thump thump*. Young Bok held his breath. He fiddled with his rice container. It was the rare occasion that Yang Sil packed white rice for Young Bok, but when she did, she was always careful to disguise it as grain by adding sesame seeds. It was one such day, and Young Bok was wary of being caught. Maisoba squinted, suspicious eyes small and hard. He tapped his wooden sword on the desk and eyed Young Bok's face. Young Bok froze, hardly daring to chew. The rice in his mouth was sticky and warm with saliva. After a moment, Maisoba exhaled loudly and passed on.

Next to Young Bok, Sok Sae Cho, one of Young Bok's best friends, was eating white rice and beef. He chewed with great enjoyment, hardly even glancing up at Maisoba. Sok Sae Cho's father was a town council member and a wealthy merchant. He was a smooth man, quick to bow, to laugh, and to smile with Japanese officials, with none of the bitter reserve of his fellow Koreans. He ran the school supply store, roomed a Japanese school teacher at his home, one of the largest in the entire village, and bribed the teachers to treat his son well. The rumors and gossip surrounding the family were unrelenting: *lack of honor, spoiled, shameless.*

Sok Sae Cho *was* rather spoiled, quick to show off his wealth and privilege with meat lunches or new shoes. But he was smart and studied hard, and this quickly earned Young Bok's respect.

A few times a week after lunch, there was an hour of physical education or labor, centered around cultivating land, weaving straw ropes, or caring for animals belonging to the school or teachers. Throughout much of Young Bok's grade school years, the children dug trenches.

Young Bok's hands blistered from the effort of plunging a shovel deep into the dirt, hitting stones, jumping with bare feet on the shovel handle. Down, down, down. Dirt in his nails, his nose, sticking to his sweaty forehead. During the warm months, he and the other boys took off their shirts, working with their backs to the sun. They passed off the stones they struck to the younger children who balanced them on their heads and walked away with shaking arms.

When school ended at four o'clock in the afternoon, all the students shuffled their belongings into their bags and stood up to leave. Maisoba always gestured to Young Bok and said, "After your bows, stay to help me grade papers." Such was the perk of being the top student in the class.

All the students filed out by class year into the main courtyard. In even rows, they lined up to bow and salute to the teachers before they exited the school grounds. Then, Young Bok returned to the empty classroom, where he would spend the next hour sitting at a desk across from his teacher, grading tests and papers. It was dull work, painful even, especially when he heard his classmates laughing and yelling as they planned an outing for chestnut picking or sledding after newly fallen snow. Every afternoon, Young Bok grasped the tea kettle and poured fragrant, steaming tea into his teacher's cup. Maisoba rarely said anything, sometimes staring out the window holding his cup, always sitting with his back straight as an ironing board. When an hour had passed or the stack of papers had shrunk significantly, Maisoba waved his hand at Young Bok and dismissed him. Sometimes he smiled, but other times his eyes and mouth remained hard. There was always a thoughtfulness behind his eyes.

As a retired sergeant from the Japanese military, Maisoba retained a strict sense of discipline and hierarchy. When he entered the classroom in the morning, he bellowed, "*KIOTSUKE*," the military command for attention. The children stood by their desks unblinkingly, with hands stiff at their sides.

If a single student made a mistake in the course of a lesson, Maisoba seized the *bokken* at his side and shouted, "*Kyodo Sekinin!* Collective responsibility!" A light burned deep inside his eyes, and he loped around the room with the notched wooden sword in hand.

Smack! Smack!

To each child, he dealt a blow to the head with a practiced flick of his muscled arm. Whimpers of pain followed in his wake, glares at the student who had failed, resentful eyes stared at Maisoba's roaming back.

When the blow came to his head, Young Bok's eyes filled with tears. He repeated a whispered cry in his head, *I was his friend. I did nothing wrong.* For Maisoba, Young Bok sat in that dull, silent room every afternoon. He poured tea, graded papers, and silently obeyed.

Furthermore, in Korean culture, the head was never to be hit; it was the most disrespectful possible punishment. It was no accident that Maisoba had chosen the head, and in Young Bok's eyes, it aligned all too neatly with the imperialist thinking: *There will be no smart Koreans. This is slavery education.* It was unjust, and the little flame of anger in his heart swelled against the Japanese system.

***

"Cleaning day's tomorrow, isn't it?" Young Bok squatted over the pit in the ground.

"Who has the tickets?" asked Chung In Sun.

Kim Ing Mo and Sok Sae Cho grunted next to him over a series of pits, fanning away the flies, "Chae Jin Shil, Lee Dak Ho, Lee Jae Hwa…" They continued listing names. "Not sure though. They may have passed it off to someone else."

In 1937, the Government-General of Korea banned the use of the Korean language in government offices, and by 1938, the ban extended to the use of Korean at schools. The principal at Young Bok's school enforced it by giving tickets designating bathroom cleaning duty to anyone who was heard speaking Korean. In the week between each bathroom cleaning day, the tickets passed between students, friends even, dropped like a scalding hot sweet potato.

The four boys could hear their poop sloshing down into the holes, the odor rising like a warm wave to slap them in the face. The flies buzzed and hummed.

"Ha," Sok Sae Cho's laugh clogged in the sticky warm darkness. "Someone missed again." They skirted a pile of poop on their way out of the bathroom. The swarming of the flies was a sickening song of contentment.

The next morning, Kim Ing Mo, Chung In Sun, and a few other neighborhood boys came early to meet Young Bok at his gate to walk to school together. Young Bok was still eating, but when he heard their laughing voices at the door, he hurriedly gulped down some *juk*, rice porridge, and dashed toward the courtyard and outside gate. His father's stern voice called him back to the room where the rest of his family was still eating. Sang Chul laid down his chopsticks.

"Abeoji…" Young Bok's eyes darted toward the doorway where he could see his friends peeking at him, making faces and waving at him. *Hurry up, let's go to school.* If he used Korean in front of his friends… Behind his back, Young Bok's hands were two twisted spiders fighting each other.

"Abeoji and Uhmuhnim…" Young Bok continued the rest of the farewell in Japanese, head bowed low. He refused to meet his father's eyes. The room went silent; the family froze mid-bite. Sang Chul's knuckles were white.

Sang Chul slammed his fist down on the wooden tray. A chopstick flew and stuck upright in the oil paper floor. The dishes on his tray clattered, soup trembling and sloshing onto his lap. "Do not speak that *Jjokbari* language to me!" A grain of rice spit in his vehemence stuck to the corner of his mouth. Young Bok watched it bob and jerk with each yelled word. His father's neck veins protruded like small rushing rivers.

"I'm very sorry, Abeoji," Young Bok bowed his head low, staring down at his feet. In a quieter voice, hardly daring to glance toward his friends who were now openly staring through the doorway, he repeated his farewell in Korean. "*Abeoji, hakyo danyuh ogaesseumneeda.*" (Goodbye, Father. I am going to school. I will see you later.)

Sang Chul dismissed him with a brief nod.

Young Bok bowed again before rushing out of the room. The click and clank of chopsticks on bowls resumed.

Young Bok had scarcely stepped out of the gate before one of the boys tapped him on the shoulder. With a rueful smile, the boy held out a ticket in the palm of his hand. It was slightly damp with sweat; he had been clutching it in his fist, waiting for this moment.

Young Bok glared, raising his small fists in challenge, "Give it to me, and I will punch you."

There was hesitation in the boy's face. The other three boys watched on in interested silence. The boy took a step backward.

Young Bok himself was no threat—he was scrawny and small. But everyone knew his older brother Cheotjjae was *jangsa*, strong and well-built, just like his father. Even a winner of the Ssireum competition once.

The boy closed his fist over the ticket again, bowing a silent apology. "Okay, okay. I didn't hear anything. That's fine with me. Just don't tell anyone you spoke Korean and I didn't give you the ticket."

They walked a little way like that, Young Bok still huffy at the injustice of it. The boy challenged Young Bok to a race, and by the time they had run about a half mile on the long dusty road, they were laughing, breathing hard, and grinning at one another, waiting for the other three boys to catch up.

CHAPTER TEN

———

Cotton matured by mid-August; blue buds growing hard and darker before the mouths opened and white cotton bloomed. Yang Sil blinked in the fields against the hot sun, picking the white bolls of cotton from their prickly beds. Once she had carted the harvest home, the seeds had to be teased apart from the fluffy cotton and hung on the walls to dry. They would then be stored away for the next season of sowing.

Yang Sil beat the cotton with a stringed bow instrument to separate the fibers into small rolls. These puffs of cotton could then be attached to the end of a handmade wooden spindle and twisted and spun into thread. While spinning her thread, Yang Sil gathered with the other women from the village to pass the time. They sang songs passed down from their mothers and their mothers' mothers, gossiped, and exchanged tidbits of news.

Once she had a roll of cotton thread, Yang Sil could begin the process of weaving the threads with a handmade loom. She strung the cotton threads lengthwise through the heddle, a wooden beam with holes bored for the threads, and tied them off at the ends. The heddle hooked to a rough straw slipper by which she could use her foot to move the loom up and down. A boat-shaped wooden shuttle was used to weave another long thread lengthwise through the warp threads. It took around twenty to thirty hours to weave a single roll of cloth.

After this, Yang Sil cut the cloth and sewed it into whatever clothing her family needed. Most of the clothing Yang Sil wove was simple and white, as she had no time for embroidery, elaborate dyes, or patterns. For the required gray fabric of her children's school uniforms, she smoked some of the cotton threads over the chimney of the fire, blackening them to a fine ashy gray.

For the summer months, Yang Sil wove *mosi*, fine, delicate fabric from ramie. When the ramie had been harvested, she stripped it of its outer husk with the bent blade of a knife and tied it in rough bunches on a drying line, fibers protruding like the legs of dried squid. The inner layer, she soaked in water and then dried. With her teeth, Yang Sil broke down the inner husk to draw out the stringy fibers before brushing through the fibers. Then, she rolled together the fibers by hand until they became soft and silky. These were tied into regular bundles with a cross of thread to wrap them. Then, the raw threads had to be inserted into the yarn guide and starched with a rough brush before the weaving process on a home-made loom could begin.

Though Yang Sil was respected for her skill in weaving, her cooking skill was even more renowned by the villagers. Young Bok remembers that Yang Sil helped with the food preparation for nearly every birthday, wedding, and funeral in their twenty-house village. No big event was complete without Yang Sil's kimchi.

The village said proudly, "Our Yang Sil makes the best kimchi."

"Her touch makes it taste better."

"She has a generous and serving spirit."

Young Bok loved hearing these things about his mother. He was already proud to be her son, but hearing these words, he always stood a little taller and smiled a little wider.

In late autumn, *kimjang*, kimchi preparation, began. *Kimjang* was largely a community affair, and the women usually coordinated to do theirs on different days in order to help one another. They gathered, chattering, with their large bowls and heads of cabbage. At home, many had already dug great holes for the *tok*, ceramic jars, where the kimchi would be stored. These jars were wide enough for two or three people to stand abreast up to neck level.

Yang Sil knew how to select the best heads of cabbage, rinsing and soaking them in salt water. Then, she added turnips and radishes before delicately peeling back each leaf of the cabbage and stroking it with a mixture of salt, red pepper, garlic, and ginger. Yang Sil's hands would smell of *kimchi* for days after. The women stacked the tightly bundled cabbages into the large jars and left them to ferment for a couple weeks. Underground, they would be protected from the heat and the cold.

The family ate some of the *kimchi* soon after *kimjang*. It was crisp and fresh, still sweet with natural cabbage flavor. The rest would be eaten throughout the winter and grew progressively more sour and ripe as time passed.

In the fall, usually around the end of the tenth lunar month, Yang Sil made *maeju*, a brick of fermented soybean, for sauces. To make *maeju*, soybeans had to be boiled, crushed in the mortar, and then shaped into a brick shape. Yang Sil hung these from the ceiling rafters to dry for two to three months, like crooked presents. After this, she washed the dried brick to remove dirt and soaked it in salt water. Another couple months and the blackish mixture became *ganjang*, soy sauce. The solid residues, *doenjang*, were skimmed off and used as soup bases. *Gochujang*, spicy paste, was made from a mix of glutinous rice, *maeju*, red pepper, and salt.

Young Bok loved walking into the courtyard and looking at the merry gathering of covered pots of sauces: small for the *gochujang* and *doenjang*, medium for the *ganjang*, and the large tops of kimchi pots poking up from the ground.

Yang Sil also raised silkworms, hatching larvae from eggs in a storage room that she heated with the *ondol* flooring. She fed them carefully with mulberry leaves, sometimes standing in the dark room to listen to the quiet sound of their chewing, their little legs whispering against the leaves. Starting as small as grains of rice, the silkworms grew to near finger length. After about a month had passed, they wove thick cocoons of silk thread nearly a mile long and Yang Sil plopped the cocoons into a pot of boiling water. She stirred with a long pair of chopsticks until they softened, and the silk ends unraveled like loose spiderwebs in the pot. She used a *jasae*, a special instrument, to twist together the fibers and then wound the silk using a spinning wheel. The thread alone took nearly fifteen hours to make.

Whenever Young Bok heard his mother working on the loom to weave silk cloth, his mind immediately flashed to New Year's Day.

Don't close your eyes. In their shared cotton mats on the floor, Cheotjjae, Duljjae, Setjjae, and Netjjae whispered to each other. Through the curtain dividing the room, they could hear

Daseotjjae, the baby, crying in the other room, where she slept between Yang Sil and Sang Chul.

Don't fall asleep. Netjjae had already drifted off, but the elder three struggled to keep their eyes open. There was an old saying that if anyone slept on New Year's Eve, their eyelashes would turn white. They had never lasted through the night, but a delicious fear of the suspicion kept their sleepy heads from drooping too long.

In the morning, Yang Sil spread out new white *hanboks,* traditional Korean clothing, which she had woven for each of the family members: a blend of new silk and fresh cotton. For each of the boys, there were long-sleeved *jeogori,* pants, and silky warm vests to go over it.

"It's like wearing nothing. So light but so warm!" Young Bok exclaimed.

Smoothing down the vests, Yang Sil looked into each of her sons' eyes and smiled. The lines around her face softened. Young Bok knew she was tired from the cooking preparations for the New Year's celebration, but there was no sign of it as she bustled around the kitchen, feeding them *tteokguk,* rice cake soup.

When the meal was finished, all four boys performed *sebae,* bowing, before their parents. Slowly sinking to their knees, they folded the left hand over the right, pressed their hands to the ground, and brought their head to their hands in a low bow. Sitting back on their heels in unison, they chanted, "*Saehae bok mani badeuseyo.*" Sang Chul and Yang Sil passed back the New Year's blessing of much luck in the coming year.

Already smiling, the four darted outside into the crisp, frosty cold. The sun had scarcely risen to wink over the snow-powdered roofs, but the streets were alive with the patter of small feet, laughter and greeting calls between neighbors, and the smell of rice cakes and their sugary red bean filling. The fields were empty for a day, every farmer taking a rare break for the holiday. Young Bok and his brothers stopped at every home, bowing to the elders and receiving money and food in return. They avoided the handful of Japanese homes, but for the rest of the twenty-house village, the atmosphere was intimate, as between family: everyone was a brother or a sister, a mother or a father to the others.

When Young Bok and his brothers returned home, chattering and animated from the outing, they sat down to a meal of fresh fruit, *tteok*, rice cakes, five-grain sticky rice, and *yakwa*, a sticky fried dough soaked in honey and ginger. There was *bindaetteok,* called *chisim* in the countryside, a fried mung bean pancake with vegetables and a little meat. Ordinary rice cakes with sesame and honey tucked inside like pot stickers, gluey rice cakes dusted with red bean crusted powder, cake-like airy, fluffy rice cakes made with baking powder, and homemade sticky, firm sweets crafted with rice, raisins, and chestnuts. They ate for almost the entire day, laughing, joking, and carefree. When it grew dark, they played loud games of *yut*, moving little painted men around a board with the rolls of four patterned sticks.

With full bellies, they tumbled into their beds, New Year's blessings still on their lips.

CHAPTER ELEVEN

———

In 1939 and 1940, the Government-General of Korea announced that the emperor had "graciously allowed" all Korean subjects to choose Japanese surnames. The new change would align Korean registration with family, as in Japan, rather than the present system based on lineage. The current family registries had an average of two mistakes per registry: ghost registries when the head of a family passed away, repeated registries as families moved between towns, unreported births, incorrect ages. All these inaccuracies would prevent the implementation of a military draft in the future. Therefore, though the Korean people were only "encouraged" to take this offer, anyone who did not take one of these names lost access to mail delivery, ration cards, or formal recognition by the colonial bureaucracy. Their children could be denied entrance to school or deprived of job opportunities.

Within six months, over three million households, 75 percent of the population, had registered new names.

Sang Chul sat with quiet fury, erupting every few minutes in a tirade, "First, they take our freedom. Those *Jjokbari*..." He spit into the dirt. "They kill us and tell us we are worthless. They ruin our clothing. They cut the *sangtus* off old men."

Young Bok pictured men yelling in the streets: harsh barked Japanese commands and angry voices and pained moans. There was the glinting click of swords and knives in the streets and the swish of thick calligraphy brushes in pots of dark ink, like day-old blood. Korean men with traditional *sangtus,* thick hair buns, were yanked to their knees, old and young alike, to face the shame of the blade, to watch their black and silvering and white hair fall to the ground. Those in traditional Korean white clothing were told to hold arms out to their sides as Japanese soldiers slashed dark ink in sweeping Xs across front and back, legs and arms. The shame of some left them crumpled on the dirt, others moaned in grief, and then there were those with anger behind blazing eyes, fists clenched so tightly their arms shook with the effort of restraint.

"They dishonor us," Sang Chul continued. "They take our language. They take our publications. They take our rice. They take our men and women and children. And now they will take our names?"

Ansan Kim, Sang Chul wrote. It was their clan name, a name meaning peaceful mountain. Sang Chul had never learned to write Japanese characters, and he handed the ink brush to Young Bok to write down possible Japanese names. *Kaneyama,* Young Bok wrote. *Kaneda, Kanegawa, Kanehada.*

"We are the Kims," Sang Chul muttered fiercely under his breath. Down came his fist in his lap, again and again. "We are the Kims."

Kane was the equivalent of Kim in Japanese, but each ending meant something new: *kaneyama* was mountain, *kaneda* was rice field, *kanegawa* was river. They settled on *Kaneyama,* the closest equivalent to their clan name.

Then, new names for each of them, foreign names that were strange to the tongue and jarring to write. Sang Chul helped Young Bok pick a name that meant the same as his Korean name. *Kaneyama Inghang. Kaneyama Inghang.* The letters burned against his eyes. "My name is Kim Young Bok. Kim Young Bok," Young Bok whispered. And then in a refrain of his father, "We are the Kims."

Young Bok had already known why his father disapproved of his attendance at the Japanese school, but the loss of their family names cemented his understanding. How could his father possibly approve of education by a nation that had stripped their family and the entire Korean nation of its dignity?

When Young Bok's two older brothers had dropped out of elementary school after only two years, Sang Chul approved of their decision. "You don't need that Japanese education. That's more than enough Japanese school for you."

But Young Bok labored on at school. He was determined to succeed. He would stay at the top of the class, and he would go to high school and then college, an ambition which Sang Chul did not understand.

One night, Sang Chul glanced over at Young Bok as he pored over his math homework. Sang Chul angled his tongue over his teeth to remove a fiber of meat lodged behind his canine. He stood up, grunting a bit, before treading heavily back to his seat with an abacus in hand. Young Bok had often seen his father use this abacus, his experienced hands flicking the beads around to quickly calculate large sums. It was true that Sang Chul had never finished elementary school, but he was still a bright man.

"Add up the numbers from one to one hundred," said Sang Chul.

Young Bok, pencil in hand, looked up at his father. "I don't have to do that. I know how to use the formulas."

Sang Chul jerked his head in Young Bok's direction, a sign to continue anyways.

By the time his father had counted up to forty-five, Young Bok already had the answer written neatly on a sheet of paper. "Abeoji," he pointed.

Sang Chul squinted at the number, "No, you don't know." He returned to his abacus. Young Bok watched Sang Chul's fingers fly across the wooden beads, his father's mouth twitching slightly as he counted without sound. When he had finished, Sang Chul was silent for a moment. He wrinkled his forehead. Rubbed his nose. Faced Young Bok. A subtle change came over his face. "It's correct."

Another pause, and then as though the words almost pained him, "Mm, school has something useful."

Young Bok tried not to smile too widely. He bowed his head, "Yes, Abeoji."

CHAPTER TWELVE

The smell of new things—rubber erasers, tang of pencil lead, dye of school uniforms—made Young Bok's heart beat fast as he stepped into Sok Sae Cho's father's store. He imagined writing with a sharp pencil on a clean, crisp notebook. Wearing a neat uniform to the first day of school with a new bag slung over his shoulder.

Yang Sil was already counting out money by the counter of the store, and her forehead was crinkled in concentration. When she caught Young Bok watching, she smiled and hid the bills behind her hand, waving him to continue shopping.

When Yang Sil returned to her counting, Young Bok stood very still, grinding his teeth and furrowing his eyebrows. Then he slipped a couple notebooks back into the pile of store goods. He only really needed one for the school year. And the school bag… He realized how tightly he clung to the strap. *You don't need it, Young Bok.* He returned it. He could do with one uniform, too. He nodded to himself, and then trotted up to his mom. "All ready, Umma!"

"Mm? Good, Setjjae." Yang Sil reached out to stroke Young Bok's head. "Only one uniform? Let's buy another." She picked up another school uniform from the stack and held it up to check his size.

Young Bok took it from her hand. "Umma, almost everyone has only one uniform. It's alright if we make more at home. You don't have to buy another one." He folded the uniform neatly and set it back on the pile.

Yang Sil pursed her lips, and Young Bok knew she was calculating in her head. They both already knew they couldn't afford another uniform.

"Umma, really! It's fine. The ones you make at home look the same."

Yang Sil nodded and smiled a little, only with her mouth. "Alright, Setjjae."

They bought the schoolbooks for that year, too. They were fairly new, published by the Japanese Ministry of Culture and Education and edited by the Government-General of Korea, as part of the 1938 Ordinance of Choseon (Korean) Education. It was an ordinance with phrases like *kukche myongjing* (the emperor is the nation), *naesun ilche* (Japan and Korea are one), and *ingo dallyon* (building body and mind through hardiness and perseverance). Phrases that Young Bok could not fully understand. What he *did* know was that a single curriculum had been implemented across the entire nation of Korea. What he *did* know was that the new textbooks loved to repeat the same phrase in different ways: Japan had built up an "intimate, organic, and mutually beneficial relationship with the rest of Asia" during the thirteenth and seventeenth centuries (Wray, 1973). Everything pointed toward a history of unflagging and persistent development forward, a nation united by their divine origins, loyalty to the Imperial family, and devotion to morality and progress. Japan did not need the

West: there were prime examples of scientific, technological, and agricultural heroes from their own history, people like Hiraga Gennai and Seki Takakazu. As the books told him, Japan's greater goal was to unify all sister Asian nations: "Our mission is to restore to life the peoples of Greater East Asia and let them achieve their own place" (Wray 1973).

You are a lesser people. The Japanese are your superiors. These were the truths pounded into Young Bok's head every day, despite the claims of supposed *naesun ilche* and "equality" between the Japanese and Korean. In his ethics textbook, Young Bok could turn to the dog-eared page in the middle and read that the Koreans needed to "catch up" to the Japanese. He could plow through essays titled, "Three Reasons Why Korean Rice Is Bad" and "Korean Houses are Small and Weak" and "Koreans Don't Take Baths." Or he could read about how Korea was a nation of people lacking "national vitality" whom Japan had rescued, how Japan had fought off the Chinese and Russian people, and how the Koreans were so impressed with Japan's successes that they joyfully sought annexation.

Young Bok also read the terms *naichi* and *gaichi.* Japan was the inner area, *naichi,* the homeland, and Korea was the outer area, *gaichi,* the territories. In Young Bok's head, this was a euphemism for calling Korea a slave nation.

And maybe they were just that.

Living in a society where all the Japanese were more well off than the average Korean, where Young Bok was told again and again that Japanese society was superior, it truly began to feel that the Japanese were superior. After all, even the Koreans who traveled to Japan for an education returned richer and more powerful than when they left.

The oppressive reality made him hot with anger and help-lessness, and his feelings were like little pebbles in the back of his throat, threatening to choke him. He could choose to swallow them down, accept them, but he knew that if too many sunk to his stomach, they would kill him. Every day Young Bok fought his anger back, chanting in his head, *My grandfather resisted the Japanese during the March First Movement, and now he is leading followers of Chondogyo in the Koksan.*

And every day, Young Bok was reminded that the little flame of Korean spirit had not yet sputtered out. He saw the sly looks two Koreans would exchange when a Japanese approached, the subtle leaning in to murmur, "*Jjokbari onda,*" or "Japanese coming." Even little children in their play stopped to whisper and then giggle.

Yet despite his hatred for the imperialist system, Young Bok sought to succeed in the classroom. He wanted to be educated: high school, then college. If he scored perfectly on an exam or ranked first in his class, his mother smiled. And that was enough.

At home, Sang Chul fumed, "There was a Goguryeo dynasty for seven hundred years, the Silla for one thousand, the Bakjae for six hundred, and so on. Three thousand years of Korean history and culture! How can it be erased with only a few decades of persecution?"

Sang Chul told his children stories about the creation of Goryeo, and then the Choseon dynasty. He told of bloody battles, courageous generals, court conspiracies, techno-logical advances. Deep into the night, he told the story of their forefathers.

Yang Sil told them the story of the sun goddess, the *amaterasu omikami*, who was considered to be the emperor's ancestor.

In legend, there was once a Korean woman, an advisor of the emperor of the Goguryeo dynasty, who traveled across the sea to Japan. She appeared before a large company of Japanese men and said, "Obey me, and I can lead your country well. I am wise and knowledgeable and will help your country prosper."

The men scoffed at her, laughing so hard they clung to their bellies.

The woman was very calm. She called out in a clear voice, "If you don't want to listen to me, I will go back." She disappeared into a nearby cave.

That very moment, the sun disappeared, and the sky was as dark as night.

The men shouted with fear, tumbling to the ground. They cowered and bowed until their foreheads were pressed deep into the dirt. "Please come out. We will be obedient."

From the depths of the cave, the woman's voice echoed, "Are you sure you will listen to me?"

"Yes! Yes! We will."

The woman emerged after some time, and over her head, like a bright crown, the sun burst out.

"A sun goddess! A sun goddess!" they yelled, bowing to the ground again.

"*Yeosin*, goddess, they called her," said Yang Sil. "Our children, the Japanese emperor was first a *Korean* woman. She was cunning and knew well the patterns of the stars and the timing of an eclipse."

This means that the Japanese are our brothers and sisters! Young Bok thought.

CHAPTER THIRTEEN

———

Yang Sil beamed as she smoothed out the dark cloth around Cheotjjae's shoulders with one hand. "*Uri* Cheotjjae, firstborn." On the other arm, she held the three-year-old Yeoseotjjae.

Cheotjjae smiled and grasped his mother's hand, but his eyes watched Sang Chul.

He spread out his arms to show off the dark silk *dallyeong* with its rounded neckband and then adjusted his black silk *samo* hat. He raised his eyebrows, seeking approval from his father.

"*Jangsa*," said Sang Chul, with rare softness in his voice. "You are eighteen, and you will become a man today, my son."

Cheotjjae smiled and bowed his head. A faint blush of pleasure crept up his ears.

Duljjae, who had been leaning against one of the courtyard walls, straightened up and walked over to his brother, "Congratulations, Hyung." There was hesitation in his words, sadness lingering in the way he looked up at his brother. It was true that Cheotjjae would still live in the same home with the rest of the Kim family after his marriage, but he would no longer be the same Cheotjjae. Though he had not been considered a boy for several years now, he had not fully been an adult either. Now he would carry the weight and responsibilities of his own household. He would be a husband.

Young Bok stared down at his brother's boots. Just last week, he, Cheotjjae, Duljjae, and Netjjae had run shouting into the stream to cool off. Cheotjjae had torn off his clothing into a messy pile. Duljjae did the same, while Young Bok carefully folded his and Netjjae's into a neat stack beneath a bush. Butt-naked, they dunked each other under the water. Duljjae swooped Cheotjjae's leg out from under him, and he fell tumbling into the stream and scraped his back against the rough rocks. Cheotjjae came up spluttering. Sweeping the water from his eyes, he roared, "Duljjae!" before throwing his entire muscled frame at Duljjae. They both went tumbling down into the water with a splash that drenched the laughing Young Bok and Netjjae. When Cheotjjae had his full revenge upon Duljjae, he took to chasing Young Bok and Netjjae, challenging them to wrestling matches they knew he would win and would only end with a nose full of water.

He's getting married? Young Bok shook his head to clear his mind.

The entire family gathered around Cheotjjae as he mounted a donkey for the ride to his bride's home. The donkey was very skinny, and for a moment, Young Bok thought that it would collapse beneath Cheotjjae's weight. But it was a work donkey used to hard labor, and though its tail flicked with slight annoyance, it stood docile beneath the weight.

As Cheotjjae passed through the threshold of the family's home, his parents and siblings trailed after, holding wedding gifts of food and the ceremonial wooden goose. After years spent in negotiation of the betrothal process, eighteen-year-old Cheotjjae was finally getting married.

When they arrived at the bride's home, Cheotjjae swung easily off the donkey's back into a crowd of waiting people.

The usual tradition was for young relatives and neighbors to tie the groom's ankles and hang him upside from a tree with straw ropes. Chanting and teasing and laughing, they would hit the flats of his feet with thin reeds and sticks and say, "You cannot take this girl away."

They would wait for the mother-in-law to come out and beg for the release of her daughter's husband-to-be, offering money, meat, and fruit as bribes.

Only a month ago, a story had spread rapidly throughout all the neighboring towns and villages. In the next town over, one such wedding festivity had been taking place, but Japanese police had mistakenly received word that a group of Koreans had strung a Japanese man upside down from a tree. Rushing to the scene, they heard yelling and saw a writhing figure hanging by his ankles from a tree.

They fired their pistols five times. Two teenagers fell to the ground, bleeding from wounds. The others scattered.

Recently, this wedding tradition had been moved indoors.

And so, Cheotjjae was borne off into the courtyard by a loud and rowdy crowd holding coils of straw rope. Young Bok watched his brother's face as he disappeared into a sea of arms and heads. There was no telling how his quick-tempered brother would react.

The crowd strung Cheotjjae from a roof rafter alongside blocks of *maeju*.

Smack! Smack! With gusto, the crowd took turns hitting Cheotjjae's feet. "You can't take this girl," they chanted. "Why should you take her? Why should she be your bride? We can't let you have her."

Cheotjjae smiled through gritted teeth. His ears were a bright red, and the blood was slowly rushing toward his head. He clenched his hands into fists, but the rest of his body swung limply.

Young Bok breathed in sharply. In the crowd, he glimpsed two young neighborhood men who held a grudge against Cheotjjae. At last year's Dano, Cheotjjae had beat both of them at *ssireum,* and spent an entire hour after the wrestling match boasting in front of nearly half the town. "The village said that they were the strongest two." A shake of his head, "You saw how easily I brought them down. Just three moves. Three moves! I just brought in my arm like *BAHNG* and then my leg like *BAHNG* and just like that, I'm the winner!"

How could they resist such an easy opportunity to assuage their anger? They hit Cheotjjae's feet with stinging blows, and Cheotjjae's eyes widened. Amid roaring shouts and laughter, Cheotjjae swung out his arms wildly, trying to catch at these men's feet. The veins in his neck sprung out and his face grew redder and redder. His lip curled as the smacks kept coming. Young Bok cringed. In just a few moments, some choice swear words would come streaming from his brother's mouth.

Cheotjjae's soon-to-be mother-in-law broke through the crowd with a basket full of fruits and money. "Here, my friends! Here!"

The crowd broke apart, bowing as they received the bribes from the mother-in-law. They let Cheotjjae free, and he got to his feet, dusting off dirt. Immediately, he swiveled around to scan the heads of the crowd. Once he saw the two young men, he raised his fist and curled his lip. Laughing, they dashed out of the courtyard.

Later in the afternoon, Cheotjjae re-entered the courtyard with a fan covering his face, and his bride was led into the courtyard from the opposite side. She was dressed in traditional wedding attire: a crimson skirt, green top, and *wonsam*, ceremonial robe with multi-colored sleeves. The bride's wedding attire was borrowed; it was becoming difficult to afford such expenses at a time when even rice was rationed.

The bride stood shyly before the crowd, careful not to show her teeth as she smiled. Beneath her powdered face and the rouge spots on her cheeks and forehead, Young Bok wondered if she was blushing.

She must be happy to finally be married, Young Bok thought. A betrothal meant she was bound to the groom's family. If Cheotjjae had died before the actual wedding, the bride could never marry anyone else; she would become a virgin widow.

Cheotjjae and his bride faced each other in front of the elaborate wedding table filled with rice cakes, nuts, and fruit. Cheotjjae presented the ceremonial wooden goose to his bride's father.

The bride bowed twice, and Cheotjjae once. Twice again, and Cheotjjae responded again with a single bow. They passed a cup of wine, each taking a sip. After a short speech by the parents, the families and neighbors feasted together.

On the first night, the newlyweds were left alone in a room of the house. Relatives and neighbors teased and called after them as the newlyweds passed through the doorway with their rustling clothes. Neighborhood boys tried to get a peek inside by poking holes in the paper doors and windows with spit-wettened fingers or little sticks.

Cheotjjae would remain for three days and nights in the bride's home before going home alone. Over a period of several months, he would make three visits to the bride's home to exchange gifts of rice cakes and food. Only then would his bride come to live in his home.

CHAPTER FOURTEEN

―――――

"We destroyed the US! We destroyed the US!"

Young Bok pumped his arm up and down like everyone around him. There were Japanese soldiers in the streets watching them. Soldiers knocked on doors and commanded people into the streets to join the celebration. The villagers rushed out, pulling on warm layers and stepping out into the cold.

A Japanese flag waved overhead, and Young Bok looked up. A gust of wind half-furled the flag, and for a moment the sun shone through the red circle and all the faces around him were cast with a reddish glow, like blood.

It was December 7, 1941. The day of the attack on Pearl Harbor.

Young Bok wondered how many of the smiles were real, how many of the raised voices were raised in celebration, and how many were in fear. A little distance away, he could see his father walking in stony silence, his fists clenched to his sides. Young Bok wanted to reach out and shake Sang Chul. What if the soldiers were to see? And behind him, Cheotjjae strode with the same set jaw, clenched fists, and drawn back shoulders.

"We destroyed the US! We destroyed the US!"

Young Bok heard about the destruction later: Nearly twenty American naval vessels destroyed or damaged and 2,400 Americans dead.

On the 7th and 8th of December, Japanese troops landed in Thailand and northeast Malaya.

The radio announcements were triumphant, a grainy voice shouting, *"What an uproar! Japan's Imperial Forces got things off to a quick start with one splendid strike, then another in historic surprise attacks on Pearl Harbor, where the bravado of the US Asia fleet met with sudden defeat, and off the Malaya Coast, where the main forces of the British Asia fleet were utterly annihilated"* ("Japanese Announcement About the Attack at Pearl Harbor, 1941").

Korean newspapers like the *Donga Ilbo* and *Chosun Ilbo* had shut down. The only way to get news was by the radio or word of mouth.

And the radio these days only documented the victories of Japan.

On the 18th of December, the Japanese landed in Hong Kong.

On the 22nd of December, Japanese landed in the Philippines.

Cheotjjae and his wife moved back into the Kims' home, and Yang Sil repurposed her silkworm raising room into a bedroom for them. The smell of mulberry leaves lingered on.

Often, both families ate together in the courtyard. Sharing one cooking fire meant they could conserve wood. There was less rice in their bowls, and there were new wrinkles around Yang Sil's mouth and eyes.

Young Bok kept up his habit of swallowing stones that he found in the rice. Cheotjjae eyed him warily, but Cheotjjae's wife flashed Young Bok a grateful smile each time.

On the 25th, Hong Kong fell to Japan.

Word has it that Roosevelt and Churchill were shaken up and went pale upon hearing of the defeats. In a third strike, Hong Kong Island, England's strategic base for its hundred-year exploitation of East Asia, fell into ruin in only a matter of ten days. During this time, Churchill was sent reeling, cutting off contact with others and showing up in Washington. What these two headstrong countries are striving for will only lead them on a downhill path to military defeat ("Japanese Announcement About the Attack at Pearl Harbor, 1941").

Young Bok wasn't sure why they left the radio on in the background. It always put Sang Chul in a foul mood. He paced the room, growling, "*Aish,* those *Jjokbari. Aish.*"

Cheotjjae joined him in his pacing, while Duljjae sat and watched in pensive silence.

On January 2nd, Japan occupied Manila.

Occasionally while weeding the fields at home or digging trenches at school, Young Bok squinted upward to watch a B-29 passing through on its way to some Pacific Island. No matter what the Japanese said, Young Bok and many Koreans thought the Americans brought hope and the possibility of liberation. These B-29s with their silver wings were angels to Young Bok.

The planes were at too high of an altitude to be shot down, but the anti-aircraft still fired. Shells peppered the sky, in a distant rumble. Young Bok imagined the Japanese military shouting with little voices at that high soaring angel, "*We're still here. Still here! Don't forget us.*"

On the 8th of February, Japan invaded Burma.

Our barbaric enemies are already cowering in fear in the Pacific, and the fall of Manila shall mark the day of the Philippines' subjugation and reversion back to Greater East Asia. The enemy power of Singapore, which was —alas—boasting of its impenetrable stronghold before the Imperial Forces penetrated the jungle area of the Malay Peninsula and advanced southward like a raging tide, shall also vanish into nothingness in the midst of this glorious chapter in history ("Japanese Announcement About the Attack at Pearl Harbor, 1941").

Every day on his walk to and from school, Young Bok was surrounded by the shouting voices of boldface text and brightly colored images. Posters, pamphlets, and banners were everywhere: shop walls, the police station, school gates, windows of homes, and scattered across the dirt road. They talked about the "Great Asian Co-Prosperity sphere" and military recruitment. Some *kokutai*-stylized ones promoted the spiritual origins of Japan. Others showed great ugly pictures of Westerners as hairy, demonic monsters, *oni*.

These latter seemed to far outnumber the other posters. *The Western guest invaded wearing the guise of diplomacy and trade,* they read. *They carried greed, wealth, materialism, and selfishness. They are monsters!* Horrifying cartoons matched these descriptions. Monster faces with deep eyes, huge noses like an elephant's trunk, and dark hair growing all over their bodies. *YOU HAVE TO WALK A DAY TO SEE THEIR EYEBALLS*, the posters shouted. *THEY ARE NOT LIKE HUMANS. THEY ARE BEAST-LIKE. The AB (pronounced ABay), American and British, are the number one enemy. DO YOU WANT TO BE RULED BY THEM?* demanded the posters. *WE HAVE TO WIN AND KILL THEM.*

These posters terrified six-year-old Daseotjjae. She often woke in the middle of the night with nightmares. Sometimes it was enough to shift closer to her mother and go back to sleep. Other nights, she crept to Young Bok, gently shaking him awake, and he would sit with his arm around her, stroking her sweaty hair until she fell asleep again.

On the 15th of February, Singapore fell.

After the confiscation of a Singaporean rubber factory, Japanese forces shipped tons of rubber balls back to the mainland and to Korea. The school announced, "The mighty nation of Japan is winning the war. As a reward, each student will receive a rubber ball and…as a souvenir for our emperor's victory, a ration for tennis shoes!"

At this last announcement, Young Bok nudged his friend, Chung In Sun. They both looked down at their woven straw shoes, and then back at each other. With rubber tennis shoes, they could run faster and kick harder when they played soccer. Young Bok beamed. Sok Sae Cho looked down at his tennis shoes and shrugged.

On the 19th of February, Japan attacked Indonesia.

The military gains of the glorious Imperial Forces are truly great, and the Army, Navy, and Air Force should be given our heartfelt gratitude. We should also honor our courageous men who are ready to lay down their lives when charging enemy lines, as well as those who went out to conquer but never returned ("Japanese Announcement About the Attack at Pearl Harbor, 1941").

Throughout the war, the elementary school students marched all over town almost every day, singing a military march and waving the Japanese flag.

In May 1942, US and Japanese carrier forces clashed at the Battle of Coral Sea. Though there were major losses on both sides, it was the first time that the US Navy had checked a major Japanese offensive. Soon after, the Government-General of Korea announced that by December 1944, all twenty-year-old Korean men would be drafted into the Japanese military. The Japanese government was desperate for manpower, but a gradual shift gave the semblance of strength and control.

In June, the Battle of Midway marked a turning point in the War: the first major US victory against the Japanese.

In most of the villages, Japanese officials had set up singing towers with loudspeakers for radio broadcasts. The crackly voices of announcers continued to praise the emperor and the Japanese Imperial Forces. *Victory, honor, glory.*

Young Bok entered fifth grade, and his teacher Maisoba was finally replaced by a new teacher, an Ainu man. The rumors flew thickly around this man: *I heard he has hair all over his body. Don't the Ainu do the iyomante ceremony and kill bears? My parents said they were a dying race.*

Young Bok knew very little about the Ainu, only that they were indigenous to Hokkaido and considered second-tier citizens in Japan. Perhaps this is what drew him to Kaneyama Masaharu because he shared a background of oppression and discrimination similar to the occupied Koreans.

Kaneyama Masaharu was a patient man, and he rarely reacted, even when the class whispered or cast him sideways glances every time he entered the room. He took the students on trips to nearby landmarks, museums, and cities. In Young Bok's sixth grade year, he took the class to Port JinNamPo. Young Bok saw the ocean for the first time, marveling at the great expanse of glistening blue water.

In 1943 the Japanese government announced the Korean Naval Volunteer Soldier System and the Korean Student Volunteer Soldier System.

Many Korean elites and socialites acted as microphones of Japanese authorities, whether by choice or by coercion. Kim Hwal Lan, the first Korean woman to receive a doctoral degree, gave speeches and wrote articles persuading mothers and wives to support the draft.

In the *Maeil Sinbo*, Mo Yun Suk wrote the poem:

"The nation [Japan] is more important than your mother,
The nation is more important than family,
The nation, which is more important than life,
is beckoning you to come, so go" (Palmer, 2007).

Much of the propaganda was wasted on the public because too few Koreans spoke or read Japanese.

Posters, newspapers, and radio stations proudly shouted that to die for the Japanese nation was an honor, that the dead would be enshrined at Yasukuni shrine and become gods to be revered night and day. Korean soldiers would be "the right hand of the emperor," a "humble shield of the Emperor," a "soldier in the holy war" against the Anglo-American enemy.

What did a title mean if you were dead? thought Young Bok.

Yang Sil worried over her two eldest sons: Cheotjjae was twenty and Duljjae seventeen. It was true there was only voluntary military service at the moment, but the year planned for the official draft, 1944, was drawing closer. Yang Sil slipped Cheotjjae and Duljjae extra food at meals. She spent much time crouched on the floor, shifting through the rice to remove little stones. For Duljjae who was almost always cold, she wove clothing with leftover silk and cotton, materials she would normally have saved for New Year's.

Women disappeared from neighboring villages in larger numbers as the months passed. One day, Yang Sil went to the market stand where she always bought small bags of sugar. The young market woman who she spoke with every time was gone. In her place, a little bent old woman cried. Her granddaughter had been dragged into a vehicle by uniformed men just the week before.

Yang Sil pressed her hand but said nothing. Thousands of women had already disappeared. Stripped of their families, their homeland, and their dignity, these women were thrown into horrific conditions of forced prostitution to the imperial Japanese army.

Yang Sil kept eight-year-old Daseotjjae close to her at all times.

CHAPTER FIFTEEN

———

Young Bok graduated in 1942 at the top of his class, the twenty-fifth graduating class since the founding of his elementary school. As he proudly accepted a certificate for no absences over the course of the six years, Yang Sil beamed from the audience.

Almost the moment he returned home, Sang Chul said, "That's enough Japanese education." Sang Chul's statement was a declaration, and Young Bok knew better than to question it. Usually only a fraction of elementary graduates attended middle school and high school, and nearly all of Young Bok's elementary school classmates would remain at home to work on their parents' farms or businesses.

For a year, Young Bok worked as a bank orderly, scurrying around the bank building mailing letters, counting money, sweeping the floor, and taking orders from the bankers. He was happy with the plump little envelope that he brought home to his parents, but Young Bok wanted to go to school. After a year of work, he finally convinced Sang Chul to let him attend middle school.

Three years later and it was the debate over high school. Again, Sang Chul demanded how Young Bok could possibly need more Japanese education. Even the day before school, as Young Bok finished packing his few belongings, Sang Chul stood over him. For nearly the tenth time, he muttered, "Why do you have to go there? For what? You already learned all that the *Jjokbari* can give you. And now you want more?"

Yang Sil pressed his arm with a silencing look. "Setjjae studies hard. He wants to go to high school, Yobo. He'll be successful."

"And the money?"

Yang Sil looked up at her husband and said, "Yobo, it's not very much. Most of it will be for textbooks and Setjjae can bring those home when he has used them. Then the rest of the children can use them, too."

***

In the spring, Young Bok attended Sunan High School, which, like most other high schools in the area, was shared between several towns. The school, a large brick building, was a five-hour walk from Young Bok's hometown. Yang Sil went with Young Bok to help him settle into the dorm, and when she left, Young Bok watched from the doorway until he couldn't see her anymore. It was his first time living away from home.

Nights were lonely and often Young Bok hugged himself tightly, turning his face toward the wall. There was a dull ache pulsing in the back of his throat and behind his eyes. He missed home. He was used to the close quarters, a room only seven feet across and about eight feet wide, but he missed sleeping next to Duljjae, Netjjae, and Yeoseotjjae.

The whispering, poking, kicking, fighting over the space. The way that Yeoseotjjae snored. How Netjjae stubbornly wrapped the blanket around his body so no amount of pulling could snatch it back.

Young Bok smelled sweat and damp clothes as a slight breeze trickled in through the open sliding door to the hallway. Back home, Young Bok knew Yang Sil would wake soon, creeping softly into the kitchen to start breakfast, humming in that peculiar half-whisper, half-song that she did in the early morning. *Was Daseotjjae able to sleep through the night?* he wondered. But he was at school, not home, and he shared the room with two strangers. In the morning, there was only the rough scritch-scratch as the boys pulled the three study chairs and desks away from the walls. Sometimes when the room was still too dark to see in the morning, they switched on the single naked bulb hanging from the ceiling. Its gentle rocking often lulled Young Bok into half sleep again.

In the evenings, when he yawned so wide he thought he would swallow his books whole, Young Bok left behind his dorm for the hills. He loved the way the moonlight shifted through the trees, the gentle hum of cicadas echoing into the night, and the smell of bark and moss and softly rotting chestnuts.

Young Bok spent most of his free time with Chae Eun Shin, Lim In Jim, and Lim In Hyung, all of them sons of pastors from his church. Because they had lived in different towns, they had never been close before. Now, they ate together at every meal. Bland vegetables, soup, rice, and very little meat. They laughed their way through it.

They spent much of their free time outdoors: hiking, fishing, and swimming. When the river froze over, they made skates, nailing a thin blade of metal into a wooden shoe, and threading double wires beneath it. Young Bok was proud that he now used only a single wire beneath the blade, a mark of experience. They skimmed across the rough ice, hours that slipped by like some of the fish deep beneath the frozen surface of the river. When they were hungry, they picked and ate chestnuts and sticky wild pears in the hills.

***

Every weekend, Young Bok traveled home to see his family. The train ticket only cost a small fee, but Young Bok knew his family was already strapped for money. Yang Sil paid for his tuition costs, and he could not ask her to take on another burden.

So this day, as on every other weekend, he went to the town market to buy rice.

He approached a market *ajumma*, a stooped little old lady with missing teeth, and held up three fingers. While the woman began filling up handwoven sacks with rice, Young Bok checked his money carefully again. Just enough to buy three sacks, around five liters of rice in total. The woman nodded and gestured with her hand to the sacks. They were all filled to the brim, and Young Bok thanked her with a bow, pressing money into her outstretched hands.

Young Bok slung the small sacks of rice across his shoulders and began the two-hour walk to the Pyongyang marketplace. He hummed, thinking about the profit he would make. Rice was worth double in Pyongyang. *I'm doing the same kind of work that my father did.* He pictured his father lugging huge sacks of dirt toward Pyongyang. *Did he hum like this? Or was he too tired?*

Young Bok loved the frenzy and excitement of the marketplace. There were screaming market *ajummas* everywhere, crying out their wares to the passerby. He loved the smell of the *kimchi*, the fresh produce, the salty dried fish. Even the iron sweet of the blood of slaughtered livestock. He liked to look at the dried persimmons and ginseng roots, things he could only imagine tasting.

When he had settled down into an empty place and bowed his greetings to the neighboring vendors, Young Bok opened his rice sacks, only to find the rice levels had fallen at least two inches below the rim of the sack. "Again?" he exclaimed. "But I tried a different *ajumma* this time! How is it that every time I'm short?"

A sharp-nosed woman approached his stand.

"Hello," Young Bok bowed his head. "This is fresh rice from the countryside."

The woman seized his bags and started to shake them. Young Bok raised his hands to stop her. "I just bought these three sacks of rice a few hours ago!"

The woman eyed him, "Oh, I never buy without measuring myself." She looked down at the settling rice and then swiveled her head to strike Young Bok with a piercing glare from narrowed eyes. "No, this is not three. It's two or maybe two plus."

"But I just bought..." The words died on his lips as she hurriedly handed him the money for two and a half sacks of rice and walked away. *Cut short again*, Young Bok thought. Still, he made a good deal of profit.

Young Bok also asked his mother to help him make long chains of one hundred pieces of garlic. They strung the white cloves in braids, with stalks upward, to keep it fresh. At the market, people always asked for a sample, saying they needed to check the merchandise was good. Sometimes, after doing so, they would simply walk away. Others would feign the garlic was not fresh, though Young Bok knew this was not the case. Still others after taking their sampling, insisted that they should get a discount as there were no longer a hundred pieces of garlic on the chain. Their voices were rough on Young Bok's ears. He knew they too had families to feed and money to scrimp, but he did not understand the swindling.

Yang Sil would often cluck her tongue at him when he told her his stories of woe. "My Setjjae is so smart, but he is not a businessman."

***

In class, Chae Eun Shin, Lim In Jim, Lim In Hyung, and Young Bok learned about history and culture, math, physics, and biology. An hour every school day was dedicated to pre-soldier training. War games where Japan always had the victory. In the fields and hills, they clung to roughly hewn wooden swords or rifles, practicing springing out to meet fellow students with a solid *thwack* to their weapons. Other days, they spent hot afternoons digging and moving stones to build trenches for bunkers in case of air raids.

Just like the blasting radios and posters, the Japanese teachers and authorities on the high school campus never admitted defeat: "The whole Pacific Ocean is under our control."

Some propaganda pointed to the number of Korean men who had applied voluntarily to the Japanese military through 1938 and on, and how this reflected a desire for the draft. In 1944, the Government-General of Korea presented the draft as a "gift from a benevolent Emperor who responded to the desires of the Korean people." The reality that Young Bok and many others knew was that colonial officials increased the number of applications through coercion, bribery, and deception. There were the visits at night, the conversations in private rooms, the threats of withheld rations.

Cheotjjae was twenty-one by this time, and too old for the military draft. Yang Sil and Sang Chul were convinced that this would protect him. It was eighteen-year-old Duljjae for whom they worried.

Midway through his first year of high school, Young Bok returned home for a weekend, as he did every couple weeks. "Umma! I'm home!" he called as he passed through the courtyard.

Daseotjjae ran up to greet him with swollen eyes and pink cheeks. "Setjjae, they took Cheotjjae." She burst into tears.

Young Bok bent down, and held his sister's face in his hands, "What do you mean? Daseotjjae, what do you mean?"

Yang Sil came out of the kitchen. "Setjjae... Your brother was drafted. For military labor." There was a single tear in Yang Sil's eye, but she didn't let it fall. Her voice was steady.

Young Bok dropped his backpack and wrapped his mother in a hug. After a few moments, she patted his back. "*Aigoo*, I'm all right," she said. She passed Ilgopjjae to Young Bok and walked into the kitchen. A few moments later, Young Bok found her squatting by the *doenjang* pot in the courtyard with a spoon in hand, unmoving.

Dinner was late.

Sang Chul didn't come to eat dinner that night. Young Bok opened his mouth to ask, but Yang Sil pointed toward the river shack and said, "He's been there all day."

There was a stone in the rice, and out of habit, Young Bok swallowed it down.

"When will he be back?" asked six-year-old Yeoseotjjae.

Yang Sil looked away.

Just like that, Cheotjjae disappeared along with the nearly five million Koreans conscripted by the Japanese for labor. Thousands never returned home.

A few months later, Duljjae was drafted to a naval academy for training.

***

Young Bok returned to high school. The teachers spent entire lecture periods going into tirades against the ABay, the American and British, the same descriptions he had been hearing for years.

You would have to drive a motorcycle a day to see their eyeballs!

Their nose is a mountain you have to climb because it is so large!

They are enemy number one!

They are non-human!

Young Bok watched their faces: eyes bulging, veins standing out like rope in their necks, spitting in their vigor. They were uglier than the people they so bitterly reviled.

We will eliminate ABay power!

When Young Bok passed village children in the town, they often played games of war, chasing each other with sticks, yelling, "Kill the ABay."

Out of earshot of the teachers, many students talked about the liberation and freedom that could come with war. It became more and more difficult to believe that Japan was winning the war so splendidly. Rations kept shrinking. Japanese soldiers took all the coal and oil for the war effort. Women and men kept disappearing. Businessmen and students who returned from Japan passed on bits and pieces of news about how difficult things were in Japan. And the voices of the Japanese propaganda were becoming increasingly hysterical.

Kim Ku, Kim Il Sung, Syngman Rhee. Kim Ku, Kim Il Sung, Syngman Rhee. These three names filled Young Bok with hope and a thrill of excitement.

Hushed nighttime conversations, moments stolen away in the classrooms when the teacher was absent, long hikes into the hills. Young Bok couldn't halt his bounding heart when he heard people say, "We have leaders helping us. They won't give up until Korea is free."

Young Bok, Chae Eun Shin, Lim In Jim, and Lim In Hyung, sometimes chanted together: *Kim Ku in China, Syngman Rhee in the US, and Kim Il Sung in Manchuria.* In the lowest moments, they and nearly every other student bent near and whispered, "We have leaders helping us."

"Kim Ku," Chae Eun Shin murmured. "He was born in Haeju, and when he was a teenager, he joined the Chondogyo movement. And then," his voice sunk to a hum as soft as a resting mosquito, "he killed a Japanese man when he was twenty-one."

"An officer," Lim In Hyung added.

"No, it was a Japanese man disguised as a Korean. He probably was part of the assassination of Empress Min," Chae Eun Shin corrected.

"I heard Kim Ku killed him with the officer's own sword. Arrested but then he escaped," Lim In Jim whispered.

"And he's part of the Korean Provisional Government in China," Young Bok breathed. "I heard he set it up in Shanghai."

Together, they said, "He's fighting for us."

"I heard my father's uncle's friend donated money to their cause," said Chae Eun Shin.

"Then there's Syngman Rhee!" said Lim In Jim.

"He was the first Korean *ever* to get a PhD in the US," said Young Bok. "And he's been in exile working toward independence for—"

"At least thirty years!" Chae Eun Shin butted in.

But most of all, they loved to talk about Kim Il Sung. One of their classmates had heard rumors from their parents, and they all gathered around him, with one student to keep watch for the teacher.

"You all already know that Kim Il Sung is in Manchuria." He paused to scan the nodding faces. "My father told me the Japanese soldiers tried to corner and kill him. But every time they got to a new city, the Japanese soldiers would hear news that Kim Il Sung had killed soldiers in another city or province or town. You know what he did? He had five or six other people share his same name so he's always moving, and they can never know which one is the real Kim Il Sung. He's been doing it for over thirty years, and he's never been caught. I don't think they'll ever catch him. He'll win us independence!"

"Sensei!" shouted the lookout student. Young Bok and the rest of the students scattered back to their desks as the teacher re-entered the room. It was some time before the teacher could regain order.

CHAPTER SIXTEEN

———

"Teachers...students...our beloved empire will take an extraordinary measure to accept the provisions of the joint declaration of the United States, Great Britain, China, and the Soviet Union," the school principal's voice crackled over the radio system. It sounded like someone had taken his voice, broken it over their knee, and twisted the broken pieces back together. "It is for the common welfare of the Japanese nation and its loyal subjects that we will now pave the way for a grand peace. The hardships and suffering ahead will—"

Young Bok caught little else. He was already out of his seat turning to other whispering students, "Is the war over?"

The usually strict Japanese teacher sat silently with his head bowed. His shoulders crumpled inwards.

Someone let out a whooping cry, then another and another. Through the walls, Young Bok could hear yelling and laughter from the other classrooms. Excited chills ran up and down his arms.

It was August 15, 1945. A day that would become known as Liberation Day, *Gwangbokjeol,* the Day of Restoration of Light.

Chae Eun Shin ran for the door and in a mad rush the other students joined him, toppling desks as they tripped over each other to get out the door.

Young Bok bowed to his teacher, and then he tore out of the room. The hallways were already full of other shouting students. One boy stood in the middle of the hallway tossing homework papers in the air.

Later, Young Bok would hear people talking about the radio broadcast from the Japanese Emperor. A voice halting at first, uncertain, as though it were toeing the edge of a lake made of rice paper. Big words, elegant sentences, queerly majestic and distant. A speech that never mentioned the words *defeat* or *surrender*.

Young Bok found Lim In Hyung and Chae Eun Shin in the crowd of shouting boys. Clinging to each other's backpacks, they shoved their way outside.

"Are we really free? Are we really free? The Japanese have lost?" They couldn't keep the smiles off of their faces.

Young Bok split from his friends the moment they stepped outdoors into the sunlight, "Goodbye! Goodbye!"

He ran almost the entire way home.

When he burst into the courtyard, panting and sweaty, he yelled, "Umma!"

Yang Sil ran to meet him in the doorway, "Setjjae!" She wrapped him in a hug.

Netjjae, Daseotjjae, and Yeoseotjjae were lying on their stomachs in the dirt, drawing Korean flags on pieces of white paper. They sprung to their feet when they saw Young Bok. Laughing and yelling, they grabbed his hands and danced in a lopsided circle.

From the side, a strong arm wrapped Young Bok in another hug. Sang Chul. It was the first time that Sang Chul had ever hugged Young Bok, and for a moment he hesitated before slowly bringing his arms around his father. Young Bok heard sniffling, and when he looked up, he saw tears streaming down Sang Chul's smiling face. "Setjjae, our nation is free. Our beautiful nation is free."

Young Bok started crying, too. He was sixteen.

News of liberation spread through the entire village. From the attic, Sang Chul brought out a dusty Korean flag, the *tae-geukgi*. He shook it gently to remove waves of dust and dirt and then held it up in the light. The colors were faded, but Young Bok remembered it was one of the most beautiful things he had ever seen. The family stood in reverent silence, and there were tears in Sang Chul and Yang Sil's eyes.

Young Bok joined his brothers and sister on the ground, painstakingly copying the *taegeukgi* onto sheets of white paper. Other families had done the same, and by the end of the day, there were flags hanging everywhere: roofs, rafters, bicycle handles, outside the school, and in every tree.

Some villagers nailed together several white boards and wrote "*MANSE*," Hurray, in bold letters.

When the Kim family walked into the streets, people everywhere were crying out, "*Manse! Manse!*" People gathered in their best clothing, white *hanbok* and pants. Some held handmade drums and dented pots and pans and danced in uneven circles, beating in time. They leapt upward, sometimes switching directions, sometimes bumping into one another. Crowds of people, young and old, gathered around them. People sang the national anthem, waving flags in time.

Throughout the day, parades began spontaneously throughout the village. And everywhere there were flags and yelling and laughter.

Later in the afternoon, the villagers built a roaring bonfire in the middle of the village.

The books were burning: school textbooks, paper-bound texts, Japanese-English dictionaries, flyers, anything written in swirling Japanese script. The air was thick with the smell of burning paper and hot ink.

Young Bok pressed through the crowd toward the bonfire, hands flying up instinctively to shield his face from its heat. People were laughing and cheering, clapping as they watched the paper curl into ashes. Across the fire, Young Bok could see his father laughing with his head thrown back. Hearty laughter that Young Bok could hear even through the roar of the crowd. Sang Chul laughing? It had been so long. Young Bok wanted to smile and laugh too. *But the books themselves are knowledge! They're not guilty of any crime*, Young Bok thought. The Japanese-English dictionaries could have been used to learn English, and the textbooks could have been used for school until the village could print their own Korean ones.

Young Bok squatted down and stared into the fire until his eyes smarted. The thick smoke choked his lungs, and at this level, he no longer saw laughing and smiling faces, only a confusing tangle of legs and shifting bodies.

The fire spurted sparks and the books...the books kept coming.

Just like the books, the Japanese were burned out of the town.

Shortly after the announcement of Japanese surrender on the radio and news that the Soviets were moving down the peninsula, Japanese homes across the village turned inside out. People and their stuffed bags of belongings spilled into the streets in a flight south and toward the harbors. Among them were many pro-Japanese Koreans who feared reprisal for their cooperation with the Japanese. Young Bok glimpsed the mayor and his wife with a cart full of valuables. Of the Japanese who lingered, there were the bank chief, police chief, and school superintendent. They were stripped of any power and made to clean the streets.

Within the day, Young Bok's village had reorganized the entire hierarchy of the town. People volunteered to take positions as teachers or policemen, roles that had been filled mainly by the Japanese. It took only a week to organize a local government, called a people's committee, with a town office, bank, post office, and police station.

Throughout the country, people's committees emerged in every one of the country's thirteen provinces.

***

Young Bok and the other villagers wove a narrative about why the Soviets had come to liberate the northern region of Korea. *Near the seaside*, they said, *the Japanese military had rows of machine guns to guard against the attack of the Soviets. The Soviets sent down their Siberian soldiers, knowing that thousands would be massacred. Later, in the treaty with the Allies, they complained, "We lost thousands to liberate Korea. In exchange for these deaths, **we** should liberate the north section of Korea."*

The reality was more complicated. American officials, headed by Roosevelt, had already suggested the idea of a trusteeship as early as 1943. Though Harry Hopkins, Roosevelt's personal assistant, had revised an American draft of the Cairo Declaration in 1943 to say that Korea would be independent "at the earliest possible moment after the downfall of Japan," Roosevelt and the British draft of the declaration stated that it would become independent "in due course" (Lee, 2006). Despite centuries of history of self-rule, the pleas for independence by Korean nationalists during the March 1st Movement in 1919, and the provisional Korean government set up in Shanghai, Roosevelt declared that national self-determination was not in the cards for Korea. At least not yet. Maybe after twenty to thirty years. The Cairo Declaration left this small peninsula country in uncertain waters for the future. With room for manipulation by the Great Powers, Korea was a brewing pot for conflict, and the US was uneasy regarding a possible Soviet occupation of Korea. The Soviet-US relationship was already built upon a shaky foundation of hostility, the US distrustful of Stalin's totalitarian, communist state, and the Soviet Union's anti-democratic policy toward Eastern Europe. But it was an alliance of necessity; Nazi Germany was pressing on all fronts.

On August 14, 1945, the night before liberation, Colonel Dean Rusk and Colonel Charles "Tic" Bonesteel stared at a *National Geographic* map and chose a line. Colonel Rusk admitted he and Bonesteel were no experts on Korea: "But it seemed to us that Seoul, the capital, should be in the American sector... We looked north of Seoul for a convenient dividing line but could not find a natural geographic line. We saw instead the thirty-eighth parallel and decided to recommend that" (Lee, 2006). It was late, and the State-War-Navy Coordinating Committee (SWNCC or SWINK) accepted the dividing line, as did the Soviets.

The decision of those two men in a lonely room turned into a permanent divide that split apart a nation and tore apart millions of families.

In the eyes of the US government, the decision had been critical. The nearest US ground troops on the night of August 14 were stationed in Okinawa and the Philippines. If a demarcation line was not proposed, the US feared the Red Army might have seized all of Korea before US troops arrived.

At the Moscow Conference of December 1945, the Foreign Ministers of US, Britain, and USSR decided upon a trusteeship of up to five years for Korea. Vocal Korean opposition to such a trusteeship was ignored.

***

Within two to three days of official liberation, a train puffed into the station at SaInJang (now Pyongsong), an hour's walk from Young Bok's hometown and four stations away from Pyongyang. Soviet soldiers waved from the windows. Young Bok and many of the other men from the town were at the station, cheering for the arrival of the soldiers. Word had it that soldiers were being planted at every stop.

Young Bok held a Russian flag and a Korean flag. *"Manse! Manse!"* he cried.

The soldiers lumbered from the train, and Young Bok's *hurray* choked in his throat. *These are not men.* They were like beasts with their unwashed bodies, thick beards and long hair, ragged and patched clothing. The filthiest people Young Bok had ever seen, with a ripe smell like rot. They must have gone several months without washing. Young Bok forced a smile onto his face. These were still his saviors; they had rescued his nation from the Japanese.

He would learn later that many of these men were criminals from Siberia, promised a pardon from their sentences if they enlisted.

One of the soldiers peeled away from the rest of the ragged group and sauntered toward Young Bok.

"*Daymne,* gimme," the man said in Russian, gesturing to Young Bok's watch.

It was a cheap Japanese watch that Young Bok had just bought from the black market. He fumbled with the watch's clasp, quick to bow his head in respect as he passed his watch to the man. The soldier grunted appreciatively, rolling up his sleeve to reveal at least a dozen watches running up his arm.

Another soldier approached Young Bok and gestured at his belt. Young Bok hesitated a moment, grasping it with one hand protectively. The market had flooded with military leather shoes and belts after the Japanese military supply had been looted at liberation. But this belt Young Bok had spent hours over, dyeing it with mercurochrome time and time again until the belt was a brilliant shade of red.

The soldier was gesturing, pointing more aggressively. Young Bok undid the belt latch and slowly handed the belt over. He stood there on the train platform, still cheering, clutching the Korean and Russian flag in one hand, and holding up his pants with the other.

Young Bok stayed on the platform until the train left the station, bearing away more troops of soldiers toward Pyongyang. When he finally walked down the main path into his village, he expected more celebrations and parading, smiling people bearing flags in the streets. Instead, there were wailing voices, crashes, and screaming.

The doors to the bank were mutilated and broken wood splintered across the pathway. The soldiers had looted the banks, staggering away, some with sacks of money, others with money spilling from their filthy boots and pockets. Now only a lone Soviet soldier wandered through the ruins, nudging ransacked cabinets with the butt of his gun.

Young Bok began to run toward home.

The sound of wailing women rose in a terrible, visceral cry. Young Bok heard later that every woman on the streets had been caught and raped. Anyone with long hair, old and young alike, was seized by the Soviet soldiers. It was now that Young Bok was grateful his home was on the edge of town, far enough away that his mother had been safe.

In the days after, the entire village mourned. The Japanese had been brutal masters, but they had never pillaged the village or raped all the women.

When the regular Russian army arrived in the days following, their clean appearances and behavior were a shocking contrast to the previous troops.

CHAPTER SEVENTEEN

Sang Chul broke through the sealed door to the attic for the second time that week, pounding at the wood until the latch gave way and the door swung downward. He hoisted himself into the musty room by his elbows, coughing on dust and kicking his legs while he balanced his elbows on the edges of the frame. The family watched. Young Bok rubbed away stinging dirt from his eyes.

"Here it is." Sang Chul held out a dusty text. "The *Dong-gyeong Daejeon*, Chondogyo Scripture."

Setjjae reached out to touch a yellowed page. Even rows of vertical inked script in Chinese characters ran down each page.

"Your harabeoji, grandfather, believed in the Chondogyo religion. See here," Sang Chul traced the page, jaw relaxed for once. "In the beginning, God created the world…"

Young Bok looked up quickly—the Christian Bible started in the same way.

"Your harabeoji always said he would be there when heaven and earth came," said Sang Chul. He let his chin fall to his chest and stood very still.

The children nodded. Heaven and earth coming—the long-awaited liberation from the Japanese—they were well aware of this phrase.

"Your harabeoji... Your harabeoji..." Sang Chul lifted a hand to cover his face. For the second time in the last two days, their strong, set-jawed father was crying. "Your harabeoji was ninety-nine when he died last year." Sang Chul held up a worn and folded note, a note he had folded and unfolded a thousand times, a note with the news that his father, Chul Soo, had died. "He died a year...a year before liberation. Just a year before heaven and earth came."

He stroked the page of the Chondogyo text with his calloused palm. "I will become a follower of Chondogyo."

Young Bok looked up at his father, "Abeoji..."

For the last nine years, going to church had been a Sunday habit for Young Bok. Wake up at first light, wash quietly so as not to wake his brothers, say goodbye to his mother already at work in the kitchen, and slip out for the one-hour walk to church.

Young Bok liked the other children he met in the Sunday school, and he liked the annual Christmas gifts that the church passed out. But most of all, he wanted to earn an award for perfect attendance. Just like the one he had earned from elementary school, he wanted to bring it home to show his mother. He wanted to present the paper award to her, hear her clap her hands together in pride, and then smile, saying, "Good job, my Setjjae."

The weekly messages also attracted Young Bok. The tall and wiry, black-robed pastor looked like an angel to him. With his arms spread wide, he would say in a deep and sonorous voice, "Let us pray." That human beings were ugly and broken and sinful; this, Young Bok saw every day. As the pastor told him, ugliness and brokenness had consequences—death and separation from God. But God wouldn't abandon humanity to the death they deserved. He was a God who loved everyone on earth so dearly that He sent His own son, Jesus, to die on the cross. Jesus took on all human sin and conquered it, symbolically and literally, by His death and then resurrection from the grave. Because of Jesus's sacrifice, God offered a relationship with the Creator of the Universe and the free gift of eternal life, and all Young Bok had to do was believe in God and in Jesus.

Some Sundays, the pastor talked about heaven and earth coming and prayed for a day of liberation from present pain; Young Bok and the congregation knew the pastor was praying for a day when the Japanese occupation would come to an end. Young Bok could feel his heart beating in his chest, a rumbling *pitter-patter-pitter-patter*, crescendoing as the pastor's voice crescendoed in excitement and confidence. Above all, the pastor talked about a hope beyond anything offered on earth, an assuredness of eternal life and a promise of a Father in heaven who loved unfailingly.

Young Bok was so used to the anger of his father at home, the fear and bitterness of his classmates. To hear about unconditional love, forgiveness, and hope for the future—these were irresistible promises.

"God brought about this liberation," Young Bok said to his family that afternoon, the day after Liberation. Before, his faith had felt very small, but now he was convinced that God had brought about Liberation Day. He could no longer keep this news or this hope to himself. "Everyone, if you would come to church with me, you could hear about God. You could hear about the way that he brought heaven and earth. You could hear about how He loves all of us!"

Yang Sil smiled. "Setjjae is right. We should all go to church." Her son asked for very little. If he was asking her to do something, it must be important to him.

But Sang Chul refused adamantly.

"You left home, Abeoji. You didn't like it! You chose to leave Chondogyo!" Young Bok argued.

Sang Chul shook his head, "I didn't like it, but my father died to see this happening. He is right. This is happening... heaven and earth came! Now I must continue his religion."

"But Abeoji—" Young Bok protested.

"I am not opposed to you going to your Christian church," Sang Chul interrupted. "But I am a prodigal son, and I betrayed my father. Now you think I will betray his religion, too?" His eyes were fierce, anger spattering from them like the spit from his mouth. "No, I cannot do that."

"It was God who saved us from Japan!" Young Bok burst out. "He brought this liberation!"

Sang Chul gave Young Bok a hard stare. "It's fine if you go to church but I won't."

"But Abeoji, Umma even told us the story about how she gave Harabeoji the honey in his water so he could survive the forty-day fast. Chondogyo's not real! It's not, Abeoji, please—"

Yang Sil pulled Young Bok's sleeve and shook her head. "He knows what I did, my Setjjae. Your Abeoji knows already."

Young Bok looked at his mother. She pursed her lips, eyes signaling him to stop the words already rising in his mouth.

Bulhyoja, infidelity. Obedience to a parent, especially a father, was the highest duty of a child. Young Bok could see the pain and guilt in Sang Chul's eyes. Chondogyo was the last possible way for Sang Chul to perform his filial duty to his father, and so he clung to it desperately.

Young Bok swallowed. "That's your obligation, Appa. I won't fight anymore."

The next Sunday, Yang Sil and all four of Young Bok's younger siblings joined him on the dusty road to church.

In the years that followed, Young Bok asked time and time again for his father to at least come to one church service. Sang Chul never did.

CHAPTER EIGHTEEN

———

Shortly after liberation, Duljjae returned home. After spending the last few months training at a naval academy, he was spared from the battlefield by Japan's surrender.

The Kim family moved to a new home, from the little twenty-house village of SaChangRi to the two-hundred-house town of SaInJang (present-day Pyongsong), so that they could be closer to their fields.

Still they waited for Cheotjjae. It had been over a year since he had been drafted.

Other sons had returned home, pale, shaken, and full of gruesome stories. Many looked haggard, bearing the news of brothers or friends slaughtered in the battlefield, starved to death in the military plants and factories, or blasted by Allied bombs that rained from the skies. The Kim family waited.

Sang Chul spent most of his time with the other village men, helping with the local people's committee and organizing the local government. When he was home, he rarely left the shack over the river.

Young Bok often caught his mother lost in thought during her tasks about the house. Yang Sil was too methodical to burn the rice or weave a crooked row into her cloth, but sometimes as she beat the laundry to clean it, there were long pauses of silence between each *smack*. He would look out and she would be standing there, holding a wet sheet limply at her side, her face to the sky and the mountains.

One time, Yang Sil grabbed Young Bok's hand. "Setjjae, there's hundreds of thousands of people who were sent to Japan, hm? They worked in the shipyards or the mines and they haven't all come home. That must be where your brother is…at least 600,000… That's what your Abeoji said he heard. Cheotjjae will come home soon. He'll come home."

***

The family was sitting down for dinner one night when they heard a limping step outside. Step drag. Step drag. Step drag. Through the gate, into the courtyard.

Young Bok held his breath. Their house was on the fringe of the village, one of the last houses hugging the mountainside. Who could it be? Was it maybe…?

Sang Chul was standing immediately, knocking aside his bowl as he stood in haste.

Cheotjjae. He stood in the doorway, with the sun a halo around his face and his body. For just a moment, they were sure that it was as though he'd never left, that he was still the strong, youthful man-boy who lifted stones and weeded the fields and lounged in the little lean-to over the river. Still the handsome, broad-shouldered man who had been married just four years ago. But when the sun faded, Cheotjjae was bent over a cane, his body weary and folded inwards in parts where it should not have been. The skin hung loose on his frame and there was an emptiness in his eyes. An exhaustion.

He smiled when he saw Sang Chul stumbling toward him. For a moment, the rest of them froze, watching Cheotjjae's slow and painful progress across the courtyard. Then Yang Sil burst out, "Cheotjjae!"

They surrounded him, Sang Chul laughing and patting his son on the back, Yang Sil crying and holding his hand tightly, Duljjae sobbing, Young Bok smiling up at his brother, Netjjae and Daseotjjae and Yeoseotjjae clinging to him and crying. Cheotjjae's wife held back a little shyly at first, but Cheotjjae put out his hand toward her, and she drew close and pressed his hand.

The handle of Cheotjjae's cane was so worn that Young Bok could even see the way he had gripped the cane, the outline of his fingers, the place where the nail of his thumb dug into the wood. *He must have traveled so far.* Young Bok looked up at his brother. There were lines of pain around Cheotjjae's mouth.

Yang Sil shooed them all away after some time, and she and Sang Chul carefully guided Cheotjjae into his room. Young Bok watched from the courtyard, as his mother spread out a bed roll and blanket with gentle hands. She paused twice to reach up a hand to Cheotjjae's face, to gently hold his cheek and look into his eyes. Sang Chul sat on the floor next to his son, angry and quiet. "What did these *Jjokbari*—" Yang Sil hushed him.

She passed out of the room to get some watery *juk*. When her back was to Cheotjjae, she let a few tears fall. Her lip trembled. "My poor baby," she murmured.

After a few days, Cheotjjae was well enough to sit up in his room, propped against the wall. Yang Sil, Sang Chul, and

Cheotjjae's wife sat in the room with him, while the rest of the children crowded the doorway. Cheotjjae smiled a little when one-year-old Ilgopjjae grabbed his finger with a little curled up fist—a baby brother whom he had met for the first time.

They finally asked him their questions, toeing delicately over the whens, hows, and whys until Cheotjjae began to speak, to painfully spin the narrative of the last year.

After he had been drafted, he was shipped off to Kobe, Japan. He spent several months in the Kawasaki Heavy Industries Ltd. military shipyard, building destroyers, submarines, auxiliaries, and escort craft. When they asked him about how he was treated, he only shook his head.

"There was an accident with the equipment." He looked down wearily at his crippled leg and tapped it lightly with his hand. "I was in the hospital and couldn't walk. For a while, I wasn't even sure that I would ever be able to walk again. I thought they might…take my leg. Then one day, the bombs—they just came down and down. I just lay in that bed very still. It smelled like smoke and people were screaming everywhere."

"They bombed the hospital, and all the patients were moved by people rushing in with wheelchairs or carrying them out. But I was left behind." Amid the confusion, the screaming, the running, panic, flashes of light, and darkness, Cheotjjae slipped out of consciousness. "When I woke up, I had somehow ended up on the lawn outside of the hospital." He paused, a look of confusion frozen on his face. "I still don't know how…I couldn't walk at all, and everyone had left the hospital. I was saved by an invisible power." He nodded. "An invisible power."

What he didn't describe was the US Boeing B-29 Superfortresses with their long wings and the bombs tumbling from their bellies. The scream of air raids and the fear for ten full days in March as the bombs fell and fell and fell. Five thousand four hundred and twenty-four tons of incendiaries ravaging over half of Kobe. The silver bellies of the B-29s gleamed red. Hundreds of B-29s surging through the sky so close he could read their identification numbers, felt like he could reach out and touch them. The eruptions of the magnesium thermite incendiaries, the brief silence when the bomb was falling and the moments of thinking that perhaps this time it wouldn't go off, this time there wouldn't be more screams and fire and smoke. The smoke billowing in giant columns upward, blown by the wind up into the sky farther than the eye could see. There were fires everywhere. Summer heat, choking smoke, and the smell of burning wood, chemicals, and flesh.

And people dying everywhere.

He had been lucky. He lived. He returned home, and the family was finally whole again.

CHAPTER NINETEEN

———

By late August 1945, the headquarters of the Soviet 25th Army had arrived in Pyongyang. The Soviets recognized the local people's committees, formed under the nationwide Committee for the Preparation of Korean Independence (CKPI), and they slipped behind the scenes, allowing the committees to continue their decolonization process in the North. By October, the Soviets formed a North Korean Branch Bureau of the Korean Communist Party, and the people's committees were organized into the Five Provinces People's Committee and a Five Province Administrative Bureau to oversee the country. Though there was a Christian Korean Democratic Party and a Chondogyo Friends Party, Communists took effective control of these organizations.

That same month, thirty-three-year-old Kim Il Sung appeared in Korea for the first time in about a decade. He was welcomed on that sunny October day by a crowd of seventy thousand people as "General Kim Il Sung," the legendary anti-Japanese guerrilla resistance leader. On a high podium, he delivered an impassioned speech. Behind him, the stout Soviet command saluted in full uniform, a visible image of Soviet backing to Kim's leadership.

In that year of 1945 and in the years that followed, Kim Il Sung was shrouded in deep myths, truth mixed with the unrealized desires of the people, lies mixed in with envy or frustration. Too many voices said too many different things, and Young Bok found it impossible to sort fact from truth: "*Kim Il Sung and his guerrilla forces liberated Korea. He was at Chongjin in early August with the Soviet army to fight against the Japanese Kwantung Army.*"

"*Kim Il Sung fought in secret for our independence against the Japanese ever since the 1930s until Pearl Harbor.*"

"*Kim Il Sung was picked by the Soviets… They picked him as a leader.*"

"*Kim Il Sung occupied the Korean town of Pochonbo on the border with Manchuria in June 1937 and had several hundred guerrillas beneath him. But then he disappeared into the Soviet Union in the 1940s because the Japanese drove him back.*"

Most prominently, Sang Chul's voice as they looked at the newspaper pictures of the October speech: "This Kim Il Sung is too young to have played a role in the anti-Japanese struggle. Do you see him, Setjjae? Look at all that dark hair, that smooth face. He's much too young. He's an impersonator of the real, legendary Kim Il Sung."

By January 1946, Soviet military police laid strict controls on their troops. Soldiers were to be shot on sight if they were caught raping a Korean. The looting and stockpiling of valuable goods rolled to a stop, but the Soviets still requisitioned supplies, issuing redeemable receipts for everything. It did not mend the problem. Young Bok heard tell that in Pyongyang the Russians had requisitioned two-thirds of the food supply without compensation.

Pyongyang wasn't too far from Young Bok's hometown, but politics felt distant when he was busy in the fields and in school. It was difficult to keep up with the shifting landscape: the continued trusteeship of Korea (*Would his country ever be united?*), Kim Il Sung *(the imposter?)* who now headed the Korean Communist Party. Then, in February 1946, Kim Il Sung was named the chairman of the newly established North Korean Interim People's Committee (NKIPC). In Kim Il Sung's words, it was a "model for the future Korean Provisional Government" that would only function "until such a time as the united Korean government is established" (Cumings, 1981).

With March came warm breezes and rainfall. Spring. Across the nation, poor peasants and agricultural laborers banded together into councils calling for radical land reform. On the fifth, the NKIPC issued a land reform ordinance that seized land from Japanese collaborators, landlords with more than five *chongbo* (twelve acres), absentee landlords, and all land held continuously in tenancy. All land was to be distributed to the peasants, though the state would maintain full administrative and legal rights to all of it.

Posters and handbills and loudspeakers blasted the same message: "From the masses, to the masses," and "Let us remove the parasitic landlords" (Cumings, 1981). They were words that Young Bok did not fully understand. They were words he felt his neighbors did not understand either, swept up in this wave of nebulous concepts and promises that none of them could fully pry apart. They were simple people, accustomed to the coming and going of the seasons, to timing and ceremony and ritual. Everything was wrapped around planting and harvesting; there was little time for reading, little time for dreaming or outlandish ideas.

One day, Young Bok overheard his father talking to his mother in the courtyard. Vague terms began to take more concrete shape.

"Only an hour's walk from here, they are taking land." Sang Chul's voice was strained with anger, but he was trying to keep his voice low and calm. He was failing. "We have tenants, I know, but I'm a part of our people's committee. I love our nation! But...they will take our land? I've worked for this land. I carted dirt from the countryside to Pyongyang for years. I hurt this back. I sweated for this food. They will take my land and do what? Whom do these Communists work for? Do they work for the Soviets or the Korean people?" Sang Chul drew up his lip in disgust. "Yes, the land should be taken from those Japanese-loving traitors, but why should it be taken from me?"

Yang Sil closed her eyes for a moment and inhaled deeply. "If it does happen..." She laid her hand on Sang Chul's arm. "We had less before, and we've been blessed with what we have. We will find a way."

Meanwhile, the people's committees encouraged tenant-farmers not to associate with their landlords. Young Bok heard that landlords in other towns were harassed with frequent questioning by the cadres and watched by the police. Sok Sae Cho, Young Bok's elementary classmate, had his home under observation. The quiet man leaning against a tree in the village square was not subtle. The man watched and watched, sometimes sneaking a finger up into his nose. *Like a little snake*, Young Bok thought.

One day, walking home from high school, Young Bok saw some of his family's tenants ahead, their backs to him. He almost raised his voice in a greeting, but when he saw the way the two, husband and wife, leaned in close to one another, voices hushed and pausing, he closed his mouth and slowed his pace. Young Bok pretended to play with the school bag on his shoulder and look off into the distance. Really, he was straining his ears to hear.

"How can we take this land without payment? They tell us that this land originally belonged to us, but Yobo…" The man was patting his wife's arm. "Yobo, not even my grandfather can remember a day when we owned land. It is not our land."

His wife nodded in agreement. "And they have been good to us…they don't ask for more than we can give."

"But…it is land. It is an opportunity to make our own living and not pay anyone. To be free! If we had our own land to raise our children, Yobo…" The man's voice was heavy with emotion. "It doesn't make sense, Yobo, why would they give it to us for free? Still, whether we care or not, won't the land be taken and given to us? Wouldn't it be better to do as they say so we can get the best land? The Kim family has enough, they—" The man's voice had risen in his passion, and noting it, he stopped speaking suddenly. Young Bok sped up his pace and passed them. These were people his family had known for years. They were tenants on his parents' land, but far more than that, they were friends. He didn't look back.

Yet Young Bok understood what it meant to own your own land, to be able to till the land knowing that each drop of sweat and each callous and splintered nail was for food on your table, to feed your own children. He couldn't argue with that, and perhaps it was right. These people worked long and difficult days and ended up with far less than they deserved. This was true; the inequality was deep…but to take from his own family?

Young Bok shook his head.

There was no compensation when a cadre from Pyongyang took part of the Kims' land and distributed it to their tenants. The Kims were not Japanese, nor traitors, nor even wealthy. Their only mistake was in renting out a part of their land to tenants. They were lucky, though. Because they owned so little land and worked almost all of it themselves, they were allowed to keep their home and most of their land.

Sang Chul held in his curses at the Communist fools taking his land, only because he knew the danger of challenging the authorities. He'd heard that in other towns well-to-do landowning families had ended up in jail or sentenced to hard labor. Some had lost everything. With an unfriendly government and no land, they faced starvation. They moved into shacks on the edge of town, fled to nearby towns, or even fled south of the 38th parallel.

Meanwhile, Communist leaders moved into the most beautiful homes, which had originally been owned by the Japanese.

In June 1946, the government passed an ordinance on taxation. Farmers were exempted from all taxes on land and rent and only required to submit 25 percent of the total harvest to the government. The surplus, they would be allowed to sell at free markets.

At first, farmers were overjoyed with the power of owning their own land. After generations and generations of suppression, hopes and dreams for land and for rights, they were now ruled by a government that claimed a proletarian dictator and shouted slogans of "For the masses, to the masses."

They quickly learned that the land was not their own.

During *chusu*, harvest time, the government sent officials to survey the land at each farm. Though the formal ordinance said that the measurements were based on 25 percent of the harvest, Young Bok recalled it being calculated at 50 percent. When the government official arrived at their farm, Yang Sil and Sang Chul were required to harvest a certain amount of their land. After weighing the crops on a scale, the official scribbled 50 percent of this yield into a thick ledger. This would be used as the multiplier for the rest of the crops, which would be "given" to the government. Almost every time, the most fertile portion of land was chosen as the analyzing point.

Farmers ended up surrendering 60 to 70 percent of their harvest to the government.

It was too often that Young Bok heard stories about a blank-faced official demanding fifty barrels when there had only been seventy barrels of harvest. When a farmer was left with only twenty barrels of harvest to last him an entire year, there was no way he could support his many children, his aging grandmother, and his favorite younger brother.

The Communist leaders always claimed the landowner and tenant had a master-slave relationship. "Your former landlord was *far worse* than this landlord you have now. The government owns all the land; now you have a better master." Young Bok knew different. Though landlords did require half of the harvest yield from their tenants, there was humanity in their relationship. All of them worked the same land, experienced the same droughts and rainfall. They knew when the harvest was bad; they knew Kim Bong Su's five children or Lee Ae Ra's sick husband.

Young Bok knew his mother had always treated their tenants as friends, even family. She had never told their few tenants they would divide their harvest fifty-fifty. Instead, she would press their hands and say, "Whatever you feel that you owe us." When the harvest was bad, Yang Sil would always tell them, "It was a difficult year for us all, so I won't ask you to give much." It had always been that way for as long as Young Bok could remember.

When they lost the mountainside to other farmers, Sang Chul and Yang Sil said very little, but Young Bok knew that their food would not be enough. Their family had always been self-sufficient, but never prosperous. In the weeks before harvest time, Yang Sil was always scraping up the last few grains of rice in their stored bags. The apples, pears, chestnuts, and wild vegetables from the mountainside had been the family's lifeline through the lean, hungry months.

The family turned to the marketplace. Three days a week, Sang Chul, Cheotjjae, and Duljjae pushed small wagons of produce to the market in different neighboring towns. Perhaps Sang Chul was ashamed, but perhaps he had found his place among the shouting vendors and bustling shoppers. Young Bok was attending high school during these market times, so he never knew.

Yang Sil began to make *tteok*, rice cakes, with the little bit of rice she could set aside. She also made *yeot*, a rice taffy snack. To make *yeot,* she boiled rice in a large pot over the fire, rinsing it thoroughly and spreading it out on a rough cloth to dry. She squeezed chunks of rice apart, sticky grains slipping through her fingers, careful not to lose a single grain of rice. Combined with malt from barley seeds and lightly fermented, it would make saccharine. Then, Yang Sil stood sweating before a huge pot over the fire, holding a wooden paddle and slowly stirring the mixture until it started to resist the paddle. At this point, Yang Sil could take the *yeot* from the pot, a dark brown, sticky mixture, and with a little wooden post that she had set up in her kitchen, she began to pull the mixture. Young Bok liked to watch her sometimes as she did this, the quick fluid movements of her hands and arms as she slung the taffy over the post and then pulled, slung, and pulled. The taffy slipped into golden smoothness and then clear white as Yang Sil roped it again and again. When she was finished, she dropped it onto a wooden table in the kitchen and chopped the *yeot* into bite-sized chunks before rolling them in rice flour. The chewy snack sold well in the market, and with it, Yang Sil could buy a little extra rice to feed her family.

When Young Bok was home from school, he sometimes woke to find baskets of pears and apples in the kitchen. They were firm to the touch, fragrant, with the residues of crumbly dirt still clinging to their skins.

"Umma, where did you get this fruit?" he asked. *I know we can't afford to buy this.*

"Last night the farmers who now own our mountain came and brought this for us," Yang Sil replied. "I told them not to come." Yang Sil lowered her voice. "You know that the government would punish them if they were caught. I tell them not to, but they still come often. Do you know what they tell me? Setjjae, remember Yoo Ra's umma?"

Young Bok nodded.

Yang Sil continued. "She told me, 'You were so good to us for many years. Now you have lost everything. How can we not help you?' She is so kindhearted. They all risk so much to bring us this food."

Young Bok knew that if the new "owners," namely the government, had treated these former tenants better, they wouldn't remember to care for their old landowners.

Still, even with their neighbors' generosity, there were long and hungry nights.

"Hyung, my stomach hurts. It hurts," Yeoseotjjae pulled on Young Bok's arm. His eyes were red-rimmed and teary, and his face strained with the pain.

Young Bok squatted down to the same eye-level as his nine-year-old brother. "Yeoseotjjae… Umma is making some *juk* tonight so your stomach won't hurt, okay? Don't cry, it's okay."

"Hyung," Yeoseotjjae rested his head against his brother's shoulder. His shoulders were thin and small, and Young Bok rubbed them slowly while his brother took stuttering breaths.

The last season had decimated the harvest: drought and flooding had ruined the rice paddies with sand. Along with the rising measures that had to be paid to Communist authorities, there was simply not enough rice. In the fields, farmers lay down in the terraces exhausted. The government sent in soldiers with rifles on their backs to work the farms and keep output high. Young Bok mourned the loss of a peaceful and happy village.

He got used to the constant pang of hunger, always thinking of food, always metering out each mouthful of food. He learned to chew slowly, to keep his eyes on his plate and away from his mother's pained eyes. He tried hard to think before complaining about the food they ate. Sometimes, his only meal was a bowl of thin *juk*. Other times, only a cob of corn.

Yang Sil grew inventive, desperate to feed her large family. She collected bark from pine trees to make pine bark cakes, similar to rice cakes. She stripped away the outer bark until she reached the thin brown film covering the white inner core. This thin film, she peeled away and pounded with rice flour.

Eaten one or two at once, these pine bark cakes were quite tasty—chewy and slightly nutty. However, after eating pine tree cakes day after day for nearly a week, it caused painful constipation, so terrible that Young Bok cried when he tried to relieve himself.

One day, he pushed away his plate. "I don't want it anymore."

Yang Sil turned away for a moment and her hands flew up to her face in two quick swipes. When she took his plate from him, her eyes were still wet. She smiled, but Young Bok felt guilt rising up in his throat like sour bile.

CHAPTER TWENTY

Yumulchui, the teacher scratched onto the blackboard. *Everything is matter.*

How many times will we go over this same concept? Young Bok wanted to smack his face into the desk but instead he blinked for a long time, squeezing his eyes shut so tightly that he saw little white stars blossom.

"Ideas and faith are all invisible products of the concrete brain. There is no spirit or supernatural. Everything is man-made. There is an acquired genetic inheritance of the matter of ideas. If a man is a Communist, then his children will be born Communist as well," the teacher droned on.

Every class. EVERY CLASS, it is Marx and Engels, Lenin and Stalin, the revolution, Communism and Communism and Communism. Everything is matter.

"Capitalism, *jabonchui,* is the enemy of the people," the teacher shook a finger at the sky and his eyebrows suddenly arched with his passion. "Religion is an enemy of the people, too. It makes people into slaves! God is an evil product of human thought."

The teacher passed back last week's tests. Young Bok stared down at the perfect score on the paper and then circled his pencil on the page in a tiny dark circle, pressing harder and harder until the pencil tip broke through the paper. No one could accuse him of being anti-Communist if he excelled on the tests. No one would bother him or his family. No one would throw him into jail. He pasted a smile on his face when the teacher congratulated him. The teacher had no idea how difficult it had been to memorize the information for this test, how much Young Bok had to fight his own anger and frustration to stuff each fact into his head, grinding his teeth, clenching his fists.

In Young Bok's next class, a Korean-Soviet woman taught Russian to the class. She liked to shake everyone's hands in the morning firmly, saying *zdravstvuyte*, hello. Her hands were so dry, it was like holding a cold little lizard.

Many of the teachers were Koreans who were second, third, and even fourth generations of families who had lived in the Soviet Union. Their parents, worn down by the loss of children and aging grandparents to starvation, had fled to Manchuria and later toward Russia throughout the late nineteenth century and early twentieth century. In 1937, a paranoid Stalin charged these Koreans with disloyalty and forcibly relocated over 170,000 of them to Soviet Central Asia, places like Kazakhstan and Uzbekistan. Many died en route of diseases, starvation, or train accidents. Those who survived arrived in nearly uninhabitable fields and lands, exhausted and forced to begin their lives all over again. It was some of these Soviet Koreans who returned to Korea after the Communist takeover. Though Young Bok understood they carried their own painful past, it was nearly impossible to see them beyond the Russian language and Communist values and history they taught.

"*Chto eto?* What is this?" The teacher held up a newspaper in her hand, prompting the class to chant together in Russian: "*Eto gazeta.* It is a newspaper."

Young Bok looked across the room at Chae Eun Shin. For a split-second Chae Eun Shin's mouth twisted, and he scrunched his eyebrows together in an expression of distaste. Young Bok echoed the look. Just a moment, and then they were both back to blank faces, chanting, "*Eto gazeta. Eto gazeta.*"

"*Kak pozhivayete*, how are you," the teacher droned. "*Tovarishchi*, comrades..."

When class was over, Young Bok rushed to the bathroom to wash his hands. He looked into the mirror at his face and quickly corrected his expression. Loosen the jaw, flatten out the eyebrows, return his eyes to a blank expression. He scrubbed his hands in the sink roughly, passing his palms over his knuckles again and again. He could still feel the lizard hand in his grasp.

That afternoon, Young Bok met with his superior. Under the Communist system, every member of society was incorporated through a network of underlings and superiors, and everyone only knew the people directly above or below them in the hierarchy. The superior passed orders to the underling, and they passed these on to their inferiors. These orders were never to be revealed to anyone else, even family.

Young Bok's superior was a Korean man with terrible bad breath. "What is your comrade doing?" he leaned in close. Their conversations were so frequent that Young Bok often thought he would get used to the stench, but it was freshly pungent each time. He struggled not to flinch, to breathe normally. He was required to give all the details of how his inferior spent his free time, who he talked to, what he said, and how he studied.

Young Bok had little to say: "My comrade is a good and hardworking student. He was almost always studying in his room this entire week." It was true; his underling was a year below him, a quiet student, unobtrusive, who kept to himself.

"Is that it? You're not hiding anything? You're not lying?"

Young Bok held his breath as the man leaned in closer. He shook his head vigorously, breathing out to dispel the smell. "I'm not lying, sir. The only other thing I know is that he visited his grandmother last weekend in the countryside."

Some people went to jail for hiding information from their superiors or even for being suspected of hiding information. Young Bok's status as a top student in school bought him some freedom from suspicion and bad-breath-man did not concern himself too much with Young Bok's affairs. He grasped Young Bok's shoulder firmly. "You keep studying hard, alright? You work hard, alright?"

Young Bok nodded and bowed. He walked toward the lunchroom to meet up with Chae Eun Shin, Lim In Jim, and Lim In Hyung. These days, they only talked about what happened within the day, and even these words were carefully curated. There was an unspoken code of "don't ask, don't tell." They knew they might have to report to the superiors on what had been said in the conversation. It was better to just study, eat meals, and shift through each day just like the last.

***

Through the open door of the church, Young Bok could hear chanting and the uniform marching of small feet, "*Manse* Kim Il Sung! Hurray Kim Il Sung! *Manse* Kim Il Sung!" He paused in the middle of the Sunday school lesson until the voices had faded a little.

Young Bok knew that the children he taught faced the same type of indoctrination he faced every day at school: everything was matter, Christianity was the *soyang jeong gyo*, Yankee religion, and obedience to God meant obedience to the Yankees.

Manse Kim Il Sung! *Manse* Kim Il Sung! Six days a week, the students would march throughout the entire town, and almost like broken cuckoo birds in that clockwork town of Pyongsong, they would shout, "*Manse* Kim Il Sung! *Manse* Kim Il Sung!"

A couple of Young Bok's students came charging into the Sunday school classroom, ruddy-faced and panting. One of them covered her mouth, laughing and saying, "We had to demonstrate but we ran away."

Young Bok smiled and nodded, gesturing for them to sit. He had never told his students to abandon their exercises to come to Sunday school, but they always did. Perhaps it was wrong to be so joyful over it. Yet it encouraged and excited him, convicting him of the power of the gospel message he taught and of the desire of these children to learn.

He smiled again and returned to his message. Time was short, and he only had a half hour to impress these children with God's great love for them.

"Jesus loves everyone. Everyone." He spread his arms wide. "You know who that includes? Me. You. And you. And you.

And also, Kim Il Sung. *All* of us are under God. This same God, He loves us so, so much that He sent His only son, Jesus, to die on the cross for all the wrongdoings we have done. You know what this means? We have the gift of eternal life! God is powerful. But children, we have to be careful of Satan. Believe in God because He can and *will* conquer Satan." His students nodded back at him. They all knew what he meant when he said Satan. A word on all their minds but one they wouldn't dare to say aloud: Communism. "I have to study here well because while I am here, I have to live," Young Bok continued. "I want all of you to study hard in school too. God calls us to do our best in everything that we do! Remember this: even when you are scared, you must remember that God loves you very much."

Young Bok smiled at these familiar faces, faces he had grown to love dearly. He had learned how to direct this Sunday school class of a hundred children with silent hand motions: raised motions for the children to get to their feet, downward motions for sitting and prayer time.

He laughed a little, remembering the first time he had taught Sunday school, about a year ago now, in mid-1945 when he was sixteen. He had lost track of what he was saying half-way through a sentence, and stopped, looking blankly at the sea of little upturned faces. Panic had swelled up inside of him, and his nervous habit emerged: he gritted his teeth. He had left the service murmuring to himself, "What am I doing? I'm not eloquent…the words never come out the way I imagine them. Why am I doing this?"

Then there was the warmth of a firm hand on his shoulder, and he looked up to see Pastor Chae Shin Myuk with his kind eyes and dimpled cheeks. Young Bok bowed so abruptly that for a moment he wondered if his head would separate from his body. "I apologize. I was too nervous and...I'm not a good speaker. My friend Lim In Hyung is so much better at speaking. Someone like him should be doing this role. I'm just—"

"Young Bok." Pastor Chae's voice was a little stern. "Why are you teaching this Sunday school class?"

Young Bok bit his lip. "I want the children to learn about God and the love that He has for them, but I'm not good at this! I want to do it, but I can't."

"Young Bok, let me tell you about Dwight Moody. Do you know who he is?"

Young Bok nodded. He had heard about this American evangelist.

"Moody...he was a very poor speaker," said Pastor Chae, pressing Young Bok's hand for emphasis. "But he wanted to teach. He wanted to share the love of God to the world. It is said that he went into the lonely hills and put out ten stones to practice his preaching. He told himself, 'I will not go back to teach children until these stones agree with me.' He preached and preached until his voice was hoarse. One day, he was so enthusiastic in his preaching that the stones finally nodded and agreed. Then," Pastor Chae paused meaningfully to look at Young Bok, "he was ready to teach. It's a silly story, but the important part, Young Bok, the important part is that it all started with Moody's deep love for God; he simply did not allow his own weaknesses to stop him."

"I want to be like Moody," said Young Bok. "I want to practice and practice speaking so I can show my love for God and for these children."

"And so you will," Pastor Chae smiled.

And so he did. Young Bok's small class of five students grew to a hundred, and eventually he even became the Sunday school superintendent.

***

Young Bok had thought that with the liberation, the deaths and the arrests and the persecution of Christians would end. The Japanese government had mandated that Shinto shrines be erected in churches and schools, and Young Bok's pastor, Chae Shin Myuk, Chae Eun Shin's father, had been jailed for his refusal. Like thousands of other pastors across the nation, he had disappeared into a filthy jail cell. After the liberation, the pastors had poured out of jail, churches had reopened, and the Communists had claimed that religion was free: Christianity, Buddhism, and Cheondoism (the Chondogyo religion). *Religion was free. Politics were free,* they claimed.

Free. If this is freedom, what does freedom mean? Young Bok scoffed. This so-called "freedom" meant that there would be no real accountability for the raping and pillaging done by the Soviet troops, that Korean Communists would even defend them, that if people spoke against them, like in Sinuiju, about 140 miles northwest of Pyongsong, they would be silenced and jailed. This "freedom" meant that in this same town, a thousand students could protest, hundreds could be killed and injured, a thousand go to jail, and their voices would still go unheard by the press. This "freedom" meant that persecution of Christians only intensified as churches and Christian nationalists became involved in nationwide protest movements for political representation and religious freedoms. This "freedom" meant that the Communist system always came first before faith. This "freedom" meant that churches were burned down and torn apart and church leaders were executed, that ministers were forced to tug around oxcarts through town, bearing a label of "national traitor." This "freedom" meant that Kim Il Sung would not listen to the roaring cries of ten thousand protestors on March 1, 1946, when they demanded religious freedom and political representation. This "freedom" meant Kim Il Sung would label these protests as treason and conspiracy, an excuse to crack down on churches and crush anti-Communist activity. This "freedom" meant that the very first election held on November 3, 1946, would intentionally be scheduled during Sunday church services, and authorities would demand that all people must go and vote. This "freedom" meant that ballots were serially numbered, that Communist guards watched every move, that anti-Communist ballots went into a specially labeled "black box," that people were rumored to disappear after placing an anti-Communist vote. If this was freedom, Young Bok wanted no part in it.

Young Bok remained confident in his faith. "Even if I die now, I'll be in paradise. I don't need to fear disobeying because then I will be in heaven," Young Bok used to say. Hardship bred strong believers. Many of Young Bok's friends who would escape south in later years became pastors, elders, and seminary professors.

Still, even though Young Bok was bold in his faith, his reality was one of fear. Things he said and things he did could mean more than punishment for himself. It could mean the arrest of a church member, the disappearance of a friend, the death of his family members.

He fought so his hatred of the Communist system did not translate over to a hatred of the Communist Party members themselves. Just as his church never denied them entry, so Young Bok strove to look at these people and to see them in the context of their circumstances, to be able to say for some, "it is for their own survival that they have chosen to be Communists." After all, if Christians hated the Communists, what made them different from anyone else?

Then again, few Party members strayed into the church, unless they were monitoring worship services. If they patrolled too frequently, they risked being labeled as "church sympathizers." In the Party's eyes, regular churchgoing was a steppingstone toward sabotage and conspiracy against the Communist ideology.

CHAPTER TWENTY-ONE

Chuseok, the harvest festival, fell on the autumn equinox between late September and early October. On that night, there would be a full harvest moon, round and plump like a ripe peach in the sky. It was the longest vacation in the year: five days of celebration and freedom after the fall harvest.

Most families spent the holiday visiting the tombs of their ancestors. They ate new grain, rice, and fruit from the harvest, bowing to the graves and praying before they ate the feast.

Sometimes Young Bok envied these families. Bowing solemnly together, touching the little patch of ground where their grandparents and great-grandparents were buried, tending the flowers, passing on stories.

But his grandfather's tomb was hidden somewhere in the Koksan, and his grandmother's name and story had been lost to time long before he was born.

Instead, the Kim family set up tables at home, and on Chuseok Eve they made *songpyeon*, stuffed half-moon rice cakes. Yang Sil kneaded rice powder into chestnut-sized balls, and together they filled them with sesame seeds, red bean, or chestnut paste. Afterward, Yang Sil steamed them in layers of pine needles, until the whole house was fragrant with the sharp, clean scent. Then, she arranged the *songpyeon*, new fruit, grain, and rice from the harvest in front of the picture of Kim Chul Soo. The entire family bowed once to the food and then three times to their ancestors. Though Young Bok had never really believed it, he had always been told that the spirits of their ancestors would come and taste the food. After bowing, the family gathered around the table to eat the food. How Yang Sil had managed to scrape together so much, Young Bok never knew.

Young Bok had fully expected that the Communists would end the tomb-visiting ritual. After all, they had repeatedly drilled him at school, "When you are dead, no soul is left over. The concept of a soul is just invisible matter, a product of the brain." Yet surprisingly, Chuseok continued. Much later, in the 1990s, after Kim Il Sung had died, the tradition conveniently kept Kim Il Sung's memory and influence alive. "A political tactic of propaganda," said Young Bok.

***

Perhaps it was because he had not eaten so much in such a long time, but the unhappy gurgling of his stomach woke Young Bok in the middle of the night, and he crept outside to use the bathroom. When he returned, he heard a muffled wailing sound from his parent's section of the room. Sweeping back the dividing curtain, he whispered, "Umma?"

My mom is dying, was Young Bok's first thought. Yang Sil was on the floor clutching her stomach and writhing with pain. She let out a muffled wail. Young Bok saw a piece of cotton that she gripped between her teeth; even in her pain, Yang

Sil did not want to wake her family with her cries. Her dark hair slipped from the neat bun and clung to her sweaty face.

"Umma, what's wrong? Tell me what to do! Umma!" Young Bok grabbed his mother's shoulder. He was scared. His mother was always composed and quiet, but now she lay on the floor with veins standing out in her neck as she groaned, wrinkles in her face sharp and deep, and her arms wrapped around her stomach so tightly that Young Bok feared she would break.

Yang Sil did not respond. Another strained wail.

"Umma! What do I do?" Young Bok started crying.

My mom is dying with pain. My mom is dying. Young Bok ran for the doctor. Tearing out into the courtyard, he left his shoes behind. Left foot. Right foot. Left. Right. Swallowing his fear and gasping for air. *Faster, Young Bok, faster.* Even when a stone on the road gashed his foot, he paused only for a moment to regain his balance. He dashed back tears and ran. *Umma. Umma, I'm getting help.* He pounded on the door to the doctor's home, yelling, "My mom is dying!"

The doctor's home was dark and still. The stars were bright in the sky. Young Bok pounded again and again, shouting until his voice was hoarse. "Doctor! Doctor! My mom is dying! Please help me! Save my mom!"

Finally, the sound of shuffling feet in the courtyard.

The doctor opened the gate. It was too dark to see but Young Bok heard annoyance in the doctor's voice. He handed Young Bok a black leather bag with his equipment inside. "Run back," he said. "I'll come soon."

Young Bok sprinted home, feeling as though his lungs would burst with each lunging step. It felt good to feel pain, to know he could do something to help end his mother's pain.

When he rushed through the door, he found his mother in the same position he had left her in. Gently grasping her shoulder, he told her, "The doctor is coming, Umma. The doctor is coming."

But half an hour passed and his mother was still wailing, and the doctor had not come.

Young Bok ran back to the doctor's home. "Doctor! Doctor! Doctor!" This time the doctor did not answer the door; his son did. He was the only medical student in the entire town, and Young Bok's friend, but Young Bok had no time for niceties.

"Excuse me," he impatiently shoved past into the doctor's courtyard.

The doctor was shaving in front of a mirror. A delicate swipe with his razor, and then he brought his face close to the mirror to examine for stubble.

"I'm coming, I'm coming," he waved Young Bok away, eyes intent on his reflection in the morning half-light.

Young Bok gritted his teeth. He had no choice but to leave, sprinting home again. The sun was rising now, and as Young Bok ran home, he could see stains of blood on the road from his cut foot. His wound had clotted while waiting with his mother but split open again as he ran. He could feel gritty bits of dirt and a stinging pain with each step. *Back to Umma. Get back to Umma.*

Sitting there in the half-light, holding his mom's hand and stroking her back, Young Bok kept up a steady murmur of words. It made his heart ache too much to listen in silence while his mother groaned in pain. "Umma, if I were a doctor, I would come running right away! I would listen as soon as someone asked for my help. I would drop everything and run to them."

Yang Sil groaned again. Young Bok wiped away her tears of pain, his voice choking. "Umma, just hold on a little more. The doctor is coming. He's coming."

"Umma," he eased Yang Sil's head into his lap, and stroked back her sweaty hair so he could see her eyes. "Umma, I'll become a doctor. I'll study hard in school and find a way to go to medical school. Umma, you'll be so proud of me! I'll take care of you and make sure you're never in pain again. I promise, Umma, I promise. You see that black bag? I'll take one of those with me to every house in the village, and I'll listen to anyone who asks for my help. I'll make sure no one has to wait for help."

When the doctor finally arrived after another half hour, he calmly pressed Yang Sil's stomach until he found the source of the pain, grunted, and passed a little bag of powder to Young Bok. "It's likely a stomach ulcer."

He left within five minutes.

CHAPTER TWENTY-TWO

———

In the hot courtyard, Young Bok felt the sweat dripping down his face and down the back of his high-collared school uniform. He desperately wanted to roll up the long sleeves and pants.

The high school principal was shouting, "Again! Again! Sing it again!"

"Donghae mulgwa Baekdusani mareugo daltorok

Haneunimi bouhasa uri nara manse," the students sang.

"Until that day when the waters of the East Sea run dry and Mount Baekdu is worn away,

May God protect and preserve our nation; hurray to Korea."

The Communist government had recently changed the Korean national anthem. Though it was still sung to the Scottish folk song of "Auld Lang Syne," as it would be until 1948, the line that once went *"Haneunim* (God) protect and preserve our nation" became "the people protect and preserve our nation." And when it came to this new line, all the students yelled *Haneunim* as loudly as they could.

The principal pounded his fist on the podium. "Stop! Stop!" With each slam of his fist, beads of sweat flew in all directions. The other teachers were visibly uncomfortable.

Chae Eun Shin turned his head very slightly toward Young Bok. Young Bok could see his twitching lips and the laughing glint in his eyes.

Young Bok fought to keep back his own laughter.

"Again! Again!"

"Haneunimi bouhasa uri nara manse," the students roared. Young Bok was beaming; he could not keep the smile from his face. Looking at the faces of his peers and friends, he was thrilled that this was his country, and these were his countrymen. They sang until their voices were hoarse and rough, until each note of the rising melody felt ingrained in Young Bok's throat.

The principal was fired because he could not control the students.

The new principal was brought in from the far northern region of Hamgyong-do. It was a recurring tactic used by the Communist party: prevent unity against a common enemy, the Communist regime, by bringing in Communist leaders from different parts of Korea. How could the Korean people unite against the regime when they feared and hated one another? People in Young Bok's town hated people from the Hamgyong Province. They were known to be the worst, most brutal Communists. *Ppalgaengi,* Red Commies, who were willing to kill and rob from their own countrymen.

In later years, Young Bok heard that people in Hamgyong Province always believed the people of South Pyongan Province, Young Bok's province, to be the most terrible and brutal Communists.

Young Bok was walking down the school corridor one Friday, carefully counting out his money. *Just enough for three sacks of rice. Or should I maybe do four this week?* he thought. He heard raised voices from inside the principal's office. The door was slightly ajar, and Young Bok peered inside.

The principal sat in a wooden chair at his desk while a dozen high school soccer players crowded the room. Some of them leaned against the walls with a couple of their shirt buttons undone. *The bad boys,* Young Bok thought. He never dared to break the dress code, but he had a grudging respect for those who did, though it was a childish way to rebel. Five of the soccer players sat on top of the principal's desk. They wore their metal cleats, still grassy and muddy from practice, and swung their long legs. The dangerous points nearly grazed the principal's neck and face.

"Go home to Hamgyong-do, you filthy *ppalgaengi*, or we will kick you!" they shouted. Sharp kicks to punctuate their words. Their cleats stopped scarcely an inch from the principal's face. They spit other ugly words into his face, but Young Bok pressed himself against the wall before running down the hall, out of earshot. The less he saw and heard, the better. He could be punished for a failure to report such an event.

The next day, the twelve soccer players were in jail. Young Bok knew someone else must have witnessed the event and reported it, if not the principal himself. He never expected to see them again. People had disappeared for less, and none of those students belonged to important or influential families.

But they did return. All twelve of them.

When they walked down the hallway on Monday, people stared. After what they had done, how could they possibly have returned? The story spread throughout the school. For at least a week, it was the only subject of conversation.

Apparently, the principal had rushed to the police station the moment that he heard his students were in jail. He begged for their release, but a policeman had turned him away. "There's nothing I can do. These students need to be re-educated."

"I will teach them and make them supporters of Communism," the principal cried out, grasping the policeman's arm and gazing into his eyes. He too had children back home. "That's my job…to teach them. Please let me do this."

The policeman paused a moment. "I will talk to my superiors."

After some time, he returned and, nodding to the principal, he directed him to the holding cell where the twelve boys were. He shut the door and stepped away with a heavy tread.

The soccer players were disheveled, hair rumpled, faces bloodied, sleeves torn. One had clear tracks of tears down his face, though he puffed out his chest and glared. The principal saw the fear in each of their eyes. He knew they hadn't been thinking of their families at home, their friends, or even their own lives when they had sat there swinging their cleats at his face. They had been angry and foolish, but they were young.

He crouched down to meet their glaring eyes. "Please listen to me. You must make your choice now: prison or school?"

They chose school.

After this event, Young Bok was convinced educators could not have bad hearts: "Communism might force people to do terrible things, but humans are still good inside."

CHAPTER
TWENTY-THREE

———

It was 1946, Young Bok was seventeen, and he liked a girl in the church choir. He liked her!

Every Sunday, Young Bok woke far before the ringing of the church bell, mostly because he liked to arrive early at church, but also because he loved to stand outside and listen to the rich, stirring sound of the bell. It struck a chord within his heart, something deep inside of his soul singing out in response to that musical *cheondang cheondang,* like a sweet voice crying out, *Come to church! Come to church!*

The church had been built by American missionaries and was a single story of brick, stucco, and tile. In the large room with its cold wooden floor, the nearly two-hundred-person congregation split: men on the right and women on the left. That morning, Young Bok kneeled several rows from the front of the congregation. He could hear rustling as the man next to him nodded rhythmically to the pastor's prayer. Usually, Young Bok would have been focused on the prayer, on the beautiful call to a humble and open heart to God. Usually, he would have been thinking about how his pastor sounded like an angel with his sonorous, deep voice.

But today, Young Bok was thinking of the choir girl. *My first love.* She was tall and slender, with a beautiful soprano voice. Young Bok had grown up going to Sunday school with the choir girl, but he had only talked to her a handful of times. One time, it was "*You dropped your pencil, Young Bok,*" and "*Thank you*" in blushing response. Or "*Hi, Young Bok,*" and "*Oh…hello.*" Just thinking about their interactions…Young Bok's heart pounded fast.

He could imagine exactly how she was standing in the front left corner of the choir box: one hand folded over the other, her hair carefully combed back, the slight lift of the eyebrow when she was intrigued or focused. Maybe the sun was glancing off her hair. Maybe she was smiling now? Young Bok opened his eyes furtively, glancing at his neighbors' bowed heads. When he raised his eyes to look toward the choir girl, he found her staring straight back at him.

His heart thundered and he jerked his head down and squeezed his eyes shut. *Why did we both meet eyes? There is no reason why we both should open our eyes while praying. Does she…like me?*

This is lust! Young Bok's brain screamed, *This is a sin!*

After all, it was forbidden to date or even to like someone by Korean tradition. Marriage was only by introduction; there was no free love, no "I love this girl and I want to marry her." That was forbidden.

Young Bok's mind flickered to a passage in the Bible speaking about how lust in the mind was already adultery. Now he laughs at his dramatic reaction, but in the moment, he was panicky, thinking only, *I've committed adultery! I have to repent!* He bowed his head down deeply to his chest and rubbed his hands together. The rustling man next to him was still for a moment, and Young Bok felt the silent heat of staring eyes. *I'm sorry, Lord, forgive me,* Young Bok prayed. *Please forgive me!*

Young Bok never knew exactly why he opened his eyes, or why the choir girl had been gazing steadily back at him with her beautiful dark eyes. But she had stared, and Young Bok was sure he had caught that gentle smile just starting to pull at the corners of her mouth when he had ducked his head again.

Nothing could ever come from this first love. Young Bok's parents did not know the choir girl's parents. And even if they did, betrothal and marriage had to come from careful planning and consideration. Feelings were…unreliable.

As Young Bok reached the age of eighteen, the discussion of marriage became inescapable.

First, it was the gossiping village *ajummas* who clucked their tongues when they saw him pass. Then it was his friends and high school classmates talking about their own arrangements and marriages. Finally, it was his own mother.

On weekends when Young Bok couldn't make the long trip home from school, Yang Sil would travel to his school on the Monday after. Without fail, she always arrived bearing a whole boiled chicken in a basket, an expensive treat.

Young Bok always took her hand. "Umma, let's eat together!"

"Oh no, Setjjae," Yang Sil would reply. "I already ate." Or sometimes, it was, "I'm not hungry." She always had a reason. Tearing off a drumstick, she would hand the tender meat to Young Bok, smile, nod, and settle back to watch him eat.

Young Bok loved to eat the bones clean, but he knew that his mother would refuse to eat until he said that he was finished. So, he ate the meat roughly, leaving strings of meat and skin on the bones and tossing the bones into the basket. When he had "finished" and washed his hands, his mom began to chew off the bones.

One day in 1947, shortly after Young Bok had turned eighteen, Yang Sil was watching Young Bok gnaw on the chicken bones. "Setjjae..."

"Yes, Umma," Young Bok looked up at his mother, mouth full.

"Setjjae, you remember our neighbor's younger daughter, Hee Young. She's ladylike, isn't she? Pretty manners." Yang Sil paused, looked searchingly into Young Bok's eyes for a moment. "She can carry heavy buckets of water from the well. She's strong, hardworking, and pretty, too..."

Of course, Young Bok knew this girl, two years younger than himself. He knew her older sister was the prettier of the two, the town beauty, mostly because her mother never stopped boasting about it. Young Bok also knew that eighteen was the matchmaking age, and by this age, his elder brother, Cheotjjae, had already been married. By the time a man turned twenty, he was "old."

Yang Sil reached up to wipe some grease from Young Bok's face with a deft stroke of her thumb. "Would you like to marry her?"

Young Bok swallowed. He looked down at his hands before he turned to face his mother. "I would like to marry her," he smiled. "But Umma, I want to finish medical school first. Can I wait until I am twenty-one or twenty-two?"

Young Bok knew that most mothers wouldn't accept such a request. The older he was, the worse his marriage prospects would be. He would be the talk of the town too, and Yang Sil would hear no end to it.

Truthfully, he simply wasn't ready. He could do almost anything his mom asked him to, but he could not see himself as a husband or a father yet. There was so much he still wanted to do, so much more he needed to learn...

Yang Sil was nodding slowly. She patted Young Bok's hand. "Of course, Setjjae. You study hard and become a doctor. We can talk more about this later."

She smiled a little now. "You know I am so proud of you, right, Setjjae? Your Umma is so proud of you."

Young Bok felt tears pricking his eyes. He grabbed his mother's hand. They were rough, browned by sun and calloused from farm tools and the laundry beating stick. His own hands were much paler; the only callouses were from gripping his pencil. "Umma."

"Mm, Setjjae?"

A pause. "Nothing...just...thank you, Umma." He wanted to say, *I love you.*

CHAPTER TWENTY-FOUR

In February of 1948, Young Bok graduated at the top of his eighty-person class, tied with his friend Ee Yoon Young. Only Yang Sil made the five-hour walk to watch him graduate, but Young Bok knew his entire family was proud of him—the first member of their family to graduate high school!

At the ceremony, he and Ee Yoon Young received handsome certificates, bearing big red stamps and a signature from Paek Nam Un, the Minister of Education. The certificates granted the holder admission to attend whatever higher university they desired at no cost and without an entrance exam. A full ride. Young Bok was proud of the gilded award, the feel of the new paper, the importance of having everyone applaud, the smile on Yang Sil's face. But he and Yoon Young both knew the lie. They wouldn't be attending the universities they wanted; in fact, they wouldn't even be in the country at all. The top two achieving students from each high school were selected for a special program: three to four years of training in the Soviet Union. Upon returning to Korea, they would be expected to serve as political leaders or important party members in the Communist government.

If they refused to go, they risked imprisonment.

So, Yoon Young and Young Bok smiled and bowed to the applause, but Young Bok knew he was smiling too widely, the strain shaking the corners of his mouth.

Later, Young Bok gritted his teeth. How could he leave behind his town, his church, his family, his mother? Yet, at the same time, what if this was his chance to finally be free of the Communist regime? Sometimes he lay awake at night thinking about how he could use the trip to the Soviet Union to escape North Korea. He would pull out his school textbook in the dark room, and to the music of his brothers' snores, he flipped to the page with the map of Europe. "If I have to go, then I have to go," he would mutter to himself. He traced different paths each time on the black and white map. "I could go through this way, then here, then to East Germany, and then maybe, maybe I could escape!" He knew these were dreams, that he would always be watched closely in the Soviet Union. That there would have to be false papers and passports and, most of all, money, which he did not have. And then where would he go even if he made it to East Germany? England? The United States? What would happen to his family? Surely, they would be punished for his flight. Never being able to talk to them again, maybe never returning... He couldn't run and leave them behind. He had to find a way to excuse himself from this program.

In March, the excuse came in the form of a terrible and infectious rash from mange. Young Bok's entire arm was covered in an ugly red rash, leaky with yellow pus. For the entire month until his planned departure in April, he never washed or cleaned his arm. Then, he went to the organizing officer of the abroad group. "I was among the candidates selected for the trip to the Soviet Union. I have mange now, what should I do? Do you think I could still go?"

Young Bok rolled up his sleeve, and the officer's disgust was visible. He took a step back and held a hand up to his nose. "How long has it been?"

"A month and it hasn't healed yet."

A sharp intake of breath from the officer. "I don't think you should go at this time. If the group is infected, it would be shameful. For your team's sake, I hope you won't mind being excused from the program to cure your disease. However, we cannot guarantee that you can go to the Soviet Union next year."

Young Bok carefully shielded his smile with a low bow. "No, no, I sincerely apologize for what happened. I thank you again for the honor."

In early April, all the chosen students gathered in Pyongyang and boarded the train to leave for the Soviet Union. Young Bok waved goodbye to Ee Yoon Young from the station. He would never see him again.

***

"If you wanted to come here, then you should have applied when school started. It's too bad. You're too late." The board members at Pyongyang Medical School were shaking their heads.

Even when Young Bok presented his stamped certificate and explained his circumstances and the two-week period where his skin condition had healed, they still shook their heads.

Young Bok left the board meeting and wandered around Pyongyang for about half an hour before he decided that the only next step was to approach the Minister of Education himself. When he had located the correct building, Young Bok entered, clutching his certificate with sweaty palms. If all went smoothly, he would be able to follow his dream and enter medical school. If the Minister was angry… Young Bok shook his head. Better not to think about it. If he argued his case respectfully and logically, he would likely avoid any punishment. But then again, this was not just any Communist official; it was the North Korean Minister of Education.

Young Bok gritted his teeth together and hid his shaking hands behind his back. He bowed to the secretary at the front desk, "I have an important matter to discuss with the Minister of Education."

The secretary did not look up from her desk. "He's busy. You cannot see him."

Young Bok squared his shoulders. He was *going* to go to medical school. "I am a graduate with the Minister's award. See this one!" He waved the certificate in front of the secretary, raising his voice. "The Minister. Mr. Paek Nam Un. I *have* to see him! Is this certificate even valid? Is it a fake? I have to see him! You have to let me see him!"

Fortunately, the Minister heard him. The door to his office swung open, and Minister Paek Nam Un stood in the doorway in a smart suit jacket, hands folded behind his back. "What is happening?"

The secretary stood quickly and bowed. "This young boy wants to see you, but you are too busy, so I did not permit him to go in, sir."

The Minister approached Young Bok. He tightened his tie and straightened his collar, looking at Young Bok with heavily hooded eyes. He looked dimly like a tired frog. "Who are you?"

Young Bok bowed deeply, chin almost brushing his chest, "My name is Kim Young Bok, sir. Thank you for this certificate. I am honored to receive it. But sir, is your certificate false? Does it have no value?"

Young Bok did not look up, but he heard a tone of surprise in the man's voice. "Of course it has value!"

Young Bok straightened to face the Minister. "I went to Pyongyang Medical School, but they said that I could not be accepted, as the school was filled and I missed the time to apply, sir. I was chosen to go to the Soviet Union, but I couldn't go because of a rash from a skin condition. You gave me this certificate that said that I could attend anywhere I wanted to go. What did you mean by giving this to me if it has no real value? Because of my skin condition, I am too late and cannot go to school!"

The Minister nodded. He ran a tired hand through his styled hair and gestured Young Bok to follow him into his office. "I will write a memo for you," said the Minister, already scribbling a note. "You bring this to the dean. I am sure he will accept you." He signed the page with a flourish.

Young Bok beamed and bowed low, accepting the paper with both hands. "Thank you, sir!"

As he left the office, he read the drying black ink: *Kim Young Bok is a bright and good student. He was selected to attend the Soviet Union but could not due to health reasons. Please consider him for admission to Pyongyang Medical School; he is well-qualified.*

Young Bok went directly to the dean of the medical school and showed him the note. While the dean read it, Young Bok said, "The Minister of Education said that this certificate is valid. It's not fake; it's a real one."

"Oh. Well." The dean pursed his lips. "The Minister said okay, so I'm okay." He turned to one of the professors in the office. "One more in your class. Direct him to the hospital for complete treatment of his mange."

Young Bok said a quick prayer: *Thank you, God. I tried my best and you helped me.* In all of it, he was learning again and again that though he had to trust God fully, he couldn't simply wait around to be fed and provided for. He had to work to achieve and survive.

Young Bok could not wait to tell the news to his family. He was to be the second person in his entire town to go to medical school.

***

Pyongyang Medical School had four classes of thirty people each: three medical and one public health. Young Bok saw only one familiar face, a troublemaker high school classmate notorious for his frequent fist fights and hot temper. He was most notorious for his vicious head-butting that left bloody and broken noses in his wake. Young Bok actively avoided him.

Though he had enrolled late, Young Bok slipped easily into the rhythm of the classroom. Exams took place orally every couple weeks, and Young Bok got used to the jolt in his stomach each time he was called to the front of the classroom. The professor extended a metal cup in which exam questions were written neatly on flat sticks. The students had only a couple minutes to think before giving their answer.

In Young Bok's biology class, a white-haired professor spoke about the acquired characteristics in apples, as proposed by Trofim Lysenko, a Soviet biologist. Lysenko had been the director of the Institute of Genetics of Academy of Sciences of the USSR since 1940 and rejected the existence of genes and inheritance for the concept of acquired characteristics. By 1948, across Stalin's regime, education and research in standard genetics was outlawed. Some geneticists were arrested, while others died from undisclosed causes. Young Bok knew this so-called "biology" that his professor now spoke of was in the vein of Communist thought. It fit cleanly with the concept that the Communist ideology was passed down from father to child; in other words, a Communist would give birth to a Communist child. Young Bok had held his tongue for so long, but he could no longer be quiet. After all, this was biology they spoke of—truth he could see just by walking outside.

"Professor," said Young Bok, "the crabapple plant does not make good apples, but neither can the apple seed be planted on its own. You have to graft an apple sprout into crabapple roots in order to make good apples." Young Bok had seen it a million times, even helped select a crabapple stalk with healthy roots and a slender stalk from a favorite apple tree. With the deft swoop of a farmer's knife, a stalk of the crabapple plant was cut open at an angle to expose tender white pith and sweet tree sap. Then, a small branch of the desired apple was sliced in an identical angle. The two pieces were lined up and bound together tightly with a piece of white string. Usually, the two pieces grafted so cleanly there would be nothing but a thin scar between the two to distinguish the pieces. Young Bok continued, "Why would grafting be necessary if all plants have acquired characteristics? Growing without grafting should be inherited then!"

The white-haired professor smiled very slightly, more with his eyes than his mouth. "I'm teaching Lysenko's experiment, but I suppose they didn't use our Korean apples to experiment." He lifted one eyebrow very slightly, and Young Bok felt the unspoken words pass between them: *The Communist ideology could not dictate biology.*

The professor disappeared within the year. The school committee ruled that the teacher was not faithful to Communism, naive and unable to handle a class. He was supposedly moved to the "northern provinces," but Young Bok never knew what had really happened to him.

Young Bok tried to avoid thinking about him because the guilt was unbearable. It was he who had asked a question with a dangerous answer, but his teacher had been punished. It was *his* question. His stupid pride.

***

While at Pyongyang Medical School, Young Bok found a role model in Professor Chang Kee Ryo. Like Young Bok, Chang Kee Ryo had been born into a rural village. He was a devout Christian who graduated from Gyeongseong Medical School in Seoul in 1932, becoming the Director of Surgery at a hospital in Pyongyang in 1940. He rose to great fame, widely known as the top surgeon in the nation. A quiet and composed man, his core values were simple: Let your heart motivate you. While you are alive, serve others. If something isn't right, say it; don't deny the wrong in a situation. Take responsibility for problems, even if this means paying for them yourself.

Young Bok heard stories that Professor Chang had operated on Kim Il Sung in a secretive appendix surgery. Before beginning the operation, he had all the staff in the room pray for a successful surgery. His status as a top surgeon granted him particular privileges. Why else would Communists bow their heads in prayer to a God they did not believe in? Years later, many people pestered Professor Chang: "Why didn't you kill Kim Il Sung? Are you a Communist sympathizer?"

To this, Professor Chang had a simple response: "That would have been wrong. I cannot kill another human."

Young Bok heard much later that during the Korean War in the winter of 1950. Chang Kee Ryo had had to leave behind his family in the North. Caught up in the withdrawing South Korean army aboard an ambulance transporting emergency patients, Chang saw his wife and children in the hordes of refugees moving south. Perhaps they saw them and waved, perhaps they said goodbye. But more likely, they did not see him above the shoulders and heads of so many trudging people, carrying the burdens of sorrow, exhaustion, and household belongings. Only Chang's second son was with him in the ambulance. Chang's family was unable to escape south, and after the war, the South Korean government offered to search for them in the north. Chang turned down the offer, saying, "God will take care of them. I cannot have the privilege of the government searching for my family when so many others are missing."

Meanwhile, he set up makeshift tents in Pusan to treat the endless stream of war victims. This would later grow into a hospital of 190 beds, Pusan Gospel Hospital.

Professor Chang often used his own salary to discharge patients who could not pay for their own release, and he was constantly raising funds to help the poor. He was a humble man. Even when he became the Chief of Surgery at Seoul National University, he continued to live in a simple one-room home in Pusan, where he kept a picture of his wife on the wall, looking forward to the day when he would meet his wife again in heaven.

Young Bok deeply respected and continues to respect Professor Chang to this day. His picture is framed in Young Bok's office.

CHAPTER TWENTY-FIVE

In southern Korea, the US directed an election in May of 1948 amidst strikes, demonstrations, and boycotting by Koreans, both rightists and leftists. The Koreans were well-aware a separate election would inevitably lead to the creation of two separate states; correctly, they predicted that such an event would extinguish the possibility of a reunification between the US-held southern Korea and Soviet-held northern Korea. On August 15, 1948, the right-wing, conservative leader Syngman Rhee was named the president of the Republic of Korea in Seoul. Three weeks later, on September 9, Kim Il Sung was named the premier of the Democratic People's Republic of Korea. And after three years of occupation, Soviet troops finally began boarding trains to return home.

This time, Young Bok did not go to the train station to see them off.

1948 passed and 1949 began. Young Bok turned twenty.

After over a year of fighting, tens of thousands of Korean boys who had been dispatched to China to aid Communist Mao in the Chinese Civil War began to filter home. Upon their return, these weathered soldiers were integrated into the North Korean People's Army.

Kim Il Sung disappeared into Moscow with great frequency, seeking permission from Stalin for an attack on South Korea. He emerged with nearly $50 million of machinery, air force, artillery, and coal, but no clearance for an attack.

The neighborhood people's committee kept knocking at the Kims' door almost every night, reminding the family to attend education classes: "Communism helps the poor. General Kim Il Sung fought all of his life to liberate us from the bourgeois." At almost every class, they sang the Red Flag song: *"Don't cry if we die while fighting our enemies… If you lift the red flag high, then we will die bravely beneath it. If anyone is a coward, he can leave, but we will protect the red flag and die singing this song"* (Cheong, 2011). Young Bok grew to hate the color red. Red on the banners and posters across the town. Red on the new, ever-present flag. Red on the armbands of the security officers and neighborhood representatives. The invisible red blood of all the disappeared and the executed. In the loneliness of his university dorm, it was too easy to dwell on hatred. Ideology and people tangled together until Young Bok's chest tightened, and he could no longer tell if he hated the people or Communism itself.

Each weekend, Young Bok stepped off the train into his hometown. He always found Daseotjjae waiting for him at the station. She was fourteen now, but when she ran toward him smiling brightly and waving both of her arms, he could only see the little child he had once carried on his back. They walked home with linked arms, talking and laughing on the dusty road. There were few watchful eyes on the country road, and he could almost feel the pressure and tension ease out of his shoulders, out of the furrow of his brow, the clench of his jaw. He breathed in the country air, comforted by the smell the cooking dinners of a dozen different families and the sound of laughing village children.

Daseotjjae loved to wash Young Bok's lunchbox, and Young Bok often stuffed it with penny-cheap items: pins, barrettes, and candy he bought in Pyongyang.

On one occasion, Young Bok heard a piercing scream from the kitchen. He ran across the courtyard and into the kitchen to find Daseotjjae on the ground, clutching a human finger bone with a shaking hand. Her mouth was a wide O and she stared unblinkingly at the bone. Young Bok laughed until tears ran down his face. "I'm sorry, Daseotjjae… I'm sorr—" he cascaded into laughter again. He had been studying models of human bones in class and forgotten he had put them in his lunchbox to study later.

Daseotjjae refused to wash, or even touch, Young Bok's lunchbox for several weeks after.

***

Kim Il Sung had recently created a pro-regime Korean Christian Federation. By 1948, all Christians were required to join, and those who refused began to disappear into jails. Many were executed.

The sale of Bibles and religious materials became illegal, and the pastors in Young Bok's province gathered and decided they would each memorize one or two books of the Bible. In the event that their Bibles were confiscated or burned by the Communists, the Church would still be able to piece together the entire book. Pastor Chae Shin Myuk of Young Bok's church was in charge of the final book of Revelation. Every

Saturday before service, he spent a long night on his knees in prayer and in memorization of Revelation.

Since his high school years, Young Bok had always wanted to join his pastor in this overnight prayer. On a windy fall night in 1949, he finally had the opportunity to do so.

On his knees in the small, dark room next to the podium, Young Bok felt at peace. In the quiet, cool darkness, it was just him and God. His prayer stretched all around him like a ribbon of silent words. *God, I praise You for Your great love, for Your mercy and compassion. For being a God who is just and slow to anger. I pray for my family, that You would protect them and help bring my father and brothers to You. I pray for our country, for our Korean nation, that You will give us freedom and unite us again.*

Young Bok lost track of time in the room. The small window in the wall showed only a dark sky, stars hidden by fast moving clouds. It was still far from sunrise. Young Bok's head felt heavy on his shoulders, and he had long since lost feeling in his knees. He felt half-dead. He rubbed his neck and glanced at Pastor Chae next to him, whose mouth was moving silently in prayer.

Thunk. Thunk. Thunk. Approaching footsteps. They were the purposeful tread of someone searching for something. The congregation? But it was not morning yet. Suddenly, a burning light shined in his eyes and a rough voice shouted, "What are you doing?"

Young Bok raised his hands reflexively to shield his eyes from the light. Arms yanked him to his feet, but his legs collapsed under him, and he fell down again, legs numb from kneeling in prayer. "Get up!" a voice barked. Young

Bok glimpsed the red arm band and uniform of Communist security officers.

Pastor Chae Shin Myuk stood slowly, another officer grasping his arm. Pastor Chae nodded at Young Bok, and his peaceful face calmed Young Bok's skipping heart. *Yes, this was not Pastor Chae's first arrest.*

As they were dragged away to the local jail, Young Bok stared out at the dark village. *How easy it would be to disappear.* It was frightening, guided away by these men with their familiar faces, fearing that maybe he would not get to say goodbye to his family or even tell them where he was being taken. Young Bok clenched his hands to hide the shaking, but the chill of fear spread throughout his body. His teeth chattered and he felt goosebumps rising on his flesh. Had someone reported him entering the church at a late hour? Had it just been a routine check on the church? How was he to be punished? Was this his last breath of free air?

Once they were locked behind bars, Pastor Chae said, "In the book of Acts, Paul and Silas spent an entire night praying and singing hymns to God after they were imprisoned by the Romans. Just like us, they sat on a cold, hard jail floor. Just like us, they were afraid, and their futures were uncertain. They did not respond in fear, but in prayer and songs of praise to their Father in heaven who they knew had a perfect plan in store for them." Young Bok knew the story but propped up against the corner of that cold jail cell, feeling the panic and worry washing over him in waves, it was comforting to hear Pastor Chae's voice filling the empty walls of the jail. Pastor Chae's deep voice was a warm rumble in the pit of his stomach, and he clung to it with all his might. "Then there was a violent earthquake that shook open the doors of the prison and loosed all the prisoners' chains. The Roman jailer, believing that all the prisoners had escaped, raised a sword and was about to kill himself, but Paul and Silas cried, 'We are all here! Do not harm yourself!' The jailer fell before Paul and Silas. Do you know the words he said?"

Young Bok nodded, then realized Pastor Chae could not see him in the darkness. "Yes, Pastor Chae. He said, 'What must I do to be saved?'"

"Very good. They responded and told him, 'Believe in the Lord Jesus and you will be saved, you and your household' (Acts 16:31 NIV). Then, the Roman jailer and his entire household came to believe in God."

Like Paul and Silas, Young Bok and Pastor Chae filled the fearful darkness of the jail with hymns and with prayers for their safe release in the morning.

At first light, a policeman clanked open the door. "You both may go."

As Young Bok passed through, the man grasped his shoulder and Young Bok's heart clenched in fear. "Don't go to church with all these *yesu jaengee,* Jesus people. No more, okay? Otherwise, we'll tell your school, and you will be kicked out for going to church. Do you want that? To be kicked out of school? Pyongyang Medical School is miles from here…why do you come back here on your weekends? Just study. Don't go to church, just study."

Young Bok only bowed his head in respect to his elder.

When they had left the jail, Pastor Chae patted Young Bok's back. "You did well, Young Bok. Weeping may endure for a night, but joy comes in the morning. You know this verse?"

Young Bok nodded. *Psalm 30:5.* "God truly did rescue us, Pastor Chae!"

They parted ways.

Throughout the entire week, Young Bok spent much time in prayer. He was confident all things were in God's hands and that God had complete control of his future, but he was also terrified. He could be jailed, disappeared into the night, even executed.

Breathe, Young Bok. You are the only medical student in the whole town. The town needs a doctor, so the police won't risk reporting you. They can't risk you being kicked out of Pyongyang Medical School. Still, he could not know for sure. *God, please give me peace. I'm scared,* he prayed.

Young Bok returned to church the next weekend and the next and the next. Nothing happened.

***

A few months later, the Communist Party murdered Pastor Chae, other pastors from Young Bok's town, pastors from the next town over, and loyal members of the congregation.

Communist officials dug a long trench into the mountainside, an ugly gashed scar of fresh dirt. There among the roots and broken shoots, they strung people together with thick barbed telephone wires through their hands, like gutted fish left out to die. Only every third person was covered with dirt. Men that Young Bok had known, faces twisted in pain and death into horrid expressions, and frozen skin gray-black and icy.

Every time he passed the mountain, Young Bok was afraid that he heard gasping, the last breaths of men who were not ready to die, not ready to leave behind wives and children, friends and empty churches. He was afraid to see the bodies because then he might be too terrified to go on.

Young Bok could not bring himself to go there the first night after the murder, but others had crept to the mountainside in the cover of darkness to see whether their loved ones were alive or not.

One of Young Bok's friends had searched for his father among these bodies. He never told Young Bok about that dark, cold night on the mountainside, creeping along on hands and knees on the ground, choking on the stink of dead bodies, the fading smell of blood from the pierced hands of the men. But he found his father.

Young Bok remembered Pastor Chae's words to him: "Weeping may endure for a night, but joy comes in the morning." *Psalm 30:5*. Maybe the morning would be long in coming; maybe the weeping night would be long and heartbreaking. But he would wait faithfully.

CHAPTER TWENTY-SIX

With summer came sleepless nights lying as still as possible on the sticky dorm floor, listening to the static hum of cicadas. 1949 had been scarred by guerrilla fighting, nine months of sporadic battles along the 38th parallel. At least a dozen boys from Young Bok's hometown had already volunteered or been drafted into the North Korean People's Army, the NKPA, and there had been physical examinations of all young eligible males throughout the summer of 1949. What Young Bok and his classmates heard again and again was that the Supreme Leader, General Kim Il Sung, wanted to "liberate" the southern brothers. There were raids and bloody skirmishes at Kaesong, Ongjin, and Chorwon. *The South started it, the North started it*, propaganda, opinions—all of it melded in Young Bok's head, a complicated dialogue between things that did and didn't make sense. Who was right, who was wrong…it became difficult to tell.

Northern citizens from a five-kilometer belt along the 38th parallel were evacuated. "The ROK is preparing to attack," they were told. Farmers left behind half-planted rice fields.

On June 25, 1950, at 11 a.m., the speaker system crackled on over the Pyongyang Medical School campus. In excited tones, a voice cried,

"The so-called 'defense army' of the South Korea puppet regime started a surprise invasion of the north along the whole front of the 38th parallel line at dawn on the 25th. The enemy, who started the surprise operation, invaded the territory north of the 38th parallel line one to two kilometers at three points west of Haeju, Kumchon, and Chorwon... The People's Republic Army succeeded in repulsing the enemy force... In this connection, the People's Republic of Korea wishes to remind the South Korea puppet regime of the fact that, unless the puppets immediately suspend their adventurous military actions, the People's Republic will be obliged to resort to decisive countermeasures. At the same time the People's Republic entrusted the Home Affairs Bureau to call the attention of the South Korea puppet regime to the fact that the whole responsibility for the grave consequences arising from their reckless venture would squarely rest on the shoulders of the South Korea puppet regime" ("The Ambassador in Korea (Muccio) to the Secretary of State (Seoul, June 25, 1950)").

The teachers marshaled the students into even lines in the center of campus, where they stood sweating beneath the sun for half an hour, shifting from foot to foot, eyeing each other, and murmuring. A tense hush fell when the school dean stepped in front of the students.

"Our people's military is pushing back the South Korean invaders and passing down to the 38th parallel as we speak. Our nation is brave and already victorious. And you, all of you, have the honor and glory of being a part of this victory," said the dean. "From now on, you will not return home. You will stay in your dorms and start military exercises in preparation to fight the invaders."

The sun was a heavy anvil of heat that hammered down and down and down in rhythm with Young Bok's pounding headache. A single bead of sweat rolled down his cheek. He didn't reach up to wipe it away.

The dean continued, "You will enter the military and fight for our glorious nation soon. Until then, we will provide food and housing for you. You will have absolutely no reason to leave this campus."

God, what do I do? The fear clogged up Young Bok's throat, and prickling sweat tickled his hairline and slid down into his shirt in cold rivulets. Behind him, teachers strained to close the school gates. Two resounding thuds, and he could no longer see anything except for the blank, staring walls of concrete and wood surrounding him on all sides. Trapped. A glorified jail. Young Bok's stomach clenched. *I can't breathe.* A few other students met his eyes, and Young Bok saw the same raw fear reflected in their eyes.

His mind raced. He loved his country, but how could he fight for a system and an ideology that he so passionately hated? If he wanted to avoid being drafted, he had to act now. But what to do? He couldn't sneak off campus, he couldn't hide, and he had no money to bribe the teachers. What could he possibly… Then, it struck him. *Tuberculosis!*

The moment the students were dismissed to their dorms, Young Bok started to run. When he had first arrived at the school in 1948, he had received a tuberculosis screening from Dr. Cheon Yong Ul. An x-ray revealed a lesion in his chest, a fibrous tubercle from T-cells and macrophages engulfing the bacteria in a dormant capsule. It meant he was in no immediate danger, but in the future, the tubercle could burst open and spread active tuberculosis bacteria throughout his lungs.

But today, it could save his life.

Young Bok burst into Dr. Cheon Yong Eul's office and said, "Dr. Cheon, it looks like war has broken out and the whole class will be kept and drafted into the military. You know I have a tuberculosis infiltration. Please help me. Please. I need to go home. I can't stay here. I have to go home!"

Dr. Cheon looked at Young Bok silently over his thick-rimmed glasses. His eyes were very small, and Young Bok couldn't tell if he was tired or annoyed or suspicious. Maybe all of them.

Young Bok rubbed his hands together and bowed his head. "Please, Doctor, please. Please give me a diagnosis. Say I need rest in the mountains or rest at home. Anything… I need to leave as soon as possible! Please, Doctor."

Dr. Cheon removed his glasses, setting them carefully down on his desk atop a chest-high stack of papers. He rubbed the bridge of his nose, and then looked long and hard at Young Bok's face.

"Please, Doctor." Young Bok's mouth moved to form the words, but his voice stuck in his throat.

Another moment of hesitation, and then Dr. Cheon nodded, picked up a pen, and wrote a quick note: *This student must treat his tuberculosis. He is infectious, and it would be ill-advised to have him in the military camp.*

With a deep bow and a thank you, Young Bok tore out toward the school gates. He heard the deep grunts and shouting of the male students doing military exercises in the courtyard. He kept his head down. Better not to wave or say goodbye, better to disappear unnoticed.

The female students were guarding the gates and Young Bok scanned for a familiar face, hoping he would find someone who wouldn't ask too many questions and let him pass. *No. No. No. Cheon Chung Sook!* Cheon Chung Sook was his rival for first place in the school, but they were also friends, and coincidentally, she was Dr. Cheon's daughter. Young Bok waved and jogged up to her. "Chung Sook, I have a note from your father."

Chung Sook smiled, crinkling her nose in the way she always did. After she read the note, she looked up into his eyes with an unreadable expression. She blinked four times in rapid succession and looked away while folding the note into halves again and again until the note disappeared into her hand. For a moment, Young Bok was afraid she would not let him pass, that she would call out to a teacher to stop him from leaving. But Chung Sook gazed back up at him with a small smile, nodded, and strained to pull open the gate, just wide enough for him to pass through.

Young Bok didn't look back until he heard the creaking gates shudder closed behind him. Then, just for a moment, he looked over his shoulder at the walls of his school, wordlessly saying goodbye to his classmates and teachers and education, wordlessly burying his dreams of becoming a doctor. He knew he wouldn't be back.

Young Bok headed straight home. There were few people on the path to the train station, and he said nothing, keeping his eyes trained downward at his feet. It would have been better if he had had something to shield his face from watching eyes, but the people on the path were too preoccupied with their own matters to bother with his. After all, war had broken out. War!

Young Bok hitched a ride on the train from Pyongyang station. By the time he arrived in his family's courtyard, he was sweat-soaked and jittery with nerves. Yang Sil ran out to meet him, wiping the sweat from his forehead and grasping his hands, "Setjjae, are you alright?"

"The whole medical school is being drafted," Young Bok panted out. "I'm sure someone will come soon to call me or capture me to bring me back. I have to hide somewhere. No one can know that I have returned home."

***

By June 28, the North Korean radio stations were blaring victory. Seoul had fallen to the North Korean People's Army (NKPA), and the army marched steadily south. Suwon, then Osan...

Family meals were silent, Young Bok always well aware he was another mouth to feed, another burden on his mother's weary mind, another secret to hide from the neighbors' prying eyes.

As July crept in, Young Bok spent hours inside his house with a blanket over his head, fiddling with the radio. His fingers slipped over the little dial, his head spinning from the heat and the crackling noise of static and occasional grainy voices. Sometimes it took hours, other times only minutes to find the right frequency for the South Korean radio station.

For a period, Young Bok remembered the South Korean radio announcer promising again and again, "We will come up in one day to liberate you. You are suffering now, but we will come! We will have breakfast at Sariwon, lunch at Pyongyang, and dinner at Sinuiju." Confident and powerful, the voice promised that the South Korean ROK army would sweep back up the country with ease. Young Bok clung to that voice beneath the blanket in his room, repeating the words later in an excited whisper to his siblings and parents. *Liberation by South Korea would be like heaven and earth coming—we could finally be free!*

Under cover of night, the family spent a week digging a rectangular bunker against one side of the kitchen wall. When they were finished, it was large enough to fit four full grown men and Sang Chul concealed it with a wooden door and a stack of firewood for the kitchen stove. Other families used similar shelters to hide their husbands and sons from the draft, but the Communist officials quickly learned of the trick. They began to carry long, sharp iron poles whenever they visited homes. After the pounding on the door and the brusque interchange with the family, the Communist officials took the poles and plunged them into the dirt of the home again and again, often stabbing and killing the hidden men below.

Sang Chul decided Young Bok would hide in the mountains if anyone came looking for him.

As the weeks passed, the South Korean army withdrew and withdrew, two hundred miles on foot in the blistering heat and humidity of summer, attacked by clouds of hungry mosquitoes. Meanwhile, the North Korean radio announced the NKPA held the entire country, except for the very southeast tip of the country, the Pusan perimeter. Their motto became "Pusan by Liberation Day." The South Korean radio fell silent. Or maybe Young Bok just couldn't find the right frequency.

Late one night, Yang Sil shook Young Bok. He groaned, stretching his arm and leg across Netjjae who slept next to him. "Setjjae!" his mother's urgent voice woke him with a start. He sat upright quickly, rubbing his eyes and squinting in the dark room.

"Setjjae, they are looking for you. Get up, Setjjae, get up. You have to go!" Yang Sil pressed a packed backpack into his hands.

Sang Chul stood in the shadows of the doorway. "You'll hide in the mountain tunnels like we planned."

Young Bok nodded and Yang Sil grasped his hand in hers. "Take care, *Setjjae*. Make sure you take care of yourself. Make sure you sleep well and eat well. Don't get ill—"

"Yobo, Setjjae has to go," Sang Chul interrupted.

Young Bok stood, gulping back a lump in his throat. As he passed through the doorway, Sang Chul grasped his shoulder firmly and said, "Take care, Setjjae."

Five miles from home, a series of tunnels wormed through the mountainside. Young Bok would hide there for the next five months.

CHAPTER
TWENTY-SEVEN

The mountain tunnels were a labyrinth of stone. Some were narrow, formed long ago by the snaking path of hot lava, while others were recent, man-made, and wide, roughly hewn away with tools and explosives. Young Bok rarely ventured too deep into the tunnels; he did not want to stumble across a mass burial site.

It took him quite some time to find the best tunnels: which ones were dry, which ones shielded him from the wind, which ones branched off so he could make a quick exit when needed. He'd learned the latter the difficult way when a routine search party had stumbled across the smoke from his cooking fire. He had dashed deeper into the tunnel at the sound of their approaching voices, wedging himself into a tight shaft, gashing his arms and legs in his frenzy to hide deeper and deeper, so tight he was afraid he wouldn't be able to wiggle out. He wondered if this was how the cocooned silkworms felt as his mother dipped them in the boiling water. Great darkness that should have been safe but was not. Great darkness that was a trap, a taunt of not knowing and waiting, where the only sensation was his trembling, his cold sweat, his heart pounding and pounding. The voices and footsteps of the search party faded away. When he emerged several hours later, the sun had long set, and the ashes of his fire were cold and scattered.

A handful of other young men were in a similar situation as Young Bok, avoiding conscription and the war. At most, there were five all together at once, spread out between the tunnels. Newcomers brought fragments of war news, but for the most part, Young Bok knew very little about the happenings in his village or across the nation. The men talked together sometimes about their homes and families, but usually they had very little to say, squatting in the shadowy cool or slumping against the curving mouths of the tunnels, staring out at the horizon. Young Bok saw many new faces appear, but he rarely got to say goodbye to those who left. They melted away at night or snuck away at daybreak and whether they lived or died, he never knew.

Young Bok was always moving, rotating between three different caves. On the rare occasions that he built up a fire, he cooked large portions of food at a time before stamping out the flames and disappearing again into the shadows. He plucked wild chestnuts and stole corn and sweet potatoes from nearby fields. Young Bok often stood hesitating in the mouth of the tunnel after sundown, thinking of his own hungry family with their aching stomachs, how every bite of food had staved off a little pain and eased the long, hungry nights. He was stealing from children now, from hardworking parents, wrinkled grandmothers and grandfathers. But he was hungry, and it was all too easy to listen to the persistent voice in his head that whispered, *I have to survive.*

Every day Young Bok worried for his family. His father and two elder brothers had not followed him into hiding. Though it was unlikely they would be drafted to the army because of their ages, they could easily be sent to paramilitary labor camps. Yet, even if they worried for their lives, they could not desert their families. Duljjae had a wife, Cheotjjae a wife and toddler, and Sang Chul a family to head.

Heavenly Father, please protect my family, Young Bok prayed every day. *Please keep them from any harm. Please provide them with enough food. Please grow their faith in You, that they would come to love You more every day.* He also prayed for his father and two brothers to come to believe in God, sometimes crying in his anguish over their unbelief.

Hymns kept him sane and calm. Of the gospel songs in his church's hymnal, he remembered at least six hundred. There was a hymn for every situation, and in the dark chambers of those rocky tunnels, he listened to the echo of his voice, singing,

> *All the way my Savior leads me; What have I to ask beside? Can I doubt His tender mercy, Who thro' life has been my guide?*

and

> *My Jesus as Thou wilt!*
> *O may Thy will be mine;*
> *Into Thy hand of love I would my all resign.*
> *Through sorrow, or through joy,*
> *Conduct me as Thine own;*
> *And help me still to say, My Lord, Thy will be done.*

In these quiet moments of prayer and song, the war faded away. For brief moments, it was just him and God in the world, and Young Bok was at peace.

***

On September 15, 1950, over one hundred miles south of Young Bok, the US First Marine Division launched an amphibious attack on Inchun, a port nearby to Seoul. With each high tide, landing ships ground into the shallows and unloaded thundering tanks, tractors, artillery, bulldozers, jeeps, and crates of ammunition. Well behind enemy lines, the US troops hoped to cut off supply chains of the NKPA with a swift capture of Seoul.

From a new arriver in the tunnels, Young Bok learned Netjjae's engineering technical school was planning a visit to the northern port city of Hamhung for a site tour of the Hungnam Fertilizer Complex. His stomach plunged. *Netjjae will be drafted.* In this war time, there could be no reason for a school to take its entire population of male students for a tour of a distant town.

Young Bok spent a long time sitting on the cold stone ground, arms crossed, staring pensively at an impassive wall. Netjjae was eighteen now, three years his junior, but Young Bok's mind was drifting back to when they were much younger. To a time when they used to sit back-to-back every day on the hard bedroom floor, hunched over low wooden desks, working to the busy rhythm of their *scritch scratching* pencils. Young Bok humming a song under his breath, and Netjjae nodding his head in time. Listening to the droning of cicadas in summertime, and sometimes picking out the voices of their younger siblings playing outside. Whispering

Daseotjjae or *Yeoseotjjae* with a little snorted laugh that said they were older and more mature. Young Bok liked explaining difficult questions and concepts to Netjjae. He liked that Netjjae wrote with his face close to the paper, with a look of deep concentration, turning his head to show that he was listening to Young Bok's explanations. It was a simple, quiet kind of brotherhood. Comfortable.

He had to stop his brother from being drafted. He had to warn him. Young Bok knew Netjjae's train would have to make a stop in Pyongsong, Young Bok's town, to refill the water in the boiler before continuing further northeast toward Hamhung. It would be his one chance.

Young Bok did not hesitate much. He was terrified of being caught, terrified he might be drafted, arrested, or even executed on the spot, terrified his family might be punished if he were found. But he was more terrified of doing nothing, of being too cowardly to warn Netjjae of his likely fate. Besides, he was disgustingly dirty after weeks in the tunnels, hair grown long and tangled. For anyone not looking too closely, he would be unrecognizable.

On the day of the trip, Young Bok stood waiting on the platform by the hissing, spitting train. He hunched his shoulders and kept his eyes downward, but he snuck frequent glances toward the doorways of the train, searching for Netjjae. A handful of older men, and then a wave of teenagers in high school uniforms. Among them, Netjjae. Young Bok lurched forward, keeping his head down. Netjjae was looking in the other direction when Young Bok bumped into his left shoulder. "Netjjae," he whisper-shouted, two quick exhaled syllables. Young Bok grasped his brother's arm, cast a quick glance around, and pulled him away from the platform.

When they were a little distance away from the train, Young Bok grabbed his brother by the shoulders and looked into his face. In the last several months, Netjjae had grown several inches, and for a moment, Young Bok was disconcerted when he had to look slightly upward to meet his brother's eyes. He hadn't seen his brother since April, when Netjjae's school semester had started. "Netjjae," he said.

"Hyung?" Netjjae wrinkled his nose very slightly but didn't comment on the smell.

He wanted to say "It's so good to see you" or "I'm glad you're safe," but there was so little time. "Netjjae," Young Bok whispered instead. "It looks like they may be drafting you and all your classmates. I've been away from school…hiding in the mountains since the war started." He didn't elaborate on the details, but Netjjae's eyes widened a little. "If I were you, I would leave now. Come hide in the mountains with me. We'll be safe there. Let's go together." Young Bok grabbed his brother's wrist, already pulling to go. The train would leave soon.

Netjjae's eyes were troubled. They stood like that for a moment, Young Bok grasping Netjjae's wrist, staring into his eyes, hoping…but he already knew what his brother would say.

Netjjae looked down for a moment and took a deep breath. "I can't."

Young Bok loosened his grip on his brother's wrist.

"If I were just a normal student, I could, but I'm the president of our class! How can I just run away?" Netjjae looked up. His tone was angry, and his shoulders were squared, but his eyes were still a frightened eighteen-year-old boy's eyes, asking Young Bok to tell him he was right. "My fate will be the same as the rest of the class." Netjjae glanced toward the train station where his classmates were already boarding amid the rising steam. "I can't leave them like this. Thank you, Setjjae, but I have to go."

"Netjjae!"

He broke away, gently pulling Young Bok's grip from his wrist. A last lingering look and he walked away. He turned once to look back. Said something? But the steam was too thick, and the clattering of the trains and shouting of the conductor drowned him out.

Nearly forty years later, Young Bok would learn that Netjjae and his entire class had been stopped at Wonsan, a town nearly eighty miles south of Hamhung. There, all the engineering students were drafted into the North Korean tank force, which was notorious for shackling their own soldiers to the tanks with ankle chains. *Be victorious or die*, they were told.

All Young Bok knew at the time was that his brother was boarding a train toward an uncertain future, that the train was already pulling away from the station, that he had never fully said goodbye, only called out his brother's name. There was nothing he could do but return to hiding in the mountainside.

***

From the mountainside, Young Bok watched ant-sized men lugging military equipment and weapons into a train tunnel some distance away. Shortly after, there was the hard tic-tac of a plane's gunfire, and an American plane swept into view. From its belly, bombs tumbled with whistling shrieks. The mountainside was ablaze with crashing explosions and choking smoke far into the night. For several days, planes bombed the tunnel. One pilot navigated the plane parallel to the tunnel in an attempt to shoot directly in, but the wing caught a rocky outcrop and the plane plummeted downward.

Young Bok did not know if the pilot survived.

What he did know was that it made little difference whether the Americans destroyed the bridges or the railway tracks into the tunnels. Almost immediately after a bombing, Korean villagers in the nearby towns were mobilized to work, dragging straw bags stuffed with sand to fill the gaping holes where the tracks used to be. Within a few hours, tracks would be laid on top, and the train could resume its smoking course to deliver supplies to the North Korean troops.

Sometimes, Young Bok imagined he saw his father's broad back among the laborers, and just for a moment he wanted to call out, *Abeoji*. But it was just for a moment. After all, it would be more than just his own life at stake.

Leaflets from the Americans tumbled from the sky, sometimes in Korean, sometimes in English. They often read something like, *Tomorrow at 6 a.m. we will bomb this area. Civilians, please evacuate!*

Young Bok laughed sometimes, clutching a leaflet in hand. *Why would they tell us this? They should just attack if they want to win the war!* The reality was that the North Korean army officials would see the leaflets first, and any civilian caught running away was captured. A fist shook in their face. "You are believing in propaganda and betraying your country. Stay put. Stay in your home." And while the powerful ran away, the farmers and their children fell dead in their homes and fields. Villages collapsed into charred beams and broken kimchi jars. Dead bodies flooded bloody streets, twisted and scarcely recognizable.

In mid-October 1950, 150,000 Chinese men crept across the Yalu River, at the border between China and North Korea, in the cover of nighttime. The Chinese Army adhered to strict radio silence and marched eight hours at night, from 7 p.m. to 3 a.m. Any soldier caught moving in the daytime was shot on the spot. Crews used brooms and pine boughs to smooth over their tracks in the dirt and each day was spent in caves, mine shafts, or railway tunnels, away from the roving eyes of the US planes. Meanwhile, the US and ROK forces kept pushing steadily northward along the peninsula with little resistance. "On to Yalu," cried the men. Morale was high. The first ROK forces who reached the Yalu River on October 25 sent back a bottle of its waters to Syngman Rhee. That same day, US and ROK forces at Unsan Valley in North Pyongan province heard the eerie cry of bugles, wildly clanging gongs, and a cacophony of shouting voices. The Chinese army ambushed them in a barrage of fire and grenades.

As October slipped into November, snow began to fall. Temperatures slipped below zero and Young Bok shivered; he had brought no extra layers of clothing. The fields and trees were bare of food, and he could not start a fire for fear it would alert search parties. It was too cold to even open his mouth to pray or sing. Young Bok forgot the sound of his voice. *I am going through the tribulations of the end times*, he thought.

The days were endlessly long, full of blindingly white snowy skies and skeleton trees craning beneath heavy burdens of snow. Young Bok thought often of home, how Yang Sil was probably spooning out fresh rice from her black-bottomed pot and kimchi she had folded away into marinated barrels. Daseotjjae would be helping her mother, neatly sweeping the courtyard with a broom. Ilgopjjae would be playing with a handful of snow in a corner of the courtyard. The entire family would all huddle together in the main room of the house at dinner time, telling stories and burning wood to heat the floors.

He couldn't think too long of home before a lump rose in his throat. The tears stung when they flowed out, and sometimes when he left them too long, they froze on his face. The bitter winds howled, gnawing at his fingers and toes. It had been nearly five months since he'd seen his mother's face.

And still, the snow fell and there was scarcely any food to eat.

This way of life is too tiring. I want eternal peace, God. I want to go home to heaven with You.

Take me, God. I want to die.

CHAPTER
TWENTY-EIGHT

———

Young Bok lost track of time in the dark tunnels of the mountainside, but he thought it to be late October or early November when he finally heard word from another man in the tunnel that the UN and South Korean ROK forces had liberated Pyongyang. He heard later that Pyongyang had fallen weeks earlier with earsplitting explosions, the rain of mortar fire and machine guns, the heavy tread of tanks, and close-quarter combat over barricades made of earth-filled bags and broken furniture.

Young Bok and half a dozen other young men emerged eagerly from the tunnels, breathing in the frigid November air, smiling and nodding at one another. The winter cold had been bitter, and they longed to sleep on the heated *ondol* at home, eat their mother's food, and see their loved ones. As they squinted under the blank whiteness of the sky, they saw a group of soldiers inching upward at the base of the mountain. The tunnel men began to cheer. Young Bok waved makeshift Korean and US flags and shouted, "Hurray! Hurray!" His throat was dry and crackly from disuse, and it hurt to yell, but he gloried in the sound of his voice, the raw scratch in his throat, the nearly tangible words that roared from his mouth. The wind picked up his voice and swallowed it, but he yelled and yelled. His smile cracked his lips, and he began to taste blood.

As they drew closer to the climbing soldiers, Young Bok started. Guns. Guns not slung across the soldiers' shoulders but held at the ready. Aimed straight at them. There was nowhere to hide.

He could hear someone trying to speak, but the snowy mountain and the wind seemed to snatch up the voice, scattering it beneath the crooked trees and icy snow. The men from the tunnel froze, eyeing one another. The snouts of the guns followed them, like some strange breed of rigid snakes, and the eyes behind them saw flesh and blood, not fearful, young men desperate to go home. Young Bok saw a flash of movement on his left. He could hear that one of the young men was running, slipping on the ice and snow as he scrabbled back up toward the tunnels. And then there was the cracking report of a gun, a scream, and Young Bok felt hot blood spray across his face. His throat constricted. *Don't look back.*

The voice again, closer now. Sharp, barking. Young Bok's mind was racing so quickly that he could barely focus on the words. "Come down with your arms raised. COME DOWN." The tunnel men stood wavering, lifting their hands. To go down surely meant death, but to run… Young Bok swallowed the bile rising in his throat. The wind bore down on him, and it carried the heavy, sickly sweet smell of blood. Every fiber of his being told him, *RUN.* Run back into the tunnels. Run back to the quiet and the cold and the hunger. He could live through it all again. But again, the sharp voice: "MOVE." He moved, tripping on his feet because he didn't dare take his eyes off the men and their guns.

Closer and closer to the faces and bodies below, until he could see the dirt and mud on their faces, their ragged uniforms, the exhaustion in their eyes and their sagging shoulders. These were…North Koreans. These weren't the US or the ROK soldiers; they were leftover North Korean military retreating back northwards, somehow caught between enemy lines, bearing stretchers of wounded soldiers.

"Line up!" Rough hands grabbed his shoulders, jerking him into place. Five other men to the right and left of him beneath that cold, blindingly white sky. He breathed in sharply and then his ears exploded with the sound of gunshots. He was reeling, ears ringing with the sound, and yet he could still hear the slight whistle-scream of the bullets in the air and the terribly dull sound when they connected with flesh and the men from the tunnel screaming and all of it crackling out across the mountainside. The men crumpled around Young Bok.

A spurt of warm blood. Young Bok looked down, saw red, and he fell to the ground, face bruising against a rock as bark, dirt, and snow sprayed up around him.

His whole body felt numb. *Why am I dying now when we are so close to freedom, when heaven and earth are almost here?* But then it was just *Umma. Umma.* He had wanted to see her face one more time.

The ground was so cold.

Young Bok closed his eyes.

***

I have died. I have died. I have died. But he could still hear the footsteps of the soldiers and the echoing call of their rifles. Young Bok nearly sat upright then, shocked by this realization. *I'm alive!* Thirty minutes, an hour, he didn't know how long, but he stayed pressed against the cold ground until the mountainside was silent again. Even after, he lay still.

When he finally opened his eyes and sat up, he felt all over his body for a gunshot wound, waiting for his shaking fingers to sink into bloody flesh. But though there was blood all over him, staining his clothing and his hands and neck and abdomen, it was not his own. He had not been shot. He was alive. Alive!

Around him, the five other young men lay splayed as they had fallen, and the snow was spattered a deep and ugly red from their blood. He crawled to each man, shaking them. There had to be another survivor like him. It couldn't only be him. But all the bodies were already cold from the wind, and they were stiff in his arms. When he put his hand beneath their noses to see if they were still breathing, their staring eyes haunted him, reflecting the empty white sky above. He drew away, rubbing his hands together, trying and failing to get the blood off, and then for a long while, he sat propped up against a tree, blankly staring at the landscape, away from the five dead men. *It's a miracle you're alive, Young Bok. Think of that. God certainly saved you. Think of that. It was good the soldiers were in too much of a rush to check whether you were dead. Think of that. Think of that. Think of...* And there was the great, blank sky above and there was the blood on the snow and there were those great, staring eyes reflecting that great, blank sky. And he was surrounded by death, and not even wind could take away the smell of flesh and blood. *Why did they shoot?*

Why did they shoot? He began to sob. They had been so close to freedom, and all they had ever wanted was to go home. He didn't even know their names. Their families would never know what had happened. Why was he alive? Why?

He wanted to go home. He wanted to believe this nightmare had never happened. He wanted to pretend it never happened. He left the bodies in the cold under that piercingly white sky, and he crawled toward home. Trembling from the cold, he crawled for at least a mile on his hands and knees, tearing his pants on the rough ground, his hands raw and bleeding. It was only five miles to home, but the journey felt like an eternity. Over and over, Young Bok kept asking himself why he hadn't waited one more day in the tunnel. One day more and he wouldn't have nearly died. One day more and he wouldn't have had to watch all those men be murdered.

When Young Bok finally crawled through the threshold of his home, his family crowded around him. He could say nothing at first. Only in response to Yang Sil's worried eyes and exclamations, "It's not my blood." His lip was cut, and a bruise blossomed on his cheek bone from the rock he'd fallen on. Yang Sil brought rags and water and scrubbed away the blood from his face, his neck, his hands, his knees. Brokenly, his voice faltered out, "Umma." She held him tight.

***

Cheotjjae and Duljjae told him about the parades throughout the whole town as the UN forces pushed northward. MacArthur was hailed as a god, and when the UN and ROK soldiers passed through Pyongsong, the villagers gathered in the streets and welcomed them. Sang Chul, Cheotjjae, and

Duljjae helped serve food and water to the UN forces, food that Yang Sil gladly offered up despite the shortages.

It was 1950 now, but it felt almost like their first liberation in 1945. A town in celebration, free of fear. But there had been too many deaths. Perhaps they were liberated, but how could they forget all the burning towns, all the suffering families, all those murdered?

Young Bok's village set up a YMCA Information office with one of the church's pastors as its head. They designed handmade paper cards to prove their members were not Communists, and the YMCA president had a little seal with which to stamp them. Whenever American planes dropped leaflets, Young Bok was responsible for gathering copies and translating the ones written in English. Many were targeted toward North Korean soldiers, calling them to surrender and promising good treatment.

The local Communists had already gone into hiding and Sang Chul immediately joined a party of villagers who volunteered to catch them. Cheotjjae and Duljjae tried to convince him out of it.

"Appa," said Cheotjjae. "We are joining this committee, so you don't need to. You're an old man, Abeoji."

Duljjae echoed, "You should not do it. We will do it!"

Sang Chul snort-laughed, focused on his rifle. "You have to catch the ones your age, but I know the older men who are filthy *ppalgaengis*." He spit into the dirt. "I can hunt them down just as well as you can. Just *bahng*." He imitated a gun with his hand, scrunching one eye as though taking aim.

Whenever Sang Chul cleaned the issued rifle, polishing the wooden handle and testing out the sight of the gun,

Cheotjjae and Duljjae sat down next to him and did the same. Young Bok got used to the little metallic clicks as they took apart their rifles, wiping down the barrels, the magazines, and the bolts from the barrel chamber. All three were out nearly every day. When they returned, they were raucous, sometimes drunk, sometimes spitting into the dirt at those filthy *ppalgaengi,* Reds.

Blood stains on their shoes. Blood stains on their hands and faces. Blood stains on their rifles and on the cloths that they used to clean them. Blood stains on their clothes that lingered even when Yang Sil scrubbed them in the icy cold river water. Blood stains that layered new blood upon old blood upon old blood.

CHAPTER
TWENTY-NINE

Young Bok sat cross-legged on the floor, helping Yang Sil weave bags from straw. He was not an expert, and the straw kept unraveling because he did not rub it between his palms fast enough. He clenched his teeth and tried again, faster this time. He had lined up the straw unevenly. Some of the pieces were too dry, and rather than come together, they crackled and broke apart in his hands. He scrunched his brow into deep lines. Yang Sil laughed a little at his frustration, and nudging him gently with her arm, deftly demonstrated how to urge the straw into a single thread. "Like this, Setjjae. Like this."

Young Bok nodded. He tried again. *Just rub the straw, rub the straw, Young Bok.* The strand unraveled. Huffing with frustration and uncomfortably warm, he tossed down the straw and stood up. He pulled open the door a crack, breathing in air that smelled of nothing but icy snow. Clean. Fresh. Sang Chul grunted at him to shut the door. He closed it. His siblings' voices crowded the room—so many voices that he could barely listen to his own inner voice. The voice that was telling him that for the first time in nearly fourteen years, he was not studying. He hadn't touched a book since he had fled his school in June, months ago. He had no plans for his future. And what was the product of those last few months? Only a pile of unraveling straw threads in the corner.

Just like the bravado and promises of the UN troops. The UN and ROK forces had spread themselves dangerously thin as they pushed northward toward the Yalu River, at the border between China and Korea. The northern part of the peninsula was about 400 miles wide, and there were gaps of nearly twenty to thirty miles between units. Radio communication was poor, and supply lines were stretched nearly to the breaking point. Regardless, UN and ROK troops were confident of victory. What else could explain the way the Chinese melted away into the mountainsides after offensives? An all-out offensive had been planned for November 24. The UN and ROK forces pushed to the Yalu, but on the 25th, the Chinese launched a counteroffensive. A barrage of yells, bugles, drums, grenades, rifle fire, and surging men. Then south went the UN and ROK troops, units ripped apart by the onslaught of Chinese soldiers. Across the Chongchon River, men fleeing through the river and emerging into winter air that froze their clothes and boots to ice. Withdrawing and withdrawing to a defense line around Pyongyang on November 29.

Dinners were heavy with unspoken words, clinking chopsticks, and averted eyes. Cheotjjae's lips kept twitching as though he wanted to say something, but Sang Chul's eyes glared down at his plate, and so Cheotjjae stuck to swallowing his rice, stones and all.

They were all thinking the same things: *Was this their last dinner in their home? Should they stay? Should they flee south?* Young Bok's mind invaded the dinner table's silence with rumors of war news. *The Chinese hadn't even fired a single shot, and the US and ROK forces are fleeing. They don't have any motorized vehicles, just handcarts and ox-drawn wagons. The US and ROK armies are just running; they're terrified of the hordes of screaming Chinese soldiers. The Chinese are coming. The Chinese are coming.*

After dinner, Yang Sil steadily wove straw bags, and Young Bok wondered whether they were for traveling or whether they were part of the normal upkeep for the farm's needs. Every night, he lay awake with his eyes wide open. Ilgopjjae and Yeoseotjjae didn't fight for the blanket, and Young Bok almost missed his nightly struggle with Netjjae. But he was warmer. He felt guilty for thinking it.

Sometimes Young Bok thought he heard the thundering of battle, only to find it was the pounding of blood in his head. Sometimes he smelled smoke. The smoke of burning villages? The smoke of bombs? The smoke of a kitchen fire?

One day in the beginning of December, the radios urged them to escape, blaring out, *The UN forces are withdrawing. The UN forces are withdrawing.*

Sang Chul set his jaw. "Sooner or later, the Red Chinese will come. We will leave tomorrow."

They buried their valuables in the dirt bunker in the kitchen. Yang Sil insisted on keeping all of Young Bok's schoolwork and awards: his six-year-absence-free award from elementary school, his high school certificates, his notebooks, and textbooks.

"We'll come back soon," they repeated. "We'll be back soon." The dirt fell crumbling from Sang Chul's unhesitating shovel. Young Bok couldn't help but feel as though this were a funeral, a funeral of so much more than silk clothes and pots and toys and school materials. How much he was saying goodbye to, he was not sure yet.

In the meantime, there were preparations to make. Yang Sil baked soybean cakes for each person: one large plate-sized lump and then three fist-sized clumps. Sang Chul disappeared for several hours to the black market. When he returned, he had five thousand South Korean won and a sack of small gold nuggets. The South Korean won, he distributed to the elder members of the family, to hide away in little pouches that Yang Sil had sewn into their long underwear. The younger children carried gold in their pockets.

They set out before sunrise on the morning of December 3, 1950. The air was still and bitterly cold, broken only by the lonely call of a single rooster. There were eleven of them: Sang Chul, Yang Sil, Cheotjjae and his wife and child, Duljjae and his wife, Young Bok, Daseotjjae, Yeoseotjjae, and Ilgopjjae.

Young Bok was twenty-one. Ilgopjjae, only seven.

They walked mostly in silence, south toward the Taedong River, which ran through Pyongyang. Once they crossed the bridge, they would continue walking south until they reached the port city of Haeju. From there, they would take a boat to Incheon or some other port in South Korea.

They stopped briefly after an hour of walking to eat their first meal, *jumuk bap*, a fist-sized rice ball with sesame seeds and salt that Yang Sil had hurriedly made in the darkness before the rest of the family had woken.

With so many other refugees inching southward, the roads were congested with people, and the going was slow. Young

Bok tried to carry his youngest brother on his back over his knapsack, but Ilgopjjae refused to be picked up. He wriggled away from Young Bok, stubbornly demanding to be let down. "I can walk myself," he repeated, stamping his foot on the ground. "I can walk myself."

When they stopped for the night, Ilgopjjae's feet were swollen with angry, red blisters, but he did not cry. In the distance, the family could see great geysers of flames rising from Pyongyang, casting an evil red light across the night sky. They learned later the US Army was burning supplies and rations as they retreated, some piles the size of football fields. The poor of Pyongyang dashed themselves into the fires trying to retrieve clothing and food. The American guards fired warning shots. People screamed.

At noon on December 5, the UN Command declared Pyongyang enemy territory, and the temporary pontoon bridge was destroyed. It was a practical matter. The enemy could slip past at any time, and too many refugees would clog the roads that the military needed for a smooth withdrawal. They fired machine guns at the refugees crossing the Taedong River, but still they came, still the nameless bodies and desperate faces surged forward.

It was almost sunset on December 5 when the Kim family finally reached the Taedong River. People were everywhere, a bewildering broil of the screaming and the tired and the lost. The original Taedong Bridge had been destroyed in October when the North Korean army was retreating from Pyongyang, but its twisted metal skeleton still hung creaking over the river. Hundreds of people crept their way across it: old *halmonis*, little children, people carrying giant packs of belongings. Young Bok could not keep his eyes away from all the movement, all the people clinging to the icy cold railings.

Others forded the freezing river itself. When they stumbled and fell beneath the water, some came up gasping for air. Others did not resurface.

Cheotjjae's daughter was a very small toddler, and they could not risk carrying her across a bridge when much of the way would have to be on hands and knees. They dared not swim either, so they walked up and down the river for two or three hours, looking for another crossing. Other families did the same, and they would call out to each other, "Excuse me! Do you know where there is a crossing?"

As they walked along the river, they heard news of a place about four miles further north where the river was shallower and the ice was strong enough to cross. By the time they reached it, the sun had long fallen, and the moon hung bright in a frozen sky. There were already people crossing. Young Bok could hear the shifting ice, the spiderwebbing crack sound as they trekked across. The ice was too thin.

Sang Chul led the way, and the rest of the family followed him carefully, spread out at least a few feet between. The ice shuddered beneath Young Bok's feet and sweat dripped cold down his back. He tried to remember where his father had stepped, delicately toeing the ice ahead, stopping when it threatened to give way beneath his weight, stepping and stepping again until the ice felt solid, and he dared to creep forward again.

When all eleven of them crossed, they walked almost all night and into the next day.

They neared Sariwon, about sixty miles from where they had started their journey in Pyongsong. They paused for another meal by the roadside. It had been four days of almost constant walking, and Young Bok could feel his feet plodding on even when he was sitting on a little ledge by the road.

Sang Chul pulled a map from his pocket, one he had ripped from Young Bok's textbook. Spreading out the folds against his lap, he traced the two routes that the family was considering. There was the path to Seoul, a long and hard journey through the mountains that would take weeks. Or there was the port city of Haeju, which was just a full day's walk away.

Cheotjjae and Sang Chul were absorbed in the same arguments they had been for the last few days. "Haeju or Seoul? Haeju or Seoul?"

Young Bok pulled his mother to the side. "Umma, we have to go to Haeju. If we go by the road to Seoul, it will take weeks, and the Communists and Chinese are coming down. Haeju is only a day away."

Yang Sil nodded thoughtfully. Daseotjjae and Yeoseotjjae nodded along with her. "We should go to Haeju." A day's walk sounded better than weeks. Their feet were blistering, and the knapsacks left lingering red welts across their shoulders.

Yang Sil sat down by Sang Chul and touched his shoulder. "Yobo, Setjjae thinks we should go to Haeju."

Young Bok crouched nearby, tilting his head to hear the conversation.

Cheotjjae folded his eyebrows together, two angry caterpillars nesting in a furrow of worry lines. "There's no guarantee we will get a boat if we go to Haeju. We have the South Korean money they want but if there's no boat for us, there will be a delay and it will take much longer. We should go by the road to Seoul because it's more direct. We have to go to Seoul." He paused, glancing at his wife and child. "It is a hard road, but it's a good one."

Duljjae joined in, "In the worst scenario, if we take the road to Seoul, we can just stay with our uncles in the Koksan for a while."

Young Bok felt the creeping loneliness of the months he had spent in the caves in the miserable cold. "I don't want to hide in the mountains again. Let's go to the boats first. I'm sure we can rent or pay for our passage. They said there's a vacuum from the UN withdrawal so the Communists can move very quickly. If we go to Seoul, we might be caught as we move down, while Haeju is only a day's walk away."

Yang Sil nodded her head. "Setjjae knows."

Sang Chul stared off into the distance past the weary lines of heavily burdened refugees. He said nothing. Cheotjjae and Duljjae cast brief glances toward their father.

Young Bok continued, spurred by their silence. "If it really doesn't work at Haeju, we can try the road to Seoul after, but if we can get a boat, we will be in South Korea within two days!"

Young Bok could see the shifting expression on Duljjae's face, but it was Cheotjjae he was worried about. Still, if Sang Chul said nothing, then Cheotjjae wouldn't either.

Young Bok addressed his father now, pointing to the map: "Appa, we could go this way. Just straight, see. But if we take this long path—" Young Bok dramatized the long snaking path into the mountains and toward Seoul. In his father's tightened lips and hardened eyes, Young Bok read a fear of returning to the Koksan. Sang Chul would never return to the mountain-lost home that he had run away from.

Sang Chul breathed out heavily before spitting into the dirt. "We'll go to Haeju."

CHAPTER THIRTY

——

On December 8, the Kims arrived at the outskirts of Haeju.

Young Bok swallowed great breaths of air, searching for the delicate tang of the sea through the sour-sweet odor of too many bodies in the crowded streets. Between shifting heads, he caught glimpses of the sparkling ocean and ships bobbing in the harbor. He imagined walking on board one of the ships, feeling cold wind ruffle his hair. The boat skimming across the water, south toward freedom. And when they arrived in South Korea...he froze. Better to be practical. They weren't on a ship yet. But he could taste the salt of the sea and if he squinted his eyes and held out his hand, he could touch the distant bows and masts of ships in the harbor. They were steps away from the docks now, steps away from freedom. *You can think about the future now. It's okay, Young Bok.* He smiled.

When they arrived in South Korea, he would study medicine again and then earn enough money so his mother would not have to work anymore. Sang Chul wouldn't have to live with endless anger held deeply in the tight muscle knots of his shoulders. None of his siblings would be hungry at nighttime and they could all...Yang Sil called out his name, and Young

Bok realized he had stopped walking. He hurried his steps to catch up with his family.

As they pushed toward the edge of town, refugees began to pass them in the opposite direction, returning northward with solemn and angry faces. Young Bok glimpsed military helmets ahead and his stomach clenched. Daseotjjae bit her lip and squeezed his hand. He squeezed back. "It'll be fine," he mouthed.

Sang Chul shouldered through the crowd until he reached the edge of town, where UN soldiers were blocking the entrance to Haeju. "Don't come any further," they commanded. "Go back to organize *chian wiwonhoe*, peace keeping committees, in your hometown. We are moving up to Pyongyang again, so you don't have to run away."

Sang Chul, Cheotjjae, and Duljjae looked at one another wearily. How could this be true? They had seen military equipment burning in huge roaring bonfires all along their journey, southward-moving trains overloaded with ragged and bloody soldiers, and endless streams of refugees.

Still, they didn't have much choice. The men were friendly, but there were rifles slung across their backs, and the other refugees crushed around them, voices grumbling for them to move on already. Sang Chul looked the soldier square in the face and said, "Why not?" He threw his hands in the air with a derisive snort. "Why not? We'll go back."

They returned on the road that they had come from, walking north back toward Sariwon. Young Bok could no longer smell salt in the air, and when he glanced back again, he saw nothing except the tired faces of other refugees.

After a couple hours, a column of men passed on Young Bok's left, wearing thick, quilted white uniforms and strange hats that looked like folded dumplings. *Chinese soldiers,* he thought immediately. With the dim roar of passing planes, they froze at a command from their officer, silently crouching down to melt into the landscape. Their sheet-covered bicycles, oxcarts, and overladen hand wagons halted, too, and Young Bok had the strange sensation of stepping into a photograph or a broken roll of film. The world frozen and bitterly cold, and yet the refugees kept stepping on, moving out of the frame of those unmoving men kneeling in the snow. The planes subsided, and once again, the Chinese soldiers filed along in silence, except for the slow treads of shoes on snow and the clink of metal on the carts and bikes.

By the afternoon, they had passed on, and Young Bok saw no more of the Chinese troops.

The wide road eventually funneled into a two-lane walkway sandwiched between two hilly farms. The Kim family walked shoulder to shoulder, brushing against strangers, keeping in stride with the bobbing heads ahead of them. The going was slow, and by word of mouth, Young Bok heard the block-up was caused at the city gate in Sariwon where many of the refugees were turned away, directed to return further north back to their hometowns.

Again, came the hum of approaching planes. Young Bok's stomach clenched. A loose strap on his knapsack rubbed the back of his arm with each step of his left foot. *Rub.* A step. *Rub.* Another step. The sound of the planes faded into the distance. *Rub.* Young Bok struggled to right the strap, falling a few steps behind his family.

The hum again of planes. He waited for the sound to fade into the distance, but the hum crescendoed into a moaning whir, and when he looked up, the planes were diving. For a moment, he stared at the nose of the plane, watching the metal and the paint details get clearer and the visored face of the pilot get closer and closer and then there were bullets spraying out. Bullets spraying into the crowd of refugees, but there was nowhere to run. Bullets spraying down, but they were like corralled animals waiting to be slaughtered, trapped on that narrow road.

Screaming. Rough, throaty cries of men strangled midway. Ear-splitting shrieks of children. Parents calling the names of children. Mothers crouching down and grasping their infants to their chests. People pushing and running, tripping. Blood and the whistling of bullets was nearly as deafening as the thundering planes with their bellies nearly brushing the ground. At least twenty people fell with each pass of the planes.

Young Bok fell to the ground, breathing into the mucky dirt and snow. For the first time, he was grateful for the military exercises in school. Fall down. Fall down immediately, they had said. Run, and the plane would chase you down, spraying a stream of bullets that would catch you in the back, the leg, the head. So fall. Fall and hope you were lucky enough to survive.

Around him, people were screaming and running, collapsing with great staggering steps as the bullets caught them.

His family. He whipped his head to both sides. *Where was his family? Where were they? WHERE WERE THEY?* Fear was bitter in his mouth and everywhere was the sticky, warm smell of blood. "Umma!" he roared. "Umma!"

Then he saw his mother to his right, clutching Yeoseotjjae and Ilgopjjae to her sides, still standing amid the swooping planes and raining bullets. Her mouth was open, and he knew she was shouting. *Cheotjjae!* her lips screamed. *Duljjae! Setjjae! Daseotjjae!*

"Umma!" Young Bok roared. "Umma, please lay down! Umma! Lie down!" *Run to her! Just run to her. Make her lie down.*

Ilgopjjae was crying, red face turned upward in a wail that seized his whole body. Still, Yang Sil stood and yelled for her children.

"Umma! Umma! UMMA!" Young Bok's voice strangled in his throat and his screams broke. *Run to her! No, no, no. NO. Stay down. Just stay down.* His screams turned into wails. He choked on tears and snot. "Umma! Umma! UMMA!" *You say that you love your mom, but you aren't willing to sacrifice your life for her, are you? God, God! What do I do?*

Yang Sil pulled Yeoseotjjae and Ilgopjjae to the ground, shielding their shivering bodies with her own. The planes roared. People staggered to the ground.

And then the planes were gone, whirring back up into the gray sky and disappearing into the clouds.

Bodies everywhere on the road.

Young Bok ran into his mother's arms. "Umma, I'm sorry. Umma…" He clung to her with shaking hands, afraid to let go, afraid to open his eyes.

The horror he had witnessed on the mountainside was nothing compared to this. Because this time it was the Americans, the ones who were supposed to be his liberators, who had killed them. This time there were mourning families, household treasures glistening with blood, wounded moaning for help. This time there were little children crouching in pools of blood, clinging to parents who stared with unseeing eyes. *Why did the Americans shoot at us? Why? Why?*

Miraculously, the entire Kim family was safe.

It's my fault, Young Bok thought. *I pushed for us to go to Haeju and not to Seoul. It was my decision. It's all my fault… it's all my fault.*

***

Young Bok learned later the massacre on this crowded road near Sariwon was a mistaken air raid by US forces. They had been informed these were Chinese troops. How they had rationalized away the presence of small grandmas and stooped grandfathers, little children clinging to parents' hands, the bulky sacks of refugees, he could never understand. While Young Bok thought it impossible his American "liberators" would intentionally murder Korean refugees, war had a way of dimming the meaning of lives. Look down the sight, pull the trigger, shoot. Order a village to be razed to the ground. Set a bomb for a tactical military location that bordered a school or a populous village. A civilian, an enemy. Sometimes they were mistakes. And sometimes they weren't.

Journalists documented interactions like the following:

"The young pilot drained his cup of coffee and said, 'Hell's fire; you can't shoot people when they stand there waving at you.' 'Shoot 'em,' he was told firmly. 'They're troops.' 'But, hell, they've all got on those white pajama things and they're straggling down the road.' … 'See any women or children?' 'Women? I wouldn't know.

The women wear pants, too, don't they?' 'But no kids, no, sir.' 'They're troops. Shoot 'em'" (Cumings, 2005).

Of the three million Koreans killed during the war, over two million were civilians.

CHAPTER THIRTY-ONE

———

All of Sariwon was a jumble of empty houses hugging crooked streets, doors left open and belongings scattered in the road, as though the city had heaved and vomited forth all its inhabitants. The Kim family found an abandoned house, and they sat on the dirt floor chewing on baked soybean cakes. Pots still hung up on the wall, a half-charred stick of wood in the fireplace, a straw shoe on its side by the doorway.

Young Bok slouched against the wall. The entire house smelled of cooking oil and kimchi, and it reminded him of home. It felt good to be underneath a roof again.

"Do we go back home?" Duljjae asked. He still clung to his soybean cake, glancing between Sang Chul and Cheotjjae. "Or do we go south?"

"If we return," Sang Chul said slowly. "We act like nothing has happened. We were all fleeing from the Chinese. We just go back home and start to work again and—"

"Abeoji," Cheotjjae interrupted. "You think they won't know what we've done? We hunted Communists. We fled south when we heard news that the Chinese Communists were coming. Doesn't that look suspicious? Don't you think—"

"Stop!" Sang Chul shouted. "You don't think I *know* the consequences? I know exactly what we've done, and I'm not ashamed of it. But we can't all go south. We can't!" He paused, knocking his fist against his knees a couple times. When he looked up again, his voice was softer. "I am not saying we should all return home. That's *not* what I'm saying." A biting glare for Cheotjjae. "What I'm saying is that it won't be possible for all of us to escape south, but you three young people *can* escape. You must go south."

Yang Sil nodded, putting her hand on Sang Chul's shoulder. "The younger children can't travel the mountain path. The road is too long, and it would be too difficult for them. But you three, my eldest sons, should escape south. There's freedom and…" Here she paused, with a little smile at Young Bok. "I know it's what you want. All of us will be fine, so you three must go."

None of them said anything for a while, and the silence was uncomfortable.

"Umma, you can't all go back," Young Bok said. "We should all go south where we can be safe. All of us."

Cheotjjae nodded. "How could we leave you behind?" His eyes were on his wife and little daughter.

Sang Chul broke in. "We have already decided. All three of you will go south. You *must* escape south."

"For the sake of your Appa and Umma, my children. For our sakes, go south and live."

"We can all go south. We can all escape together." Young Bok heard how feeble his words were, and he was ashamed. He already knew the mountain road would be too difficult for his younger siblings and his niece, and these words were only meant to fight back his guilt, to conceal the fact that what he most desperately wanted to do was to flee south.

Yang Sil and Sang Chul were already ripping the seams of the pouches sewn into their undergarments and emptying out the money. "If you..." Sang Chul paused as he counted out the money and divided it up three ways. "If you can't pass down the mountain, stay in the Koksan with your uncles. Wait there for a little while, and then escape south from there."

The money was still warm, and Young Bok swallowed back guilt and took it.

Yang Sil reached up a hand to stroke Young Bok's hair. "In the morning, you three will leave." He couldn't meet her gaze.

There was no finality to that last night. They said no goodbyes, and when they had eaten their soybean cakes, they all settled onto the floor of the house, cuddling together for warmth beneath their winter coats. It was like any other night, and though Young Bok fought to keep his eyes open, his exhaustion and his family's snoring lulled his mind into a fog. He fell asleep.

***

The next morning, they rose before sunrise. December 11. Young Bok lingered over his bag, putting his belongings in one by one. Hymnal. Bible. YMCA ID. Soybean cakes. All in the bag. Then one by one he took them out again. Hymnal. Bible. YMCA ID. Soybean cakes. And then back in again. Hymnal Bible YMCA ID Soybean cakes...

He looked up. Duljjae was still packing, but Cheotjjae stood by the doorway, bag slung over his shoulder. His wife was talking to him very quietly, grasping his hand as she talked. Young Bok returned his attention to his packing. Hymnal. Bible. YMCA ID. Soybean—

"Yobo, please don't leave us!" Young Bok whipped his head up. Cheotjjae's wife had fallen at Cheotjjae's feet and was sobbing, still grasping his hand. "Come home with us. Come home with your mother and father. Come home with your daughter. Come home, Yobo. You have to! You have to come home." With each sentence she pulled on Cheotjjae's arm, yanking his entire body. Cheotjjae's limbs were limp and with each pull, his head drooped lower. "How can you leave her? How can you leave me? Don't leave us, Yobo. Don't leave us!" Their daughter caught onto her mother's sorrow and wailed too.

Cheotjjae was holding back tears, and Young Bok looked away.

If Cheotjjae had been the headstrong, selfish boy of his youth, he would have shaken off the clinging hands and run far from there without even an explanation. But he was not a boy; he was a twenty-seven-year-old with little wrinkles around his eyes. A father who loved to hold his daughter over his head and spin around until she screamed with laughter. A husband who loved being the strong back that supported his wife when she had sprained her ankle. Young Bok already knew what his brother would say.

"I'll go back home with you," Cheotjjae's voice was gruff and soft. There was no hesitation in his eyes as he pulled his wife and daughter to their feet. "Stop crying, Yobo," he reached up a hand to wipe away his wife's tears. "I won't go. I won't go." He bent to scoop his daughter into his arms and held her tight. "I won't go."

Then Duljjae's wife fell at her husband's feet, too. "Take me with you! I want to go with you." Her voice rose to a hysterical pitch. "Please don't leave me. Please let me go with you!"

Duljjae knelt down immediately to his wife. "Yobo, you cannot go into the mountains. The journey will be too difficult. You would be tired and wish you were home."

"Please, Yobo, let's die together, whether we go or stay."

A long pause. "I will return home, too."

Young Bok turned back to his bag. Not going back. Hymnal. To the Communists. Bible. I want to be a doctor. YMCA ID. I want to breathe free air for the first time in twenty-one years. Soybean cakes. But how can you leave your family? His whole family was watching him, but he refused to look up. "We can all go to the mountain. You know we can't go back north," his voice trembled. He wanted to yell that he was unmarried and young and strong, that he had no attachments and no guilt calling him home. But it wasn't true. "Let's just hide," he jammed the hymnal into his backpack. "In the mountains." Bible. "Together." YMCA ID. He hesitated, balancing the little package of soybean cakes in his hand. "We can all go to the mountain. We'll be safer there, and we can be together. I know how to find food in the mountains; I've done it before. We can be together." He was babbling now, but he didn't care. Anything to stop the decision he knew he would have to make.

Yang Sil shook her head very slowly and took the package of soybean cakes from Young Bok's hand and placed it gently into the bag. "Setjjae..." She took another handful of soybean cakes from her own knapsack and put them in his bag. Then she neatly closed off the backpack, patted it, and eased it over his shoulder. "Setjjae," she murmured. "It's okay."

Finally, Young Bok looked up. As his eyes passed slowly over the faces of his family members, he felt a terrible ache in his chest, and his face was wet before he even realized he was crying. Everyone he loved was in this room. "Please, let's all run away together," he repeated. "Please." Watching each of them, trying to memorize their eyes and their noses and their mouths and all the lines of their faces. Trying to freeze them in his head just like that, standing together and loving him and him loving them.

Cheotjjae and Duljjae were already taking out the South Korean money from their pouches.

Young Bok plunged his hands into his hair and left them there, squatting to the ground and squeezing his eyes shut. Snot from his nose dripped down his face, but he ignored it. "Umma…Appa…how can I…." *How can I leave you behind?* "Umma, I want to be free but how can I leave?" *Tell me to stay. Tell me to stay!* "I can't say…I can't say…" *I can't say goodbye.* He drew his hands out of his hair and dropped his face into them. He couldn't say anything more.

The money was still warm when Sang Chul pressed it into his hands. "Get up, Setjjae. Get up."

Young Bok clutched the money, "Appa…" His voice shook. "Appa… Tell me to stay."

"Get up, Setjjae."

Young Bok couldn't bring himself to say it again. Because if they told him to stay, then he would stay. He gathered himself. Deep, shaking breaths. He stood up, bowed his head low, and said, "With God's help, I will escape. I promise." He would live for his mother and father and his brothers and sister. He would live for the day when they would come south, too.

Cheotjjae, Duljjae, Daseotjjae, Yeoseotjjae, and Ilgopjjae hugged him, crying and grabbing his arms, and he was lost in a tangle of warmth and tears. "Live well," they told each other. "Live well and be happy and safe." Sang Chul squeezed Young Bok's shoulder and nodded. "Be healthy, Setjjae. Make sure you escape south. You must."

When the rest of his family stepped aside, wiping tears, Young Bok saw his mother's face, expressionless and so blank he felt a deep, stabbing pain in his heart. He caught a flicker of sadness in her eyes when she put her hand to his face. "My Setjjae, my precious child, live long…" Her voice caught for a moment, and she paused. "Live long and be healthy."

"Umma…."

Yang Sil nodded, "I know, Setjjae. I know."

There were no memorable words for him to say. They had dried up in his head or clung to his tongue. He wanted his family to wait, to stay longer, but there was no time, and the sun was rising, relentless time pounding onward. *Make a decision, make a decision.*

His whole face felt taut from all his crying, but he tried to smile. It came out pained. *I don't want to say goodbye. I don't want to say goodbye. I don't want to say goodbye.*

The sun rose pale and yellow, struggling to pierce through the cold gray-white of the morning sky. The Kim family began to walk northward. Young Bok stood and watched, clinging to his backpack. *God, please, please protect my family,* Young Bok prayed. *Please let them survive and escape south soon. God, please protect them.*

Down the crooked road of the abandoned town, and each of his family members paused to look back at him, waving and smiling. Except for his mother.

"Umma! Umma!" he yelled. "UMMA!" She wouldn't turn.
"Umma!"

Yang Sil lifted her hand in farewell.

His mother knew him better than anyone else, and he knew she had done this for his sake. Because if she had turned, if he had been able to look into her face one more time and hear her voice, he knew he would not have been able to leave.

Young Bok watched until his family was nothing but pinpoints of dark in the distance, until his eyes hurt from staring into the bright snow and the sun. Even after they were gone, he stood shivering in the cold, watching the horizon.

The world was flooded with light, and Young Bok clutched the South Korean money to his chest and sobbed.

CHAPTER THIRTY-TWO

Young Bok began walking southeastward down the road, stopping only once to scoop snow into his empty water bottle. When his stomach grumbled, he tilted back his head to gulp down chunks of half-melted snow. They slithered into his stomach and settled there, like small, cold snakes.

His family swallowed by snow and light and distance.

His mother's hand raised in a farewell.

He was already afraid their faces would grow blurry in his mind, swallowed up by time too. And the money was so warm in the pouch against his chest. So warm. He stumbled along the snowy road.

The sound of a gunshot crackled through his entire body. Immediately, he was alert, heart pounding thunderingly loud in his ears, hands wet with sweat. Just around the bend in the road, he spotted a street checkpoint, guarded by several armed soldiers. Another resounding gunshot.

One step, another step. Young Bok eyed the bare trees and surrounding mountains narrowing the pass. There was nowhere to hide. He could not turn back; the only way was forward.

Hymnal. Bible. YMCA ID. All of them were incriminating proof that he was a Christian, and the soldiers would assume a Christian meant an anti-Communist. They would ask no questions, just raise their rifles and—

But the Bible said to be willing to die for your faith! Young Bok could feel his throat stick as he tried to swallow. *It's life or death, Young Bok.* The knapsack was already sliding off his shoulder, down to his wrist, and smoothly, Young Bok let it drop by the roadside. It sunk into several feet of fresh snow. He kept his eyes on the soldiers ahead; they did not notice.

"Forgive me, God," he murmured, scrunching his eyes shut for a moment. *I'm a coward.*

He kept an even stride as he walked toward the checkpoint. Head bent down, he hunched his shoulders into what was now the familiar posture of an older man.

The closest soldier peered at Young Bok as he approached. He was dressed in the thick, quilted winter uniform and earmuff caps of a Chinese soldier. "Where are you going?" he barked.

Young Bok bowed his head respectfully. Beneath the too-long sleeves of his winter coat, his hands trembled. He stared at the spilled belongings on the ground, eyes drifting toward one of the men lying still next to them. Worn shoes, torn pants, and blood… Young Bok quickly directed his eyes away. His voice came out unevenly at first until he cleared his throat. "I'm going to get my parents in the south, and then I will return and bring them north."

The soldier glanced over his shoulder at the other soldiers who were quietly talking among themselves. He looked back at Young Bok, and the sunlight glinted off the metal rim of his rifle.

Young Bok clenched his jaw.

The soldier eyed him up and down before swinging his rifle over his left shoulder and patting Young Bok down. Young Bok was grateful his family's money was well-hidden beneath his thickly woven long underwear. "We will send your parents north when they come this way," said the soldier. "You cannot pass through here. Go home to the north."

Young Bok opened his mouth, then immediately shut it again. He bowed and turned away, trying to take one even step after the other. *Not too fast, not too fast,* he repeated silently. He could feel the soldier's eyes on his back, but he walked on, terrified he would hear the sharp report of a gun.

When he finally turned the bend in the road, he closed his eyes, dropping his chin to his chest. The shame was a dull ache behind his eyes. *Coward.* Why had he survived? Why had he thrown away his Bible? If he had been killed, he could have been in heaven now. Young Bok brought his hands up to his face, pressing the base of his palms to his temples. It would take decades until Young Bok could feel at peace with his decision to throw away his Bible, decades until he could reconcile that it had been a necessary and life-saving choice, all a part of God's plan for his life.

But it was good to be alive. He could feel the cold wind again, hear the trees swishing and the soft fall of snow from the bare tree branches onto the ground. He opened his eyes again, squinting in the bright light. The world was blue for a moment before his eyes adjusted. The South Korean won was warm against his body. This was his family's hope, their love and good wishes. If only for this, he *had* to survive to escape south.

Young Bok had walked on for only a few minutes before he saw a cluster of five people. They carried small knapsacks, but he knew immediately from their varied clothing they were not soldiers. Theirs was the handwoven cloth of village mothers, the spectrum of shades of white to smoked gray. They did not see him approaching, voices rising and falling in hurried and nervous conversation.

As Young Bok started to pass, one of the young men happened to glance his way, and quickly disengaging himself from the group, he approached Young Bok. "Excuse me…" He had a soft voice, and stood slightly bent forward, head at an angle.

Young Bok nodded a greeting.

The young man continued, "We've heard there's a checkpoint ahead. Do you know? Have you seen it?"

"We heard they found identification cards or South Korean money in some people's pockets, and they shot them right away," said one of the men.

"They won't ask questions. Just *bang*. Shoot," said another.

Young Bok nodded. "They won't let anyone pass. They already killed…" He took a shuddering breath, "They've already killed many people."

The other young men, all about the same age, watched him. Young Bok wondered if he also wore the same worry lines and weary expressions they did. He wondered how many family members and friends they had already left behind, how many they had already lost to gunfire or hunger or bombs.

They introduced themselves quickly, exchanging quick formalities and brief smiles. Young Bok learned two of the men were friends, but the rest had met here by chance. It was a difficult time to trust, but they all shared the same goal of freedom in the south. An immediate camaraderie sprung up between them.

After a short period of deliberation, they agreed they would strike out into the mountains, deep enough to avoid the watching eyes of soldiers, but close enough to the road that they could make sure they were headed southwards. Young Bok was relieved to let others make the decisions. At least for a moment, he would not be alone and the memories in his head would be quiet.

They walked in each other's footsteps, sometimes sinking knee deep into the snow. The way was silent because the hike was difficult, and they were unsure whether they would be heard from the checkpoint.

Even after they had walked for at least a couple hours, the men did not stop. The single file line had become a messy fan, each man picking his way through snow drifts and barren trees. A day passed like this, and after a long night, one of the men was missing from the stumbling group. "Where is he? Where is he?" they asked each other when they bumped into one another in the growing sunlight.

With each passing night, it became more difficult to stay together. Young men kept disappearing from the group, and Young Bok didn't know if they had wandered off or if they had simply given in to exhaustion and laid down in the snow, never to wake again.

Eventually, they stopped asking after the others, gray faces drawn, blurring through the days, stumbling onwards.

At nighttime, Young Bok covered his whole head with an ear-flapped hat that tied beneath his chin. His three pairs of socks were soaked through, but he could no longer feel his feet, so it mattered very little.

Sometimes in the long nights of darkness stumbling along the mountainside, Young Bok broke out in a cold sweat imagining what would happen to his family when they returned home. After what his father and brothers had done…he prayed desperately for his family's safety.

In his half-awake state, Young Bok drifted apart from the rest of the group. The days dragged on beneath a sky dribbling with gray snow.

Young Bok walked until his eyes grew too heavy and he slipped into sleep, stumbling along for a few steps before tumbling into the icy cold of the snow and jerking awake, immediately struggling to his feet again, hands finding the places where the snow was too soft and sinking, tumbling, fighting the snow and his weary head and the trees for his balance. He broke off strong branches from nearby trees and used them as anchors at both of his sides. Still, he fell hundreds of times. It was hell, but he was determined to survive. He refused to give in.

When he had to relieve himself, Young Bok would take a large stick and dig up a hole of dirt and snow before covering it up. If he had to pee, he went anywhere that was accessible. Chuckling to himself as he staggered along, he repeated, *I'm fertilizing the plants.*

Sometimes while Young Bok trudged through the snowy sludge, when the numbness and exhaustion nearly consumed him, he began to think about the clear running water by his home, imagining the tripping of the water over the stones and sand. There was no dirt in that riverbed. How cool and fresh the water had been! He imagined himself wading into the water up to his knees, fishing for crawfish and small river shrimp. As the days passed, these sorts of memories faded away, and Young Bok missed only his family. Nothing else seemed important besides the deep ache in his heart or the names and faces of the people he loved best. He could still hear their voices so clearly in his head.

After about a week in the mountains, Young Bok stumbled upon a small village. He knocked on every door, weak with hunger, until he found an old woman in one of the homes. She gave him a freshly baked soybean cake, pressing it into his hands with gnarled, wrinkled fingers, and coaxed from him a promise that he would look for her son. She whispered her son's name, treasured it on her tongue. Young Bok could tell she wanted to tell him more. What her son had been like as a baby, his favorite foods, how he climbed trees, how he laughed, the way that heavy sacks of rice looked almost small now on his broad shoulders. *Promise, promise that you will look for him. Promise.* He promised.

She offered him a night in her home, too, with the beckoning smile of a lonely old woman. This was the only night Young Bok slept in a house. The solid ground and the stillness of his limbs was foreign to him, but he slept deeply until the woman woke him at the first light. She filled his pockets with more soybean cakes and sent him on his way with a blessing and a last plea to search for her son and tell him to send her word.

These soybean cakes were Young Bok's lifeline. Whenever he felt the pang of hunger, he nibbled on a cake and ate a handful of snow. He never ate much at a time, always careful to ration his food. He had no idea how much longer he would have to trudge southward.

On the nights when it was cloudy, Young Bok could not tell which way to go and would often realize he was walking the wrong direction only when the sun rose again. When the sky was clear, the stars were his guide. When he looked up at them, they reminded him of tired nights after the harvest when he and his brothers would lie in their courtyard or sit by the river with their feet in the cool water. He remembered lying on his back with Cheotjjae and Duljjae, watching them point out the *euhaseu*, milky way, and the seven stars of the *bukduchilseong*, Big Dipper. They taught him that by looking at the tip of the dipper, the bright northern star, he could determine all directions and find his way. Sometimes they named constellations and counted stars until their tongues tripped over the names and numbers. They talked often about whether the city kids could see such stars, and with smug smiles, agreed they could not. Those who lived in the countryside were clearly superior in their sense of direction.

Throughout the next couple weeks he spent in the mountains, Young Bok found isolated homes scattered in the mountainside. Sometimes he wondered if his grandfather's or his uncles' homes could be nearby. Whenever he saw chimney smoke rising from one of these homes, Young Bok would wait hidden in a nearby clump of trees until dark. Then he would knock on the door, licking his chapped lips and shifting back and forth on icy cold feet. When the door opened, he could feel the warmth from the kitchen on his face and his hands.

"I am a refugee. May I come in?" he bowed his head every time, a little ashamed to infringe on their hospitality, and yet so tired and cold that this no longer seemed to matter.

Every home welcomed him in, mothers and fathers, old *halmonis* and bent *harabeojis*. "Please come in!"

They gave Young Bok warm water and salty rice balls with sesame seeds, watching him smilingly as he scarfed down the food and sputtered his thanks through a mouth full of rice. When he had finished, they told him the same story of how their sons had just left home, tenderly repeating their sons' names. They always handed him carefully folded letters, saying, "Please give this to our son if you see him."

When he left after the meal, they would stand in the doorway waving to him, "Go safely." Nearly all of them were elderly people, either too old or too stubborn to leave home.

On Christmas Day, 1950, after two weeks of almost non-stop walking, Young Bok finally broke out of the mountains. He found his feet on a beaten dirt road, joining a steady stream of refugees moving southward. They were plodding and tired, weary and dusty like he was.

By late morning, Young Bok arrived in Seoul. The city lay in ruins: The blistering rain of artillery fire and falling bombs of the last several months had done their damage. Shattered windows of homes and stores stared at him blankly. Power lines and streetcar cables snarled and tangled in the streets. But even the war-torn city was beautiful to Young Bok.

He stood in the middle of the street and spread his arms and shouted, "I'm free! I can finally breathe!" He began to cry, great heaving sobs that shook his tired body. "This is how human beings were created to live! I'm free! I'm free!"

CHAPTER THIRTY-THREE

Young Bok went immediately into a nearby church to pray. He found it completely empty, except for a bent and wrinkled elder who watched silently as Young Bok knelt on his knees in prayer. Young Bok closed his eyes, and he heard the elder shuffling away to a back room. *Thank you, God, for this freedom. Thank you that I am alive! But my family...* Young Bok let his head sink to his chest. *My mother and brothers and sister and father. I don't know whether they've made it home safely or not. I don't know anything. God, please protect them. Please keep them safe.*

"I would leave as soon as possible," the elder's gravelly voice interrupted his prayer. He had a glass of water in his hand, which he handed to Young Bok. Young Bok drank gratefully.

"Soon, only the old and sick will be left here. The North Korean armies are coming." The elder talked very slowly, as though his mouth were feeling out each word carefully, "There's a pontoon bridge across the Han River. Take that and go. It is not safe to stay here."

Young Bok thanked the elder and left the church. A wind picked up outside and a single woven straw shoe shifted across the street, followed by a flutter of ragged posters.

A couple blocks down, Young Bok found a police station recruiting temporary soldiers as volunteers for a mission against North Korea. The sign read boldly, "Register to Fight the North."

His whole body ached with exhaustion, but Young Bok picked up his pace toward the station. This was the whole reason why he had come. If he fought North Korea, he could help end the war quickly. He could be reunited with his family again! He was homesick already, too tired to walk any farther south, and in bold letters, the recruiting sign read: FREE FOOD.

Young Bok signed up.

"Young Bok?" Young Bok felt a hand on his shoulder. He turned to see Lee Do Hyun, one of his former high school classmates.

"Lee Do Hyun!" Young Bok exclaimed. How good it was to see a familiar face!

Lee Do Hyun grasped Young Bok by the arm. "It's good to see you!" He was already reaching for the form Young Bok had just signed. He tore it in quick, decisive strokes and let the pieces fall to the ground. The wind scattered them as they fell, and Young Bok watched them join the debris in the street. "What are you—" Young Bok began.

"Young Bok, come with me to Busan," Do Hyun said, already guiding Young Bok down the street.

Young Bok didn't resist. He was far too tired, and his mind felt numb and blank. After they had walked some distance,

Do Hyun turned to Young Bok and said, "Many men joined that recruiting program but most of them never returned. You know why?" He snorted derisively. "The officers pocketed the money for clothes and food and rifles. The supplies that they did have, they sold off for profit. Most of the recruits died from exposure and starvation. You wouldn't want to die for something so stupid, would you?" He eyed Young Bok up and down. "You look like you've worked hard to get here. You can't just throw away your life like that."

"Thank you, Do Hyun. It has been...a long journey." He glanced at the smart uniform that Lee Do Hyun wore. "Are you a police officer now?"

"I am," Do Hyun beamed. "And I'm on a mission to Cholla NamDo to help control the Communists there."

"Cholla NamDo?" From what Young Bok knew, the last couple years in the Cholla province had been bloody ones. Protests by the people of Cholla NamDo over economic exploitation, the repression of strikes, an exclusion from the nation's politics, and independence of their own politics had been met with no response from the South Korean government. Angry guerrilla units, often led by local Communist associations, had launched violent attacks on police and other officials. Police and rightist individuals retaliated in kind, slaughtering hundreds of villagers. Thousands were murdered, villages burned, and people gloated in victory when they held up the severed heads of their enemies. Young Bok nodded solemnly. Do Hyun was brave to smile. *He might never return...* Young Bok shook his head to clear the thought.

They reached the bank of the Han River and crossed the pontoon bridge, metal beams lined up neatly over a series of military boats. In the distance, Young Bok could see the twisted structure of the Han River Bridge.

Do Hyun followed his gaze. "June. The bridge. It was exploded in June when the troops were first retreating."

They boarded a freight train that would take them toward Taegu, fighting for a space among the hundreds of others clinging to the railings on the tops and sides of the cars. Young Bok was grateful for a rest from walking, but it was freezing cold on top of the freight train. His already cracked hands began to bleed with the frigid wind, but they were so numb he could no longer feel their pain. The train bumped along, and when Young Bok looked down, he could see that much of the track was makeshift, built roughly over straw bags filled with dirt and sand. If he had not been clinging on for dear life, he might have laughed at the faces around him, the features distorted and red from the wind, hair blown into wild, tangled nests. Instead, he traveled on in a haze of exhaustion, deafened by the wind.

A young man next to Young Bok dropped from the railing after a few hours. Young Bok was too exhausted to react, and the others around him scarcely turned their heads. The thud of the body by the tracks was drowned out by the constant hiss and roar of the train engine. As the days passed, many more fell to their deaths when their arms grew too tired to hold on any longer. The train's wake was littered by discarded baggage and twisted bodies.

Almost every hour, the train stopped, waiting on repairs to the track ahead. And at every stop, more refugees tried to board.

Though the journey should only have taken four hours, it took nearly six days. When they finally reached Taegu, Do Hyun waved goodbye. "Young Bok, stay on the train until you get to Busan. You should be safe there. If Busan is taken, take an ocean liner in the port to Japan or the US. Goodbye! Survive!"

"Goodbye!" Young Bok called. "You survive, too!"

***

On midnight of December 31, 1950, Young Bok arrived in Busan, a city at the southeast tip of the country, 325 kilometers from Seoul. Legs weak with exhaustion, he lay down in the middle of the sidewalk and cried out his thanks to God. People passed by, but no one bothered him as he lay there, rejoicing and crying.

When he had exhausted all his tears and felt his eyes growing heavy, Young Bok found a spot to sleep on the sidewalk under the awning of a bank. He gathered straw and rubber from the streets for his bedding, and tucking his father's coat around him, he lay still and stared up at the clear sky and the bright stars. He felt a sense of overwhelming peace rush over him. *Thank you, God,* he prayed. *Thank you for protecting and saving my life!*

Young Bok woke the next morning, stiff and cold. His very first thought in his newfound freedom was that he desperately needed to use the bathroom. He stumbled toward the outhouses along the street, but though he shook them roughly, all were padlocked shut. He waited for the bank to open, and then searched for a bathroom in there. Wandering into a stall, he marveled at the gleaming porcelain bowl. It was the first toilet he had ever seen.

On January 4, 1951, Seoul changed hands for the third time, and US and ROK forces beat a hasty retreat as the

North Korean People's Army took over. Within a couple weeks, almost half a million displaced people poured into Busan, and the population tripled in size. Finding shelter in one of the crowded refugee camps was almost impossible, especially as admission was limited to those whom the ROK specifically targeted for relief. Young Bok spent two weeks sleeping on the same space of pavement in front of the bank. As the streets grew more and more crowded, he often woke to find a strange arm thrown over his shoulders or a strange face near his own. The winter was unusually cold, and every night, he was grateful for his father's jacket. Hundreds died in the streets of hypothermia.

Within the first couple days of his arrival in Busan, Young Bok made his way to the shipyard. The word on the street was that one could earn 2,000 won, maybe even 6,000 won (the equivalent of one US dollar in the early 1950s), working there. At first, he just stood and watched, overwhelmed by the sound of splashing waves, creaking ships, and sweaty men yelling commands. When new ships eased into the harbors, men sprang up to form uneven lines to unload them, staggering beneath heavy sacks and boxes toward a makeshift warehouse. When they were finished, US soldiers chased all the workers out and slammed the warehouse's heavy metal door closed. The men stood shivering in the icy wind until a train arrived, after which the soldiers reopened the doors and the men heaved the supplies from the warehouse into the train.

Young Bok looked down at his arms and flexed them. Wiry and thin, but strong. He was used to heavy farm work, digging trenches and carrying bags of sand. But most of all, hunger was a terrible gnawing pain in his stomach, and he had no money to spend. From then on, Young Bok began working at the port every day, hauling hundred-pound sacks of sugar and bulky wire-wrapped boards of potatoes. Most men only lasted a week, maybe ten days on the job. Young Bok stayed in that shipyard for the next three months, up through March of 1951.

Accidents happened. Men slipped on the narrow pedestrian walkways while holding heavy loads and drowned in the sea. Some fell asleep at work, tumbled into the sea, and drowned. Sometimes tanks and military vehicles ran them down on the pier.

Young Bok felt like a pack animal most days, constantly hunched beneath a heavy load, straining and grunting, the veins standing out on his arms and his neck. The US soldiers were harsh men, always swearing and yelling, "*Habba habba,* hurry up," in butchered attempts at Korean. "Gook," they often spat at him. "Gook, *habba habba!*"

I am not an animal, Young Bok wanted to yell. He walked faster, carried two sacks of sugar rather than one. He worked harder until the crying ache of his body distracted him from anger and reminded him that if he only worked harder, then maybe, just maybe, he could help win the war faster. He could free his family. Regardless, he couldn't afford anger. He needed this job to eat and to survive.

Many of the other workers spent the brief moments between shipments ranting about South Korea and its leaders. Young Bok stayed close to the ships, but their enraged voices carried far. One man's voice was so loud that Young Bok wondered how the other men nearby kept from covering their ears. "A free election? A democracy? Syngman Rhee is a dictator who purges anyone who opposes him."

Others were quick to join in, nodding furiously and adding, "He appoints mayors, village headmen, and chiefs of police. He controls everything!"

Young Bok could tell by the way they talked they were South Koreans. He knew what it had been like at home, where people did not even have the freedom to discuss the evils of the government. They could be arrested, killed, disappeared into the night. Then again, he had only been in the south for a handful of months, so perhaps he underestimated the degree of fear that these South Koreans lived under.

"In December, our government security forces massacred people in Seoul. Eight hundred of them in one week alone, just led to trenches and shot in the back of their head. They called them Communists and collaborators, but how did they know? Then," the loud man barely stopped to take a breath. "Just a couple weeks ago, a detachment of the ROK Army killed two hundred people in Kochang, JeonbukDo."

The province right next to where Do Hyun is, Young Bok realized with a start. The other men nodded again.

"The commander accused the villagers of harboring the Communist guerrillas they were hunting, and then he had all the villagers gathered at a schoolyard. He ordered all the men shot. Two hundred people. Two hundred right there in front of their children. And it's going to be covered up. I'm sure it will be."

Many men kept knives tucked away in their boots or the folds of their clothing and slit open the sacks of sugar as they walked toward the warehouse. Cupping one hand to catch the sugar as it rushed from the bag, they lapped it up greedily like water. Young Bok watched in horror. By the time the sugar bag reached the front line, it would be empty. Were they Communists sabotaging the US and ROK army? Or were they just poor, hungry men like him? After some time, he could no longer stand the wanton waste. He suggested to the other workers they only eat from the sugar sacks ripped in transport. They shrugged. One swore at him.

He approached the supervising military officers. Could they not open one sack so the workers could eat from that rather than cut as they worked?

The officer was livid, though his words were polite. "Well, now. We do that, and we are permitting military food to be given away. It would be condoning illegal activity. We can never agree to that."

Young Bok returned to his work. If he reported specific dockworkers, they would lose their jobs. Then what of the families they had to support? Would Young Bok be responsible for their starvation? He said nothing more.

With his earnings, Young Bok managed to buy a metal kidney-shaped military canteen that held about a liter of water, a set of matches, and a little sack of rice. He had one meal a day. Later, he had the luxury of buying a bag of salt to flavor the rice. He could not afford firewood, but there were enough stones and rubble in the street to start a fire, albeit a smoky and stinking one. The only difficult part of cooking the rice was getting the water with which to cook.

Everyone in Busan still used the well to pump water, but the city waterworks had been inadequate even before the population tripled in size. Water went first to the army, ports, and government facilities. The little that remained was rationed out to the regular housing districts, three buckets for five-person families, and two buckets for those with fewer than five. Women stood with their makeshift buckets of cans and wire and string in lines that stretched on for three to four hours. Usually by nightfall, the city dwellers had exhausted the public water supply.

Young Bok worked till dark, and if he had waited in line, he knew the pump would have been dry by the time his turn came. Instead, he sat by the well quietly with his little can of rice. Most girls walked by, pretending not to see him, but it never took more than ten girls until one would come close and ask him, "Do you need water?"

"Yes please, ma'am." When she filled up his canteen, flecks of dirt, rice husk, and insect pieces from the rice floated to the top. With his grimy hand, he scooped out as much of the floating bits as possible.

Sometimes when the girl was especially nice, she would say, "I'll give you some more water. Please rinse again!"

Young Bok always refused politely, thanking the girl. "It's okay. It'll be fine."

The rest of his time, Young Bok spent looking for his family. The city hall walls were filled with flyers, pictures, and notes about lost family members. Young Bok spent hours scanning them, searching for familiar faces. Nothing. As he searched, the cloth pouch of South Korean won hugged his chest, tucked against his heart, and he reached up to squeeze it tightly in his fist. He promised he would never spend a single won of his family's money until they were reunited.

Sometimes he was convinced that if he just turned one more corner, searched one last street, that he would come upon all eight of them, smiling at him. He imagined running into his mother's arms, smiling at Daseotjjae, or holding Ilgopjjae one last time.

The pain in his heart was almost too much for him to breathe.

***

Somewhere hundreds of miles away, Sang Chul, Cheotjjae, and Duljjae were lined up before a squad of NKPA soldiers and executed, jerking as they were riddled with bullets. Their bodies were tossed into an unlabeled mass grave, and their families were stolen away in the middle of the day. No one would see them again.

CHAPTER THIRTY-FOUR

The dump near the docks had already been picked clean of useful items, and Young Bok was beginning to regret the time he had wasted rummaging through the trash when he heard the clean peal of a church bell. He stopped sifting through the trash and just sat, listening. How long had it been since he had attended a church service? Sweeping debris from his lap, he stood up and began to follow the sound of the bell through the town, drawing closer to the beautiful, sonorous call. He joined a congregation amid a church service and even when the service had finished, he lingered on, kneeling on the cold floor and thanking God for the church, the sermon, and the pastor. Young Bok stayed so long in prayer that the pastor emerged from the back room behind the pulpit. Young Bok could hear his footsteps, hesitating at first, and then gathering speed, until the swishing robes and footsteps came to a halt right next to him. The pastor stood over him for some time before he said, "Get out."

Young Bok's eyes fluttered open in shock. *Get out?* He stared up at the pastor with an open mouth.

"You heard me, didn't you? Get out."

"I've been praying this whole time!" Young Bok blurted out. "Why are you telling me to get out?"

The pastor looked down at him. "Just last week we cleaned up this entire church. The church that should have been holy became a dumping place for human waste. Now," the pastor's eyes were wide and angry. "Now you're sleeping here again."

"Again?" Young Bok tried to keep the hurt out of his voice. "This is my first time here. I was just grateful for your message and your preaching. I was just praying and thanking God for it."

"Get out."

Young Bok got to his feet in a daze and left the church. What was this response? Where was the love of God here? He was alone in this city again, a refugee belonging only to the cold night streets and the shipyard.

"Young Bok! Young Bok!" Young Bok did not turn his head at first, but the voice kept calling, "Young Bok! Young Bok!"

He pivoted on his heel, looking to the left and the right, until he suddenly saw a familiar face. "Kim Yong San?" Kim Yong San had been one of his high school acquaintances, and his father had been another of the pastors at Young Bok's home church.

Yong San wrapped Young Bok in a hug, then stepped back to look at him. "It's so good to see you! Did you just come out from service?"

"I did, but the pastor... I was just praying, and he yelled at me to get out. I just don't understand..." Young Bok looked down at his feet.

"Oh, Young Bok," Yong San bit his lip. "Let me explain... Things have been complicated. Originally, the pastor and the elders welcomed all the refugees to stay inside the church. They even took most of their money out of the bank to give these people some resources. What you have to understand is that it has been weeks of these refugees sleeping in the church, cooking, and even using the church pews as a place to relieve themselves. There was poop and urine everywhere! We couldn't even have church services because of the mess, and the church elders were very angry. After all, they were the ones who had given these people money! The very least the refugees could have done was to respect the church grounds. You see, right?"

Young Bok nodded.

Yong San continued, "The pastors and elders met together and decided to distribute their remaining money to the refugees so that they could search for different shelter. That's why they are so sensitive about any refugees lingering on the church grounds. I'm sorry though, Young Bok. I'm sure you were hurt."

Young Bok smiled a little.

"Anyways, how have you been? Where are you staying now?"

Young Bok spread his arms wide. "I stay anywhere! It's a free country, and my bed and my kitchen are the entire city. I can explore Busan now like never before."

Yong San punched his shoulder. "Don't kid, Young Bok. You can come to my house until you find a place!"

Young Bok laughed. "No, it's alright. I'm doing fine."

"Young Bok, it's right next to this church campus. My father is the assistant pastor here, and I know my family would all love to have you live with us."

"Really, Yong San, I'm fine."

"Young Bok!" Yong San continued to insist until Young Bok finally agreed.

Yong San's "home" was a boxy metal military-grade tent with a simple stove in the middle. It was a small space, built for only two or three people. When they neared the tent entrance, Yong San called out, "I met Kim Young Bok from Pyongsong today!"

The tent flap lifted, and Yong San's father emerged, followed by Yong San's mother and then his two sisters and three brothers.

Young Bok bowed his greeting to Yong San's mother and father, but then turned to Yong San. "How can I stay here, Yong San? It must be very crowded already with eight people. How can you take in another person?"

Yong San pulled Young Bok toward the tent entrance. "You can't live on the street. Stay with us! It'll only be until you find a proper place, so stay with us."

Young Bok thanked Yong San and his family profusely. After months of surviving outdoors, he finally had a warm place to lay his head.

In normal circumstances, Young Bok would never have lived with Yong San's family. Not only was he inconveniencing them, but Yong San had a sister who was Young Bok's age. A young man living in close quarters with a young woman… their reputations would have been stained and the village gossip would have been vicious. This was wartime, however. Things like this could not always be avoided. Still, Young Bok was as careful as possible. He took night shifts at the port, leaving the house before dinner and only returning mid-afternoon to sleep in a corner of the tent. For most of the morning, he roamed Busan looking for his family. In his remaining time, Young Bok preached about Jesus on street corners. Through those early months of 1951, he was convinced that he was living through the seven years of tribulation predicted in the book of Revelation in the Bible. "We are in the end times! Turn to God!" he screamed to passerby. Much later, he laughingly shook his head, "Why would anyone listen to someone like that? That was not an effective way to share about God's love."

Young Bok never shared meals with Yong San's family, always aware of how he was a burden on their household. Instead, he continued to buy rice for his own meal each day. Sometimes he splurged on a can of Spam, picking chunks straight from the can with his hands and glorying in the salty goodness. When the can was empty, he slurped the remaining juice.

Every bit of extra money he had, every won and coin, he stored away for his family.

***

Young Bok had not changed his clothing for three months. By February, it got to a point where the itching from the lice was too powerful for him to even sleep. He set out to look for some DDT in the street market.

The street market, which was often called the *Gukjae Shi Jang*, or International Street Market, was not difficult to find in Busan. It was at almost every street corner and every bend of open sidewalk. People of all ages hawked military goods, winter jackets, pants, and metal scraps, while school-aged children peddled stolen cigarettes, gum, and candy. Many vendors sold what was called UN stew or *kkulkkuli chuk*, pig's soup, leftovers gathered from nearby military bases and boiled in a large pot.

Young Bok found a merchant selling DDT and carefully counted out the money to pay him. He needed new clothes too. The ones he wore were stained with sweat, and as the city thawed, Young Bok could smell a strange rancid odor from them. If he had still been living on the streets, he would not have noticed, but now that he was in Yong San's home, he was painfully aware of the odor. He bought a pair of pants and a jacket for two days' worth of wages. Young Bok could recognize the military uniforms of the US soldiers beneath grayish-black dye. "The soldiers sold their uniforms to me for spending money," the vendor explained. Whether this was true, Young Bok doubted. He had overheard many a dock-worker conspiring with US soldiers to steal shipments, bribing the soldiers with promises of alcohol and women.

DDT in hand, Young Bok walked to the sunny hill behind the church. He vigorously rubbed the DDT all over his body and his clothing, sitting in the powerful fumes of the chemical for fifteen minutes. Then he took off all his clothes and shook them. The lice came off in handfuls, enough to fill a whole wine glass! In the warm sunlight, finally free of the itching parasites, Young Bok stretched and smiled. "So nice!" he sighed.

CHAPTER THIRTY-FIVE

———

In late March of 1951, Young Bok thanked Yong San and his family for their hospitality, and set out for Taegu, about ninety kilometers northwest of Busan. There, he spent a few restless days with little to do. The UN forces had recently retaken Seoul, the fourth time the city had changed hands, and the waves of refugees moving southward had slowed.

Young Bok was tired of waiting, tired of watching each face in the street and darting down alleys after strangers who dimly resembled his mother or sister or brothers. His family was not coming. He needed to *do* something. The war needed to end.

Young Bok packed up his few belongings, and enlisted at the ROK Navy Academy in Jinhae, South Gyeongsang Province.

The Navy was unlike anything Young Bok had ever experienced before. At exactly 5:55 a.m., officers would pace the recruits' room, checking that all one hundred recruits were still in their beds. The bell rung at 6 a.m. every morning and a speaker intoned, "Five minutes to get ready." Then there was the mad rush to brush teeth, put on pants, button uniforms, buckle belts, pull on socks, and stuff feet into shoes. Some recruits wore socks to bed to try and save a few seconds in the morning. Often, they were caught by the officers who paced the room in random inspections, barking, "Put out your right leg. Left leg." If they were found wearing a sock, the officer punished the recruit however they saw fit.

At 6:05 a.m., the recruits marched out to the grounds and lined up for inspection. Officers checked the recruits' breath to see whether they had brushed their teeth, hollering for them to open their mouths and breathe out. Belt, pants, and hat had to be perfectly aligned. In the mad morning rush, Young Bok's belt often ended up a centimeter crooked and an officer would jerk his belt to correct it. The yanking was so hard that Young Bok said it hurt his intestines and shocked his bowel.

"As a member of the Navy, you are the very top of the military, above even the Army and the Air Force," the recruits were told. "You travel the world from port to port; the entire world is your field. You are patriots and ambassadors saving Korea. Korea depends completely on you."

Young Bok learned how to obey a superior's orders without question, how to quickly clamber into the row boats for a landing, and how to load and cock a gun. Over and over, the officers drilled this single lesson into the recruits: Time is life. One minute means everything. If you miss your boat, you die.

Land training in the growing humidity was brutal: running, lifting weights, strength exercises.

They did pushups an impossible number of times and held plank positions until Young Bok's arms and core felt fiery with their aching. An officer stood over the recruits and shouted, "If you can't do it anymore, raise your hand and stand." In the beginning of his training, Young Bok stood with a few other recruits. Though he was strong from months of working on the docks, he was shaking with exhaustion. It was physically impossible for him to do another pushup. Then, the officer shouted, "How come everyone else can do this, but you cannot?" A jerk of the belt in punishment. *My poor bowel,* Young Bok thought.

"Nothing is impossible," the officers shouted. "Erase that from your dictionary. All is possible."

Young Bok collapsed during a plank exercise. A jerk of the belt. *My intestines,* Young Bok winced.

Young Bok failed to brush his teeth thoroughly enough before inspection. Another jerk of the belt. *My insides will be mush,* Young Bok grimaced.

He was bewildered. How could so few other people be punished? He was not the weakest, nor did he lack perseverance. He began to pay greater attention to the other recruits, and when he did, he began to see all the shortcuts taken around him: pauses in pushups, a bent knee during a plank exercise when the officer looked away, wet toothbrushes in the hour before morning lineup. He was convinced the officers knew these exercises were impossible, but because everyone had to obey no matter what, cheating became a matter of survival. Thus, Young Bok paused in pushups, bent his knees in the planks, and woke up an hour or two before the morning inspection to use the bathroom, wash his face, and brush his teeth.

Honesty was suicide.

Every night, the inspector general paced the room at precisely nine o'clock, checking that all the recruits had taken off all their clothes and lay still in their beds. Young Bok was so tired most nights that he scarcely thought of his family when he climbed into bed, but not tired enough that he could not feel the grumbling of his stomach. He was grateful for the Navy's cafeteria, but there was rarely enough food. Meat was a scarce luxury.

One day per week, the recruits were allowed an afternoon in the city of Jinhae. As they left the Naval Academy, officers bellowed, "You are the world leaders marching on!" One-two, one-two, they marched, like the mechanical heart of some great machine, crunching boots and crinkling uniforms stretching the entire thirty-minute walk between the Naval Academy and the gates of Jinhae. Once there, Young Bok could finally let down his guard, perusing the restaurants, the merchants' wares, and the posters outside of the movie theater.

***

It was dead of night when Young Bok was jolted awake by the shouting voice of an officer. "Outside in five!" The lights blazed on in the room, and bleary-eyed, Young Bok staggered to his feet, scrambling for his uniform and his shoes. He heard the other recruits doing the same.

The officer outside was very much awake, barking instructions: "Recruits are to march from the base of the mountain near the Academy to a funeral home across the ridge. There, they will sign a visitor's book before climbing down the mountain. All recruits will be spaced five minutes between. First recruit, step forward. And MARCH!"

Young Bok strained to see the first recruit as he disappeared into the darkness of the trees.

It was too simple of a task. Something else had to be happening. Young Bok brushed aside the fuzz of sleep, shifting between his feet, trying to think. Several more recruits marched into the trees.

"NEXT," the officer bellowed.

Young Bok took a deep breath and began to march. A third of the way up the mountain he stopped, slipping behind a clump of trees to wait for the recruit behind him. After he heard the crunch of footsteps, he counted to fifteen before he snuck out from the trees. Young Bok followed the recruit at a distance, taking shallow breaths and trying to calm the creeping anxiety that all the trees hid watching eyes. He heard the purposeful tread of two pairs of feet ahead, and dashed for the trees again, heart thundering.

Young Bok heard a dull thud of fist meeting flesh, and the recruit groaned in pain, falling to his knees. Young Bok plastered his back to the trunk of the tree, breathing quickly. They hadn't seen him hide, had they?

"We heard a rumor that you are in the Navy," came a gravelly voice. A North Korean accent. Young Bok's heart dropped to the pit of his stomach. What was happening? Why were there North Korean soldiers here? He peered out from behind the tree. Two shadowy figures loomed over the recruit.

The recruit got to his feet, slowly. "I'm not...I'm not from the Navy. I'm just passing by."

One of the shadowy figures landed another punch in the recruit's stomach. The recruit bent double and wheezed. Young Bok bit his lip. Should he go help? If there were two against two...but they would hear his North Korean accent, and if they were North Korean soldiers, they would ask why someone from North Korea was all the way in the south, near a Navy Academy, clearly in the uniform of the Academy. And what would he say then? Young Bok risked another look past the trees, examining the two figures, trying to decide what he ought to do. A beam of moonlight slipped through the trees and struck one of the figures. Young Bok nearly gasped when he recognized a fourth year at the Navy Academy. It was all an exercise. The fourth years were pretending to be North Korean Communist guerrillas.

The recruit repeated, "I swear, I'm not in the Navy." Suddenly, he threw himself headlong at the fourth-year's stomach, bowling him to the ground. The other fourth year ran over and started kicking at the fallen recruit. They scuffled for a while, and then the fourth year looked down at his watch and nodded at the other fourth year.

They let the recruit get to his feet. He held up both fists, bouncing on his feet.

"Alright, alright," said one of the fourth years, holding up his hands. "You pass. You didn't reveal anything to us. Just keep going down to the funeral home now."

After a moment, the recruit let his hands fall to his sides, muttering an expression of disbelief.

Young Bok waited until the recruit had walked a little way and the fourth years had disappeared down the path to wait for the next recruit. Then, Young Bok slipped out of the forest. He walked for a great deal of time, still on his guard for any other surprise attacks. As he began to near the funeral home, he heard deep throaty screams, some long and drawn out, others in short staccatos as though they had been swallowed. Goosebumps ran up his arms. He could see the outline of the funeral home clearly in the moonlight. *Be brave, Young Bok. What's the worst that could happen?* At that moment, he plummeted into a ditch.

Someone had set up candles in the ditch, and in the dim lighting, Young Bok struggled to get to his feet. The ground shifted strangely, and he stumbled and fell. On his hands and knees, he reached forward, trying to get a grip on something to help pull him to his feet. He found a queerly round and smooth object in his hands. "What is thi—" A human skull stared back at him. Young Bok screamed. He squeezed his eyes shut, falling backward into…more bones. For a moment, he was stiff with panic. Then he flailed in the bones, hearing some of them crack beneath his feet as he desperately scrabbled to get out. "Young Bok, Young Bok," he murmured under his breath, trying to calm himself. "You were a medical student. You spent hours studying human bones. Why are you afraid of them?" He felt around with his hands. Breathe. "Rib. Femur. That's…a mandible. A patella." A quivering breath, and Young Bok struggled to his feet. He laughed shakily and to no one in particular he said, "What kind of joke is this?" Eventually, he found the edge of the ditch and heaved himself up and over the edge. He passed through the funeral home doorway, and behind him, he could hear someone resetting straw to disguise the six-foot ditch.

There was only a single candle to light the entire room. The signing book sat on a wooden podium, and Young Bok walked carefully toward it. There were two recruits lying still on the ground nearby. He eyed them as he reached for the pen. Suddenly, hands reached out from behind the podium and grabbed his leg. Young Bok jumped and nearly screamed. In rapid fire, he yelled, "I know you're not a ghost because your hands are warm so blood must be running through them. You are not a ghost so don't try to scare me. This is childish." He understood now that the still bodies nearby must have been other recruits who had fainted from fear.

He heard snickering beneath the podium as he opened the book. Some of the signatures tapered off with a long pen stroke. The recruits must have been scared in the middle of writing. Young Bok signed his name and then passed out of the room, heart pounding in his chest. The return to the academy was uneventful.

**

Later on in his training, Young Bok spent four days out on the open sea with a crew. It felt like weeks to him. He couldn't see any land, and the endless expanse of the ocean terrified him. Panicky thoughts clung to him. He was fish bait. If he died, there would be no remains, no tomb to show his family he had kept his promise and survived to escape south. His chest clenched. He was desperately homesick, hungry for land, and struck by incredible loneliness. Trees, mountains, rocks—he would have been happy with any of them. A wave of seasickness overwhelmed him, and he retched over the edge of the boat.

By September, five months after enlisting, Young Bok was convinced that he had made a mistake in joining the Navy. He was beginning to learn how to kill others: how to fight at close range, where to aim when he shot the gun, how to launch a grenade. He became increasingly convinced he had let his hot and bitter anger lead him into this decision.

The more he learned about how to kill another human being, the more he was convinced that this went totally against the Christian philosophy of love, forgiveness, and justice. He had wanted to crush and kill the Communists of North Korea and end the war but these…these were his Korean brothers. Maybe even his actual brothers. Cheotjjae, Duljjae, or Netjjae could have been drafted. They could end up on the same battlefields. Every time Young Bok aimed at a target, every time he pulled the trigger, every time the bullet lodged in the target, he felt sick with horror. This could be Cheotjjae or Duljjae or Netjjae.

How could he forgive himself if he murdered one of his brothers? No matter how badly North Korea had threatened him and his family, no matter how much they had all suffered at the hands of the Communists, he did not want to kill any of them. Not his brothers, not his fellow North Koreans. He wanted the war to be over. He wanted to see his family again. But he could not kill.

As before, Young Bok used his health to excuse himself from service. He approached the Navy doctor, who just so happened to be Dr. Cheon Yong Eul, the same doctor who had excused Young Bok from the draft at Pyongyang Medical School.

"Hello, Dr. Cheon!" Young Bok bowed his greeting.

Dr. Cheon smiled. "Young Bok, we meet again."

"Doctor," Young Bok launched straight into his request. "You already know that I have a tuberculosis infiltration. I... made a mistake in joining the Navy. I think that the men in the Navy are brave and valiant, but I am ashamed to do this kind of work. I don't want to kill anyone. I want my family to be able to find my grave when I die so they know that I successfully escaped south." He stared searchingly into Dr. Cheon's eyes. "You helped me once, please help me again." He bowed low.

Dr. Cheon nodded slowly. Once again, he said very little, but he did not hesitate for as long this time. He picked up a pen and wrote, *Tuberculosis could recur with intensive training or extended time in harsh weather conditions. Physician would recommend Kim Young Bok's dismissal.*

Young Bok left behind the Navy Academy and struck out again for Taegu, where he had heard that a few men from his hometown were living now.

CHAPTER THIRTY-SIX

———

Once he arrived in Taegu, Young Bok headed straight for the First Presbyterian Church, the biggest church in the area. There, he met four men from his hometown. All of them lived and worked in the church as elders, reverends, and pastors. They invited Young Bok to stay with them, but he refused, knowing that they already had very little space as it was.

That same day, another church elder approached him. She was an exceptionally small woman, under five feet, with short, curly hair. "Young Bok, right?" she asked. "My name is Choi Ho Saeng. I heard from some of the church leadership that you needed a place to stay. I discussed it with my husband, Elder Kim Yoon Shik, over there." She pointed to a tall man who looked to be in his late twenties or early thirties. "And we would love to have you! We have two sons and one daughter, but we have an empty room in our house and there is plenty of space for you."

Young Bok hesitated. He knew it was not appropriate for him to stay in the home of such a young family, especially, as he would learn later, as Ho Saeng was only seven years older than him. An unmarried and unrelated man living with a young couple… But Ho Saeng's eyes and her warm manner reminded him of his mother. Instinctively, Young Bok reached up for the pouch around his neck.

"Young Bok?" Mrs. Choi looked worried, and Young Bok realized his face had contorted in a full range of emotions.

He pushed back his hesitation and bowed quickly. "Thank you, Mrs. Choi. I would be so grateful."

It was by far the nicest place he had ever lived, a room to himself separated from the main house. As fall slipped into winter, Choi Ho Saeng worried over Young Bok. Separation from the main house also meant separation from the central heating system. She insisted they light a fire for him in the spare room, but then Young Bok insisted on paying for the firewood. They both knew he could not afford such an expense, and after several long conversations, Mrs. Choi yielded.

As the temperatures dropped, Young Bok bundled himself in the cotton floor mats, expecting to wake frigid each morning. Strangely, he was always warm. He wondered if all the nights on the street had numbed his body to the cold. One day, he pulled back the mats and gasped. Tiger skin. He had never seen one before, let alone touched it. It was a luxury only the very rich could afford.

He rushed to speak with Mrs. Choi. "How could you use this precious tiger skin on me? I feel so sorry!"

Choi Ho Saeng laughed. "Young Bok, I hoped that you wouldn't notice it. I knew you would feel sorry, but I'm so glad I can finally put it to good use! It was a part of my wedding betrothal so many years ago, and I never had any real use for it until now."

To Young Bok, Choi Ho Saeng was a second mother, unfailingly kind. He was endlessly thankful for her, thanking

God for sending someone who was like his guardian angel, protecting and helping him along his way.

Young Bok and Choi Ho Saeng would remain lifelong friends.

Soon after Young Bok moved into Mrs. Choi's house, he began to search for a job. An acquaintance took him to an interview to be a janitor at the First Field Clinical Laboratory of the US 8th Army. The laboratory was centered in a repurposed engineering high school and was full of harried lab workers and exhausted doctors, fighting the spread of epidemic hemorrhagic fever (EHF). EHF had plagued US troops, infecting at least two thousand soldiers and killing hundreds. Fever, a great thirst, and rupturing of blood vessels and hemorrhaging in the kidneys stopped the body from removing waste from the bloodstream. Most patients died within this hemorrhaging "shock" phase, five or six days from contraction of the disease.

In his interview, Young Bok was conscious of his North Korean accent, watching the slightly raised eyebrows and looks exchanged between his employers. It was understandable that they were concerned. For all they knew, he could be a North Korean spy. They were short-staffed, however, and needed the help. They were also well-aware that most North Korean refugees were more anti-Communist than South Koreans, good workers who did not simply work for their earnings but wanted to help win the war.

Young Bok's first job at the First Field Clinical Laboratory was as a toilet cleaner of the Honey Bucket stalls. Every day, he squeaked open the plastic doors to the stalls and breathed in the ripe smell of urine and moldering poop. He scooped the waste from the toilet into a large sack. When it was full, he heaved it over his shoulder and hauled it to the nearby field and buried it. Then, on his hands and knees, he scrubbed around the toilet. His battlefield was that of mysterious stains and poop that wedged itself in all the tiny cracks of the toilet seat. More difficult were the toilets that were just deep holes in the ground. Young Bok had to use a shovel to dig and scoop out the waste. More than once, Young Bok's foot slipped into the hole and emerged covered in dripping goop.

Young Bok and the other janitors were also responsible for dumping out leftover food that soldiers, patients, and lab workers left in the hospital cafeteria. As they had no formal mealtimes, they picked through leftover plates, taking a couple bites of anything that looked appetizing before returning to work. Young Bok was always full by the time he returned home. The janitors had a system: Any dirty or inedible food went into one black garbage bag destined for field fertilizer. The rest, they saved in large metal drums. The kitchen staff then sold most of the leftovers to subsistence merchants who worked the International Street Market. When Young Bok passed stands on his way home, he often caught a familiar whiff of what he had just eaten for lunch from the *kkulkkuli chuk,* pig's soup. What little food remained was given to the poor who came to the back kitchen door with empty containers.

Young Bok worked every day except for Sunday and never skipped a day.

Each night when he returned home, he peeled off his stinking clothing and folded it neatly in the corner. He was exhausted, and the moment he laid down on his pillow, he drifted off into deep sleep. Mrs. Choi often discovered these stacks of clothes and washed them. Young Bok would find them sweet smelling and beautifully folded in the early morning when he left for work. He knew this was no small feat, and he tried to hide the clothing from her, guilty that she worked on such a distasteful and difficult task because of him. Eventually, he found a cheap laundry service and spared Mrs. Choi the work. When his clothes grew too worn and odorous, Young Bok bought new ones on the black market. He wore variations of the same black-stained soldier uniforms for the next several years.

On holidays like Liberation Day on August 15, Mrs. Choi invited Young Bok to join her family for a meal. They talked and laughed over specially prepared food: rice cakes, *bindaetteok*, savory mung bean pancakes, and sometimes, very rarely, meat.

Young Bok loved to play with the Choi kids: Sunghyun, Eun Joo, and little Sungwan. They often went to a nearby park, and Young Bok pushed the children on tricycles. Sometimes, he liked to pretend that this family was his own: mother, father, younger siblings.

One time, watching as Eun Joo danced around a tree, he laughingly called out, "Daseotjjae, what are you doing?"

"Who's Daseotjjae?" she asked innocently, pausing her play.

Young Bok's heart plummeted. "Did I say Daseotjjae? I meant Eun Joo. Eun Joo."

"Who's Daseotjjae?" Eun Joo repeated.

The very corners of Young Bok's mouth lifted in a smile but his eyes smarted. "Daseotjjae was my little sister. I used to play with her all the time. You look a lot like she did when she was small, Eun Joo. Daseotjjae laughed and smiled a lot. She was so pretty—" *Was? Was? Isn't it "is"? Daseotjjae is pretty. Daseotjjae is pretty, Young Bok. She IS.* Young Bok sank against the tree trunk.

The children gathered around him, little voices asking, "What's wrong? What's wrong?"

He couldn't breathe for a moment, then said, "Nothing. I'm fine. Let's keep playing." Young Bok gripped the little pouch of money around his neck and gritted his teeth to keep back the tears. It was 1952. He hadn't seen his family in two years and the pain of missing them hurt deeper than he could possibly describe. It was a throbbing pain so terrible that sometimes he wished that he could tear out his heart and lungs and die on the spot.

Still, he treasured those peaceful moments of laughter under a serene sky in a park. He could almost forget a war still thundered on throughout the country.

***

Young Bok was cleaning the lab, covering for one of his friends, when he heard the raised voices of American scientists as they crowded around a microscope. The arguing went on for quite some time. Mop in hand, Young Bok wandered over. "May I take a look?"

He read slight disgust in their eyes, as they took in the dirt on his face and his faded clothing.

"What does the janitor boy want?" one muttered, putting a hand to his nose. They looked at one another but shuffled away from the microscope to give Young Bok space to look.

Young Bok peered down the microscope, keeping his dirty hands behind his back. "That's malaria vivax," he said, without hesitation.

The scientists were taken aback, "How did you know that?"

"I went to medical school for two years, but now I'm working as a janitor."

"That's really too bad! You look like you know what you're doing… You should be working in the lab, not as a janitor," said one of the scientists. The group looked at him with new respect.

Young Bok shrugged. "I need the money, and I do what I have to do to survive."

The very next day, after almost a year of janitorial work, Young Bok was approached by the microbiology lab and hired as a bacteriologist. He rejoiced there were no more bathrooms to clean, that he was finally returning to the kind of academic work he loved. Mrs. Choi and her family celebrated with him that night with a feast of food and heartfelt congratulations.

Young Bok was happier than he had been in quite some time, but when he laid in bed that night, clutching the little woven sack of South Korean won from home, he had to clench his jaw to keep from crying. If his mother had been with him, he would have run to her with the news. He could imagine yelling for her in the doorway of their house, "Umma, Umma! I'm going to be working in a laboratory now!" She would have run up to him and beamed, *Setjjae, I am so proud of you.* She would have pulled him into a hug and stroked the back of his head, and then promised to make him his favorite food in celebration: pheasant *naengmyun.*

Young Bok devoted himself to his new job, where he was in charge of sensitivity tests to detect bacterial resistance to antibiotics. He loved the repetition and exactness of collecting a sample, plating it, and then storing away the plates until the next day, when he would test the resistance of the bacteria colonies.

In late 1952, Young Bok followed the microbiology laboratory to the 121st Division American Military Hospital in Seoul. He said goodbye to Mrs. Choi and her family, thanking them for their generosity and support in the last year.

In Seoul, Young Bok did little besides work in the lab. He was still convinced the Korean War was the seven years of tribulation in the Bible. There was no point in going back to school. The world would end before he could even practice medicine.

CHAPTER
THIRTY-SEVEN

In February 1953, in an attempt to control rampant inflation, the South Korean government had issued a currency reform that would replace the won with hwan. All old bank notes were to be removed from circulation. Young Bok learned of the change too late, but he decided that he would still open his little woven pouch, try and convert the money, and then save it until his family joined him in the south.

When Young Bok slipped open the mouth of the bag and tipped it into his hands, he sunk to his knees with a half-groan, half-sob. Months of sweat and body oil had reduced it to waxy oil paper, so transparent he could see his fingers through it when he held it up to the light. It was worthless now. "Won't you come?" he cried over the bills. "Umma, why don't you come? Cheotjjae. Duljjae. Netjjae. Daseotjjae." He paused for a gasping breath. "Yeoseotjjae. Ilgopjjae. Appa. Why are you leaving me all alone? I don't even have any money to give to you anymore. Why are you taking so long? Where are you?"

***

Peace talks had dragged on for two years when in mid-April 1953, the UN, South Korea, North Korea, and China finally came to an agreement on the repatriation of prisoners of war. Syngman Rhee continued to resist, protesting the right of the Korean people for self-determination and a conclusive end of the conflict as they saw fit. Under Rhee's orders, on June 18, ROK military police helped release 27,000 anti-Communist North Korean prisoners from POW camps across South Korea. Though American soldiers searched for the escaped prisoners, many of the POWs had already found refuge in friendly South Korean homes, and to the American soldiers, they were unrecognizable in civilian clothes. On the three-year anniversary of the Korean War, June 25, 1953, Rhee appeared before a cheering crowd in Seoul, vowing to unify the nation and fight Communism to its death. The relationship between the US and ROK grew increasingly strained, and US leaders called out to Syngman Rhee, pleading him to cooperate with the armistice.

On July 13, the Communists made a final offensive, driving ROK forces back six miles. There were ten thousand casualties, a crushing blow to Rhee's insistence that the ROK forces could face the Chinese alone.

On July 27, 1953, in twelve minutes of complete silence, US Lt. General William K. Harrison from the UN Command and General Nam Il from the North Korean People's Army signed the Korean Armistice Agreement. The armistice paused a bloody war that had lasted three years and ended with borders only miles away from those set after World War II. The ROK never signed the agreement.

Over the course of the war, the US air force dropped 386,037 tons of bombs and 32,357 tons of napalm. The Korean peninsula was ravaged, hundreds of towns and villages razed to the ground, hospitals, factories, churches, and schools destroyed. Five million refugees. Four million killed, wounded, or missing, of which nearly three million were Koreans.

Ten million families were torn apart by the war, one-third of the entire prewar Korean population.

***

Young Bok turned twenty-four.

He began to think that perhaps he had been wrong about the seven years of tribulation and the approaching end times. Maybe it was time to plan for his future and return to medical school.

Along with his laboratory work, Young Bok erased classroom blackboards for Dean Kim of Yonsei University, who was also the head officer of pathology at the Field Lab. One afternoon, Young Bok cleared his throat, brushing away chalk dust from his hands. "Dean Kim," he said. "I want to attend Yonsei University to finish my medical degree. I will work hard and be successful!"

The dean looked up from grading papers. "We are not accepting any more North Korean students. They all cheated, drank, smoked, or didn't pay their tuition, and we had to dismiss all of them. The North Korean students must have thought that a Christian university would be easier than a non-Christian one." The dean let out a frustrated huff, shaking his head. "We can't take North Korean students anymore."

Young Bok grew a little heated. "I never drink, smoke, or cheat. You can ask Cheon Chung Sook! She was my classmate at Pyongyang Medical School, and she's number one in Yonsei's class now. She knows I did better than her in school."

"Yes, that is true she's the only North Korean left in class and a superb student, but Young Bok, I can't believe and trust you. I'm sorry."

Young Bok turned back to the blackboard, swooping the eraser in a great arc across the Dean's lecture notes. A cloud of chalk dust rose, and he held his breath until it settled. "Thank you. This must not be in God's will."

***

Early in 1954, Dr. Jeon Jong Hui, an assistant professor and director of the Infectious Disease division at the College of Medicine Seoul National University, approached Young Bok. "I've been observing the lab at the 121st Division of American Military Hospital, and you caught my attention," he told Young Bok. "I was recently appointed the director of the Central Laboratory, which will work out of the Seoul National University Hospital, and we are looking for diligent and earnest workers like you. I saw that you've been doing this job for almost two years—you show a lot of confidence in your work."

Young Bok bowed his head. "Thank you, Dr. Jeon."

"Would you like to continue your lab work at the College of Medicine Seoul National University?"

Just like that? Young Bok's eyes opened wide. "I would be honored!"

Dr. Jeon smiled, eyes crinkling in pleasure. He grasped Young Bok's hands firmly, "Then let's plan together and help each other."

Young Bok was hired as the microbiology and immunology technician at the Central Lab of Seoul National University. Shortly after, the First Clinical Field Laboratory returned to Tokyo. At Young Bok's request, they left behind much of their equipment and supplies, about ten years' worth, to Seoul National University.

Young Bok's name became well-known, as the only lab technician conducting sensitivity tests for bacterial antibiotic resistance in the entire nation. Anyone planning on traveling to another country had to come to Young Bok to get their serology tested, and only his stamp of approval allowed them to exit the country.

Powerful men tried to bribe him. On one occasion, a professor cornered Young Bok in his office. Waving his testing slip in Young Bok's face, he shouted again and again, "Stamp it! Just stamp it!" When Young Bok refused, the man lunged for Young Bok's stamp on his desk. Young Bok moved to block him and handed the man a hundred blank slips of testing paper. "Sure, you can have this whole pack!" He learned to keep the stamp in his pocket at all times.

***

In March of 1954, Seoul National University began accepting students to all years of medical school, and Young Bok approached Dr. Jeon. "I want to go back to medical school to be a doctor!"

"You don't have to, Young Bok," Dr. Jeon said. "I'll teach you everything you need to know. Then you will just have to take a licensing exam. No tuition!" Dr. Jeon looked into Young Bok's face, noting his hesitation. "Of course, if you want to become a scholar, then you should go to medical school. I will support you if that is what you want to do."

Young Bok nodded vigorously.

On April 1, Young Bok entered the one-room classroom with Dr. Jeon for the entrance exam. Four huge blackboards loomed at the front of the classroom, labeled with first, second, third, and fourth year. Young Bok felt a hum of excitement in his head and the strange prickly sensation of his fingers itching to grab a pencil and begin.

He scanned the third-year board for his name. When he had read it at least three times over, he turned to Dr. Jeon in surprise and said, "Where is my name? I've already done two years of medical school in Pyongyang, so why—"

"If you really want to be a scholar, you need to start from the first year."

Four more years of medical school on top of the two he had already done? Six years of medical school? He was already so old, and the tuition…

Dr. Jeon walked Young Bok to a seat. "Good luck, Young Bok."

Young Bok sweated while taking the first-year test. He didn't know these answers! Physics? How was he supposed to answer this? What if he failed and couldn't get into medical school? His answers couldn't be right. They weren't right! What should he do? He took a deep breath. *Young Bok, think.*

He glanced over at the third-year blackboard, where there were familiar questions like, *How do you classify cancer* and *What are the common symptoms of tuberculosis?*

Young Bok turned in two tests that day: He failed the first-year exam but scored first in the third-year one. The professors called Young Bok to stand before a panel of distinguished men in lab coats and wire-rimmed glasses, all heatedly discussing his future. Finally, one professor said, "Why not let him do the third year?"

"Can I still become an academic doctor?" Young Bok asked.

They agreed. After a four-year interim, Young Bok was finally back on track to become a doctor.

Young Bok quickly climbed to the top of his class with perfect scores on his exams. His tactic was to write down every single word that the professor said, even down to their coughs, which he noted as commas. Before the final exams, he rewrote all the notes to refresh his memory, and in the process, he often laughed, chuckling over a joke he had been too busy writing down to appreciate. After this, he would condense his notes and memorize them as he transferred them to another notebook.

Alongside six hours of class, Young Bok spent ten to twelve hours working at the Seoul National Lab, every day except for Sunday. He spent every free moment in the lab, even returning to the lab for a few extra minutes of work when a professor was late to begin his lecture.

Though Young Bok was on the faculty meal plan (with Dr. Jeon's help), he ate much later than the normal mealtimes. The kitchen staff was always happy to see him at whatever odd hour he arrived, smiling, and saying, "Oh, Kim is here! We saved food for you in case they ran out."

He slept right next to the lab in the call room, and the moment he touched the bed, he was asleep. As the years slipped by, his body grew accustomed to six hours of sleep every day: rising early in the morning even while the world was still dark and cold. Sometimes, even those few hours were interrupted.

Resident students on the night shift in the hospital would come charging into his office at all times, yelling, "Young Bok! Young Bok! The baby is coming! Come see!"

***

Shortly after he began school, Young Bok found that Sok Sae Il, a former Pyongyang Medical School classmate, was in his year. He and Sae Il became close friends. Young Bok later discovered that seven of his former Pyongyang Medical School classmates also attended Seoul National University. They planned an outdoor picnic together. After four years of separation, they all sat together eating rice balls that they bought from a street vendor, exchanging stories of their escapes and their families, reminiscing, and laughing.

Some had joined the South Korean police to help identify and catch northern Communists hiding out in the south. In exchange for working as informants, they received a stipend for their medical school.

"How are all of you in the graduating class already?" Young Bok knew that all these students were exceptionally bright, so he was not surprised they managed to succeed. But how had they managed to bypass the system?

"Don't tell anyone we are in the same year! We skipped a year so we could graduate faster. We told them we had finished three full years of school already," they laughed. "Tuition, you know…"

In total, eleven of them from Pyongyang Medical School had escaped south. Many others had tried, but they could not escape the draft. At least half of all the Pyongyang Medical students had been killed while fighting in the North Korean army.

They joked about the poverty they had experienced. "Remember how we used to always talk about the cattle in the North, how even a breath could blow them over?"

"Yeah, they were as thin as paper."

"What the cattle could eat, the people could eat. So why would we let them eat our food?"

"And remember how we thought that South Korea would have a life free of poverty and repression? We used to always think that the South would be like heaven on earth."

"The farmers here live in straw houses too. There are hungry people in the streets. And Syngman Rhee…"

"It's not heaven, that's for sure."

Young Bok told them about the head-butting classmate from Pyongyang Medical School who had also escaped south and lived right next door to him. "I wouldn't have minded, except that he has a habit of drinking almost every weekend. Just last week, he staggered home and spent the entire night shouting and singing."

"The entire night?" they interjected.

"I'm pretty used to it, but that night…" Young Bok planted his face in his hands. "The vice president of South Korea, Ham Tae Young, was sleeping just across the alley. In the morning, the dean of Seoul National University called me to his office, 'All last night you were drinking and singing; I heard from the vice president of South Korea. The vice president, Young Bok! This is a disgrace to our university.'"

"What did you do?"

"Told him the truth. That I wasn't the one who drank last night!" Young Bok replied. "But still, he was furious. He said,

'We will expel you. Don't lie to me.' So, I told him again, 'I did nothing wrong! If you want to punish me, you can, but you have to believe I am innocent. You know I am an upstanding student who works hard in the lab and at school. Why would I do something like this?'"

"So?"

"I didn't end up in trouble," Young Bok laughed.

The topic of the head-butting classmate triggered a long-standing joke that came up frequently in conversation.

"In the North there is head-butting, but in Jeolla-do [a South Korean province] there is biting."

Two of them stood up to reenact a scenario in slow motion.

"A North Korean man gets into a fight with a South Korean man." Their arms swung slowly, overemphasized expressions at slow motion punches and upper cuts.

"The North Korean man gets mad and knocks the South Korean man down with a head butt." Down he fell, grasping a mock bruised head.

"The South Korean man then spits out the North Korean's nose because he had bitten it off."

They fell on the ground laughing.

CHAPTER THIRTY-EIGHT

On March 28, 1958, Young Bok graduated medical school, in the top five of 125 students. It was his first graduation without Yang Sil smiling from the audience.

Shortly after, Young Bok and a couple friends opened a clinic in front of Seoul City Hall. They painted the sign by hand, wiping back sweat as they nailed it above the clinic's doors. The First Medical Clinic and Laboratory. They celebrated with dinner, splurging a little on meat, cheering for new beginnings.

Ten hours a day, six days a week, Young Bok and his friends treated patients. For half the time, Young Bok continued his work of laboratory testing for antibiotic resistance.

Sometimes his patients' pain-ridden faces reminded him of his mother, and he was thrown back into the panic of watching his mother wailing and helpless on the floor. Young Bok never turned away a patient after hours. It had been a promise to his mother, the promise of a desperate teenage boy on that moonless night with his bleeding and cut feet.

Young Bok saw a wide range of patients, but it was those with rheumatoid arthritis that stuck most powerfully with him. They were mostly older patients nursing swollen and painful joints, some with fingers crooked and deformed. Their hands were full of callouses and they were rich with stories of their children and sometimes their grandchildren. Some smiled as he spoke with them, others bit back pain and nodded stoically, and still others begged him, "Doctor, please help me. Everything hurts so much."

He prescribed little packets of aspirin and at their next appointments, they would arrive, smiling and grasping his hands. "Doctor, the pain is all gone! Thank you so much!"

But Young Bok knew aspirin was no cure, and the next month, maybe two months if he was lucky, they would be back. He could raise the dosage, give them steroids, but after that, there would be nothing he could do for their pain.

His patients brought him gifts: flowers, food, shirts, neckties. For the patients he knew he had cured, Young Bok was grateful. But for those with incurable diseases, like rheumatoid arthritis, Young Bok swallowed back guilt each time he shook their hands or accepted their thanks and gifts.

He was holding the tiger's tail. It was a wild tiger, spinning wildly, and Young Bok's hands were always losing grip on its slippery skin. If he let go, the tiger would whip around and sink its fangs into his flesh. Would he cure the disease and kill the tiger? Or would he continue playing this game, running with the tiger until exhaustion and guilt claimed him?

***

In the fall of 1958, Dr. Chang Young Chan, one of the co-founding doctors of the clinic, handed Young Bok a little sepia portrait of a young woman. "This is my cousin, Myung Sook. I've talked a lot about you with my family and they would like to make introductions between you and my cousin. What do you think?" Chang Young Chan laughed a little, and Young Bok put up his hands quickly to cover his reddening ears.

Young Bok gazed at the photo of the girl with her two braids, square jaw, and eyes that spoke of a quiet sort of wisdom. "Okay, I'll meet her. What did you say her name was agai—"

"Great!" Dr. Chang Young Chan patted his shoulder. "Her grandmother is coming here today."

And there she was, walking through the door, a short woman, soft-spoken, and slow moving. She patted Young Bok's hands gently. "You will make a good husband for my granddaughter."

Husband? Marriage? Young Bok nearly withdrew his hands. The last time he had spoken about marriage had been when he was eighteen and sitting on the grass in front of Sunan High School with his mother, eating boiled chicken with greasy fingers.

He must have stood silent too long because Myung Sook's grandmother pressed his hand again. "Young Chan has told me about what a kind young man you are. So responsible, and a doctor, too! I know you will be a good husband for my Myung Sook."

Her wrinkled hands were warm on his and Young Bok could feel the faint pulsing of her heart through her papery skin. Somehow, it reminded Young Bok of his mother, whisking him back to his eighteen-year-old self, to the feel of his mother's hand on his own, callouses and rough patches and fingers made strong from farming and weaving. The way that not only her mouth, but every part of her face smiled. The way sitting and talking with her felt almost as though he had swallowed a bowl of sunshine, warm and satisfied inside. His mother's voice when she had said, "You know I am so proud of you, right, Setjjae? Your Umma is so proud of you." He had promised his mother that he would marry at twenty-one or twenty-two, but nine years had slipped by, and now he was thirty, far past the typical marrying age.

And yet…here was this earnest-faced woman with her wide, open features entrusting him with her granddaughter, giving him a chance to finally keep his promise to his mother.

He nodded and bowed.

A couple weeks later, a broad-shouldered woman came to visit Young Bok at his clinic. She was not tall by objective standards, but something about her posture and the stern expression on her face lent her presence. She sat down for a consultation with Young Bok. He tried to keep calm beneath the steady gaze of her eyes, keeping his sweaty hands hidden in the pockets of his white coat.

At the end of the consultation, the woman stood and said, "I'm Myung Sook's mother. I wanted to see what you were like as a doctor." She paused and pursed her lips. "You seem… capable."

"Thank you," Young Bok bowed his head.

"Come to my house this afternoon for an interview," she said.

"This afternoon? Yes…yes, ma'am."

***

In the beginning, Dr. Chang Young Chan's high school-aged brother acted as the go-between to arrange the meetings between Myung Sook and Young Bok. But as time passed, they settled into an easy rhythm of Saturday night dates. They alternated on who bought dinner, meals at fancy restaurants with three sets of forks, little food stands with plastic stools and skewered fishcakes, barbecued meat, and Western food.

Sometimes they went to the movies. Young Bok let himself sink into the darkness of the theater, into this world of luxury he had never known in his village. He glanced over at Myung Sook occasionally, watching the way the light from the screen played over her face, her enraptured gaze, the way she leaned forward ever so slightly. Many of the movies were from America, and Korean translators stood in the back of the theater narrating the dialogue into microphones. When they left the movie theater, Myung Sook was always smiling, a beautiful smile that crinkled her eyes into two crescent moons.

Movies were a rare luxury, however. Most of the time Myung Sook and Young Bok spent the fall evenings outdoors, strolling through the city's parks beneath the fading light that filtered through bronzy leaves. Sometimes they stopped by a coffee house to rest their legs.

On one such walk, Young Bok slowed his pace to match Myung Sook's. "Tell me more about what your family is like, Myung Sook." They always walked a shoulder length apart, but Young Bok felt himself closing the gap a little, leaning in as Myung Sook spoke.

"My mom is the backbone of our family," Myung Sook gave him a brief smiling glance. "You already saw how strong and tall she is. She's conquered many difficulties and worked hard to take care of our family…she practically raised her two younger brothers. She's the one who made my uncle into the man and general he is today, but we always joked that if our mother had been a man, she would have been ten times as great a general as he was."

Young Bok laughed. He believed it. Myung Sook's mother was a rough, strong, confident woman. When she told you to do something, you did not question; you did as she said.

"I could tell you more about my family's story, but I'll tell you that later, maybe." Myung Sook took a sip of her coffee, and they walked on for a little while in silence. "What's your goal for the future, Young Bok?"

"My goal? Well, you already know I do sensitivity testing and see patients and such in my clinic. I enjoy my work in the clinic, and I want to be able to keep on curing patients with God's help. Did I tell you the story about my mother and her ulcer yet?"

"Mm," Myung Sook nodded. "Your mother was in so much pain, and the doctor wouldn't come right away. You wanted to be a doctor so you could help people right away when they needed you."

"Yes. It's why I want to set up a public clinic in the countryside so I can help the people in the villages. Even if they can't pay, I'll run, run, run right away when they need help." Young Bok pumped his arms to demonstrate, crunching up his face with the passion of his words.

"That's wonderful! I love that." Myung Sook smiled up at Young Bok.

"I thought it might scare you away," Young Bok laughed, sheepishly. "I know you're used to much more in your home… and I have very little to offer."

"I really do think it is a wonderful idea. It shows your heart."

Young Bok smiled. "What's your dream, Myung Sook?"

Myung Sook's steps grew lighter. "I study English literature at Ewha Women's University right now, but one day I want to go to America. My dream is to study English literature there."

"America," Young Bok smiled.

They walked on for a little while again and then Young Bok paused, looking down at his hands for a moment before he turned to look at her. "Myung Sook, I think my mother would have really loved to meet you."

"Your mother sounds like a wonderful woman," Myung Sook said. "I hope I can meet her one day."

***

In 1957, Young Bok had taken on the role as Sunday School superintendent at his church in Seoul. The church elders loved Young Bok. He was training to become a doctor, serious in his faith, and talented at working with children—quite an eligible bachelor.

Shortly after Young Bok started going on dates with Myung Sook, the church elders and deacons approached him, saying, "We didn't know you were interested in dating or marriage. You seemed so busy with all your work. It was too hard to approach you about this before, but now…please meet at least one girl we introduce you to. You don't have to marry these women, but at least meet them!"

Young Bok could not say no to them; it would have been arrogant and rude. These church elders had provided for him, supported him, and acted almost like parents to him.

They set up blind dates for him, each time with a girl more beautiful and richer than the last time. But every date brought Young Bok's mind back to his dates with Myung Sook. They could talk, really talk, without pretenses or superficiality. He was himself with her, and he loved her warmth and kindness.

Finally, he approached the church elders. "I want to thank the elders for trying to help me. I appreciate the intentions from your hearts, and it is very kind, but I don't feel comfortable meeting these women. They are all beautiful, and I'm sure beautiful people as a whole, but I cannot keep meeting them."

From then on, the elders did not force any more introductions on him.

***

Young Bok made a monthly trip to the mountainous Gangwon-do province where he and a group of other Christian doctors gave free treatment to the rural villagers. On one occasion, Myung Sook's mother told Young Bok, "Myung Sook will go with you, and she will make some delicious food for you to take on the trip."

Early morning on Friday, the usual group gathered, and Young Bok boasted to all his friends, "My fiancée-to-be is coming with food for us and all our patients to eat."

They waited for almost an hour, but Myung Sook did not come.

Young Bok's friends joked, punching him on the shoulder, "She didn't come...I think she dumped you." Young Bok joined their laughter, trying to hide his embarrassment.

The next day was Saturday, and over dinner, Young Bok stared thoughtfully at Myung Sook before looking down, swirling rice with a chopstick. "Myung Sook...I thought your mom said that you were coming yesterday."

Myung Sook's tone was even. "Was it my idea? Did I tell you I would go?"

"No."

"It was my mom's idea, not mine. I don't want to go on a trip like that before we are engaged."

"I like that you're honest," Young Bok said. "It's my mistake. I should have confirmed with you." Young Bok knew that if his mother had said he would do something, he would have done it, but Myung Sook was different.

As he would say later, "Myung Sook is special. She knew I needed someone to lean on, to embrace my heart. She was refreshingly no-nonsense and straightforward, always absolutely clear and speaking honestly from her heart. There was a freshness and warmth in her eyes I have seen in no one else."

It was from this respect and trust that Young Bok decided to take a step further toward Myung Sook.

After dinner, Young Bok hesitated. "Myung Sook, do you want to sit down for a bit?" He gestured to a bench.

They sat. Young Bok fidgeted with his hands, hearing the *clackety-clack* as he ground his teeth for a couple seconds. He took a breath and said, "Myung Sook. I haven't ever told anyone the full story about my family and about running away to the south, but I want to tell you. Would you be willing to listen?"

Myung Sook nodded. At first, his sentences were awkward, tripping over the events and stories, but as he kept talking, the story began to pour out. Describing the family he loved, their way of life in the north, his fear as he fled south, the difficult journey, and his guilt. He cried as he told her about leaving behind his family, and she patted his hand. When he had finished, his voice was hoarse, and his eyes were wet. The sun had set long ago, and they sat in the cold and empty park looking at the stars.

"Young Bok," Myung Sook pressed his hand. "Your parents would be so proud you survived. They would be overjoyed to see you thriving and healthy."

Young Bok squeezed her hand.

"Can I tell you something, Young Bok? When my mother and grandmother were first thinking about introducing you to me, we went to one of your Sunday school services to watch you. Do you know what I said?" She laughed. "I don't like him. Look at the way he cleans the kids' runny noses with his sleeve. He's probably a weak mama's boy.' But Young Bok...you are so strong. Surviving like you did, loving your family and yet being brave enough to escape south. That's not something just anyone can do. I'm sure your parents are very proud of you."

Young Bok laughed and took a sniffling breath. "Thank you, Myung Sook."

They sat in silence for some time before Myung Sook spoke again. "My family…has a complicated past. They used to be very rich, but…" She hesitated, seeming to contemplate what to say next. "My grandfather was a bad man…he left my grandmother to take care of herself. She had three children, and she was so beautiful." Myung Sook waved a hand over her face. "Everyone said that about her. They always asked, 'How could he leave a woman like that?' When my grandfather left them alone, they had nothing. My grandmother had no idea what to do; she was the youngest daughter in a rich family, and she'd never worked for anything. She said, 'We are going to die.' But then my mother said, 'Don't worry. We will find a way to survive.' My mother was the one who worked hard and raised her two younger brothers and then all six of us children. We never begged anyone for anything. My mother worked so hard to bring us to where we are now."

***

One winter day, watching an especially funny movie, Young Bok laughed so hard tears streamed down his face. He reached out to grab Myung Sook's hand but, in the process, he accidentally bumped her leg. Myung Sook withdrew her leg quickly. Young Bok apologized but thought very little of it.

The next day, Young Bok heard rapid knocking at his door. "Young Bok, Young Bok!" It was Dr. Chang's younger brother. He panted, holding his side, clearly having sprinted to deliver a message. "You have to come now! Young Bok, come with me now."

Young Bok grabbed a jacket and rushed out. He arrived in Myung Sook's home and began to bow to her mother, when she demanded, "When are you going to get engaged?"

Young Bok was shocked, frozen mid-bow. "Engaged?" It was all moving so quickly. He cleared his throat. "I don't really know."

He knew the Confucian principle by heart, drilled into him since he was a very small child. *A boy and girl after seven can never sit down together.* But still, Young Bok was struck by the chastity of his own culture. An accidental bump of the leg, and he had committed to marriage.

Myung Sook's mother leaned in close. "Christmas?"

"I have a Christmas skit I am coordinating for the Sunday school. Maybe after New Year's?"

"I understand."

On December 26, Dr. Chang's younger brother pounded at Young Bok's door, and Young Bok found himself running out of the house again. He was back in Myung Sook's mother's sitting room, where she looked him up and down sternly. "Tomorrow is your engagement. Myung Sook's uncle will speak to you now."

Young Bok was still trying to straighten his shirt and rub out a stain on his pants when the General strode into the living room. He was dressed smartly, holding a sheaf of papers in one hand, and he shook Young Bok's hand firmly with his free hand. He gestured to the couch and Young Bok sat down. Then, ever so courteously, the General went through each of Young Bok's life experiences. He had lived in North Korea near Pyongyang, yes? His parents were farmers? He had gone to Pyongyang Medical School for two years? Ran away and escaped to Taegu? Worked in the shipyards? Joined the Navy?

And left because of TB? For this one, Young Bok assured him that there was nothing wrong with him. His conscience had not permitted him to continue service in the Navy. In some ways it was impressive, and in others frightening, that the General had such top military authority that he could search all records regarding Young Bok's past. He understood the thoroughness, though. In such a politically powerful family, a Communist marrying into the family would be disastrous.

True to his future mother-in-law's word, the engagement party was the very next day. It was a small gathering of about a dozen people, mostly family members. At Young Bok's request, Professor Jeon and his wife attended the dinner and graciously played the part of his parents. Young Bok and Myung Sook kissed for the first time.

On February 23, 1959, Young Bok and Myung Sook were married. Young Bok was seven years older than twenty-three-year-old Myung Sook, the same age difference as that between his mother and father. Myung Sook's mother paid and planned the entire wedding, inviting over five hundred wedding guests, and Young Bok invited most of the staff from Seoul National University. He laughingly recalled the university and hospital were almost completely empty that day.

On their honeymoon, Young Bok and Myung Sook traveled to a hot springs resort in Busan. Along the way, Young Bok pointed out the spot under the bank awning where he spent his first weeks in Busan, the first church he had gone to, Mrs. Choi's home in Taegu.

Young Bok remembered feeling so blessed. After all his hardships, he was going to live a normal life with a wife by his side. *Umma,* he wanted to say. *Your Setjjae is getting married. You would like Myung Sook a lot, Umma. I'm keeping my promise to you, even if it is nine years late.*

He had lost his mother, his father, his brothers, and sister, but through marriage to this woman, not only did he have a beautiful wife, but a grandmother, a mother, and younger siblings. For all the formalities of interviews and observations, they embraced him, welcoming him into the family as one of their own, and for that he was endlessly grateful.

CHAPTER THIRTY-NINE

Young Bok sat at his desk in a wrinkled lab coat. Outside, night was already falling across the city and Young Bok could hear the voices of the market men and women as they packed away their wares for the night. He held a pad of scribbled notes in one hand and his head in the other. Another rheumatoid arthritis patient. His head ached, but his exhaustion was more than a physical one. He couldn't do this anymore.

The next morning, Young Bok went to Professor Jeon's office and said, "I want to find the real cause of rheumatoid arthritis and cure it."

Professor Jeon did not look at all surprised. "Seoul National University has a partnership with the University of Minnesota, as you know. I would recommend you go there and get your PhD degree. They have some of the best research on Streptococcus pyogenes." Streptococcus pyogenes was thought to cause rheumatoid arthritis.

When Young Bok told Myung Sook and her family about his desire, Myung Sook's mother fixed him with a steady gaze. "We will support you. Don't take any of the government's money or you will have to be the government's slave. You can depend on us to take care of your tuition." She was a generous woman but also a smart one, and he could see the calculations running through her head. Pay for her son-in-law's schooling, and he would come home faster. It was good that her daughter was pregnant with her first child, good that she could keep Myung Sook nearby for a little longer. Her keen eyes fixed upon Young Bok. *You will return to us in Korea. You will be back for Myung Sook.*

In mid-1959, Young Bok was accepted to a PhD program in Immunology at the Department of Microbiology, University of Minnesota, and he began applying for a visa. The visa test was notoriously hard on the Korean end, almost as though the Korean government was saying, *No, do not emigrate!* Even after a long day in the clinic, Young Bok spent hours poring over a thick book of Korean history. He was grateful for those lengthy nights when he flipped open the test booklet and saw a question about some king's fifth concubine's third son, which he had only seen from a small footnote at the bottom of a page.

In contrast, at the US embassy, Young Bok passed the English written and speaking test easily. When he was done, the staff said, "Wonderful! Enjoy! You'll do great."

Young Bok left behind all his valued possessions in a box in Myung Sook's house: papers, receipts, pictures, awards, the oil paper money. The belongings he had gathered and saved so he could show his family the evidence of all he had done in the last decade.

He left alone, though it had been Myung Sook's dream first to study in the US. It broke his heart to leave his wife and unborn son behind, to see Myung Sook waving goodbye and him watching and watching until he couldn't see her anymore.

He remembered feeling lonely and a little cold on that August night in 1959 when he boarded the plane, body tight with anticipation. It was the first plane he had ever been on, and as the plane rose over the ocean, Young Bok glanced out the window, gritting his teeth. Huge flames plumed out of the engine, fiery against the dark sky. He sat upright, gripped the armrests of the chair so hard that they left ridges on his hands. A quick glance to his right and his left. No one was reacting. Was he the only one who could see it? And then he was immediately thinking of his wife and unborn child and then his dreams of the future. If he died now... He raised his hand high. It was alright. He would calmly ask the flight attendant what was happening. He wouldn't cause a mass panic. He was calm. Calm.

"Yes, sir. How can I help you?"

Young Bok pointed out the window. "There's fire outside! Is there something wrong with the plane? I didn't want to scare anyone else, so I just wanted to ask you."

The flight attendant's shoulders shook a little and she covered her mouth with a polite hand. "Sir, the plane is functioning normally. You can only see the flames because it is dark outside, but everything is fine."

***

When Young Bok had only recently arrived in Minnesota, Young Bok's advisor worried that he would fail his classes. In a one-on-one meeting, he treated Young Bok as though he were stupid. "Do...you...understand...me...?" he would say, mouth slowly forming each word as though he were forcing them out into a gluey puddle. Young Bok had little trouble understanding

English and he succeeded in his labs and classes; it was only that his English was laced with a heavy Korean accent.

Young Bok was often lonely, missing his wife, missing the sound of his mother tongue, missing familiar faces and home-cooked food. He wrote a letter home to Myung Sook every week, talking about his work in the laboratory, the people he met, the deep and icy cold winter. Myung Sook sent him a package of thick, woolen underwear. He wore it once while working in the laboratory but sweat through his clothing because the students turned the burners up dangerously high to warm the room. He went to the bathroom and peeled the long underwear off, fingers leaving sticky wet prints on the bathroom stall. He was tempted to throw away the long underwear, but he thought of Myung Sook and how she might ask him where it was when she arrived. He rolled it up and stuck it under the lab table.

In December, Young Bok spent his first Christmas in North Dakota at Devil's Lake with John Bergstrom, his room-mate and friend. The lake was a dying one, without any fresh water, and whenever wind blew from the lake shores, the rotting smell of still water was overwhelming. John's Scandinavian parents were warm, big-hearted people. Soon after they arrived, John asked Young Bok if he wanted to go and get a Christmas tree with him. Young Bok thought they were going to a store and was shocked when they drove for a mile or two and then turned the next corner and came upon a hill covered in pine trees. The scent was glorious, cold icy freshness nipping at their fingers and noses. Together, they sweated as they dug out a tree and then wrapped the roots in burlap. They heaved it onto the truck, and John asked Young Bok, "Do you want to drive? Or hold the tree?"

Young Bok eyed the wavering tree and knew that he would not have the strength to hold it the whole way. "I've never driven before…"

John laughed. "That doesn't matter! Here's the clutch. Here's the accelerator."

Young Bok hesitated. It was his first time in the US to violate a law, but John was insistent he would do fine. It was, after all, the back country. People here minded their own business; John had grown up driving a motorcycle across the farmland from a young age.

On one of the hills, Young Bok had to stop for the other cars to pass, but by the time he released the brake, the car began to drift backward down the hill.

"Shift! Shift!" yelled John through the pane of glass in the back of the truck. For a horrible moment, the gear stuck, and Young Bok's stomach dropped. When it finally caught, he was drenched in sweat. The drive was only about a mile or two in that stick-shift Jeep, but it felt impossibly long to Young Bok.

Together, John and Young Bok planted the tree. Even sixty years later, the tree is still there, huge and casting its own large shade by the lake.

***

Young Bok was a top student, and by his second year, he received a stipend for his work in the laboratory. He told Myung Sook's mother she no longer needed to support him in paying his tuition.

Myung Sook joined him in the US shortly after, leaving behind one-year-old John with her mother and grandmother.

As the years passed, Myung Sook folded away her dreams of a graduate school education. She had a second child, Jean, and when Young Bok attained a permanent visa to finally bring John to the US, she had two children to look after, and later a third, Paul.

Eventually, Young Bok took charge of his own laboratory at the Memorial Sloan-Kettering Cancer Center. He worked twelve-hour-days as a researcher and a professor, leaving home early in the morning and returning late. His work was his life and he dearly loved it. Every day, every experiment was a step forward to uncovering the next truth, a kind of wild treasure hunt where there was clue after clue leading him toward the tantalizing end goal of knowledge. He did groundbreaking research with gnotobiotic, germ-free, miniature piglets for the next twenty-one years. By studying pigs with no inherited sense of immunity, he unlocked knowledge about the body's defenses against cancer. He would go on to publish over one hundred original papers of research, attend hundreds of scientific symposiums and conferences around the world, train dozens of graduate students and postdoctoral fellows, teach classes at the University of Minnesota, Cornell University, and Chicago Medical School, and act as chairman and head of several committees and university departments.

Young Bok and Myung Sook have been happily married for sixty-three years. They have three children and six grandchildren. When holidays or birthdays come around, the family gathers over a big meal, usually at Young Bok and Myung Sook's house, and Young Bok always loves to remark on how thankful he is for his family, saying proudly, "I have twelve children now!"

***

Every day, Young Bok carries with him the legacy of who he has been: a farm boy, a homeless refugee, a Navy recruit, a janitor, a medical student, a doctor. He is a grandfather, a father, and a husband now, but he will always be a brother and a son. And though time may fade his memories and stories, though it may have already claimed many of his family members and the oil paper money he treasured for so long, it can never change how deeply he loves his family back home in North Korea.

Young Bok feels at peace now. "God has blessed me with a beautiful life," he says.

He smiles.

EPILOGUE

In 1990, one of Young Bok's immunology students told Young Bok of his plans to attend a sports event in Pyongyang. He offered to search for Young Bok's family and pass on a letter if he found them. Young Bok thanked him, but was afraid to do anything, worried his family might face persecution if he tried to make any contact.

A year later, Young Bok found his own way into North Korea. With donations from churches and pharmaceutical companies, Young Bok partnered with the Christian Medical Association to treat tuberculosis patients in North Korea.

Before he left, a friend told him, "Young Bok, you are helping the enemy! If you cure them, they will put rifles to us South Koreans. Just let them die."

"Even the Red Cross cares for them," Young Bok replied hotly. "You are a Christian, but you say I shouldn't help because these people are your enemy? Don't tell me not to go. Enemy or not, they are suffering people and I have to help and treat them."

Young Bok thought of his mother the entire plane ride to North Korea. He wanted to tell her how much he missed her, how much he had longed to see her again, how many times he had replayed that snowy, bright day watching his family walk away from him. He wanted to hear her say she was glad he had gone, that she never regretted he had left them all behind and been unable to return for over forty years. And he wanted to tell her about his life: his wife, his children, his job. He wanted to tell her he was a doctor now, in research, and all her backbreaking hours in the fields, all her faith and belief in him, had led up to this moment. That he was happy. That he was free. That he still loved her so much.

After the requisite tour of Pyongyang and various important Communist landmarks, Young Bok finally arrived in his hometown of SaInJang, now known as Pyongsong. He had almost forgotten the smell of pigs and chickens, musty roofing straw and wet dirt. There were the wide open, grassy rice fields. The dirt roads that squelched beneath his feet after new-fallen rain. The mountain in the distance was smaller than he remembered; the river water was brown and polluted.

A round-faced Communist leader of the town greeted him. He wore the red pin of the Party and a wide smile eerily like the Cheshire Cat in *Alice in Wonderland*. "Your mother was a great lady," the man said. "She always raised two pigs, and when she killed them, she would donate one to the Labor Party and then share the other with the whole neighborhood. Such a model citizen!"

Young Bok nodded, but he was watching for familiar figures in the fields, craning his neck around new apartment rises that cast shadows over scattered huts and broke off the view to the mountainside.

The man was smiling again. "Our Great Leader built apartments several years ago here. Everyone who had previously lived where they were built had the opportunity to live in them! Or to build a new home for themselves in a different location if they desired."

They walked on for a little time, and then the man gestured toward the courtyard of a home at the edge of town. "This is where your family moved."

It was much smaller than Young Bok had expected. He creaked open the courtyard gate and stepped onto a thin walkway between even rows of a vegetable garden. He smiled. It was just like his mother not to waste any space.

He held his breath as he walked toward the doorway of the house. After all this time…what if he didn't recognize them? What if they didn't recognize him?

He hesitated, aware of the man watching behind him, aware of the open door ahead. Aware of how every moment was agonizingly long, wanting to run in but afraid.

He heard a wailing voice calling out his name, "Setjjae… Setjjae…"

He hadn't heard that name in forty years.

Already he was stumbling forward, running toward the call of his name like he had a thousand times before.

"Daseotjjae?" he called out. "Daseotjjae?" Lurching forward toward her open arms and that beautiful smile on her face, a beaming smile that stripped away all the years of hard labor, the wrinkles, and the tan. Then in a single moment of pure joy, they were in each other's arms, and Young Bok was sobbing in a way he had never known to be possible. Shuddering heaves that shook his frame, and yet he was smiling, smiling so hard his mouth hurt.

He was home. Finally home.

Then there was Netjjae standing before him and Ilgopjjae. "Netjjae! Ilgopjjae!" He hugged them, and they did not pull away for a long time. Feeling their beating hearts against his own rib cage, breathing in their smells, feeling how alive and how near they were, Young Bok was overwhelmed beyond words. He held them tight.

Small faces whom he didn't recognize peered out at him from the doorway of the house. They looked up at him with Netjjae's eyes. Yang Sil's nose. Young Bok's eyebrows. Daseotjjae's smile.

"Praise God that you're alright! You all have families, too?" Young Bok asked.

They nodded, smiling, shy and proud.

"And Umma? Appa? Cheotjjae and Duljjae? Yeoseotjjae?"

Daseotjjae smile faded, and she took Young Bok's arm. "You should sit, Setjjae." They sat on the oil-papered floor of the house. The pieces of the last forty years gradually came together.

"Appa, Cheotjjae, and Duljjae..." she began.

"They were all executed," Netjjae finished. "In 1950, when the Chinese came down and the Communists took over again. You know what kind of work they did..."

"And their wives and children?"

"Disappeared," said Daseotjjae softly.

Young Bok sat in silence.

The Communist leader had called Yang Sil a model Communist, but Young Bok could only imagine how painful and lonely it must have been to give so openly to the very regime that had killed her sons and husband. His mother had known her every move was watched, that her choices would be the death or survival of her children. Even in her grief, she had protected her family.

"Yeoseotjjae, too," said Daseotjjae. "Yeoseotjjae is...gone."

"Gone? What do you mean 'gone'?"

Daseotjjae, Netjjae, and Ilgopjjae exchanged looks. Netjjae cleared his throat. "He grew up angry and strong-willed. He watched his brothers die and disappear; how could he not have been? He... made a mistake. He..." Netjjae glanced toward the doorway and lowered his voice. "He was taken to a concentration camp."

"What did he do?" Young Bok asked. "Where is he? How is he doing?"

Daseotjjae butted in. "He was very smart. He studied hard enough to qualify for a scholarship to the Soviet Union. When he came home, he brought a bike with him. It was his most precious possession. He rode it everywhere. Kept its frame so shiny and clean. Then his boss demanded Yeoseotjjae give it to him, but Yeoseotjjae was so stubborn..."

"So stupidly stubborn," Netjjae pounded a fist lightly on his leg and blinked several times rapidly. "Do you know what he said? 'I earned it. I cannot give it to you.' The very next day, they call him out to make a public confession to all the people, to kneel on the ground and make a self-apology saying he had sinned and done wrong. Young Bok, do you know what he said? 'If you want to be unjust in punishing me, so be it. I have done nothing wrong.' He disappeared into a concentration camp with his entire family."

"We haven't heard from them in years," Daseotjjae murmured.

"Do you know where he is? Is there anything we can do to—" Young Bok stopped, reading the fear in his siblings' eyes. They understood the regime they lived under. They knew exactly what kind of punishment that dissenters faced. Everything in their tensed faces and shoulders told him not to ask any more questions, to leave bygones as bygones. "What about Umma? Why isn't she here?"

"Umma cared for all the grandchildren while we worked in the fields," said Daseotjjae. "But Young Bok…she died three years ago."

"Three…three years ago? Our Umma?" He couldn't breathe. They were lying to him. His mother would walk through the door any moment and she would hold him close and tell him how much she missed him. His mother wasn't dead. They were lying. But when he searched each of their faces, there was only grief.

"She was on her way to the bathroom one night, and she must have slipped and fell. She hit her head… I found her dead by the toilet in the morning," Daseotjjae said. She was crying now, and Young Bok realized his face was also wet with tears, his palms full of red crescents from the fingernails of his clenched fists.

"If I hadn't been so scared, I could've come and seen her. I could have seen her!" His voice cracked and he cried desperately, clutching for his siblings' hands. "I missed her by three years. If I hadn't been so scared… Umma. Umma! I could have seen her…I could have seen her."

Young Bok beat his chest with one hand, rocking slowly back and forth. "Umma… Umma…" That terrible snowy day in December and her waving hand. That had been the last day he would ever see her alive? He choked on his sobs.

Daseotjjae took his hand and spoke gently. "Do you know what Umma would always say? 'Setjjae never died. I know he's alive.' She was sure you escaped safely. She wanted to see you so much, Young Bok. She was always waiting for you, but…I think she was glad you didn't come back because it meant you were living a good life. It meant you were safe away from here." Daseotjjae paused. "Young Bok, she would be so proud of you."

"I took a picture of Umma when she turned seventy," Ilgopjjae gently placed a picture into Young Bok's hands.

Young Bok clutched at the picture. The tears kept falling and he brushed them away with the heel of his hand. "Umma." Yang Sil was smiling very slightly, her hair brushed back into a neat, low bun. There was strength in every line of her wrinkled forehead, the expression in her eyes. Hers was still the most beautiful face he had ever seen. "Umma," Young Bok stroked the picture. "Umma, your Setjjae came back to see you. Your Setjjae is home."

"You can keep that picture," Ilgopjjae said. The picture of his mother still sits in Young Bok's office. Even to this day, Young Bok tears up when speaking about his mother.

"Thank you, Ilgopjjae," Young Bok patted his brother's hand. He took a deep breath. "You were so little when I left," he laughed through tears. "You're all grown up; you have a family now!"

Ilgopjjae smiled. "I'm a photographer, too!" He spread out glossy pictures of his family, Daseotjjae's family, Netjjae's family.

My stubborn, brilliant, and strong-willed family, Young Bok thought. How much had they suffered? And yet here they all were, laughing around him.

Young Bok had been lucky to catch all of his family in one place at one time. Daseotjjae and Ilgopjjae lived in the northeast tip of Korea, Chongjin, about a three-day train ride away from Pyongyang. They had just been visiting Netjjae at the time that Young Bok arrived. The roads were unpaved and rutted, and they talked about how they often spent three days on a journey that should only have taken nine hours on a better road.

The time passed too quickly, and when Young Bok had to leave, he pressed money into each of his siblings' hands. "Take care of yourselves and your families. Please be healthy and safe."

***

In 1992, when Young Bok again returned to North Korea, Netjjae crouched on the ground, face in his hands, sobbing before Young Bok. "Young Bok, I didn't know you would come back," he said. After a flood had come a long period of drought, and then a massive food shortage that starved thousands. Some even said it was better to be in the labor camps. At least there, the workers received minimal feeding. "I let my wife's family starve to death to save my own family. If I had only known you would return with more money, I would have given some to my wife's family." When he looked up at Young Bok, there was a plea in his eyes. "I had to save my own children. I did it to save my children, Young Bok."

"Netjjae…" Young Bok clung to his brother. "I'll return every year. I promise. I will always bring money with me when I return." Every year, Young Bok brought money for Netjjae, Daseotjjae, and Ilgopjjae.

Young Bok and his family members sent each other New Year's cards and letters with pictures of their families for the next couple decades. Most took months to make their way across the ocean.

In 2012, after more than twenty-one visits to North Korea, Young Bok made his last visit to his family. With inflaming tensions between North Korea and the US, President Obama had warned that no one was to visit North Korea. If anything happened, US citizens would be on their own, and would not be protected by the US government. By this time, Young Bok was in his eighties, and his children wanted him to stop taking the strenuous journey.

By Young Bok's knowledge, Netjjae and Daseotjjae have already passed away, but dozens of his extended family remain alive in North Korea: nieces, nephews, sisters-in-law, brothers-in-law. Though he may never have opportunity to see them again, he sends them his love.

ACKNOWLEDGMENTS

Thank you to God for Your unfailing love and constancy, for being my strength and song every day!

I am endlessly grateful to my family for their unconditional love and support for me. My life has been so blessed by all of you, and words could never communicate the extent of my gratitude and love for you!

Thank you to my parents who have taught me what it means to live a beautiful life: loving God, loving others, and being loved. Thank you for being a rock in my life, for always reminding me that I can come to you with any trouble or joy, for being willing to embarrass yourselves to make me or my brothers laugh, for being a shoulder to cry on and a hand to hold, for reminding me every day that you love me. I may be all grown up now (just maybe), but I will always be your baby girl. A million hugs! Also, a special thank you to my mom for her dedication in poring over my drafts for this book and spending hours writing comments. I could not have done this without you!

Thank you to my brothers, Joel and Micah, who never fail to make me laugh. Thank you for all your silly jokes and bantering, for your hugs, for late night talks, games, and movies, for teaching me how to love people better. I really did get to grow up next to two of the most wonderful human beings. I love both of you so much, and I am so proud of the people you are becoming!

Thank you to my grandparents for all their support and love! To Nana, for always making me smile, whether it was through hugs or cards or caramel rolls. To Halmoni and Harabeoji, for our Thursday night dinners together, for reminders to "eat well, sleep well, and exercise well," and for their great encouragement and love. A special thank you to my grandfather for all the hours he spent sharing his story with me. Thank you for your patience with my questions and for your vulnerability and honesty. I hope you know what an inspiration you are to me!

Thank you to Auntie Sooyoung for her kind and loving spirit. I so deeply appreciate the time that you took to look over my manuscript and to teach me about Korean history and culture.

Thank you to my friends who have all taught me how to be a kinder and more loving person and have filled so many of my days with laughter. Thank you to all of you who were as excited about this process as I was! It would take too long to list out how beautifully you have all blessed my life but thank you for how deeply loved you have made me feel. Thank you for meals and hugs and late-night movie nights and laughing until our stomachs ache. I know I will cherish our memories for a very, very long time!

Thank you to Claire Lin for helping bring my idea for the book cover to life! You are such a lovely, talented human being and such an encouragement in my life.

Thank you to Mrs. Loecher for how much she made me love school and writing. To this day, I still remember your encouragement and kind words. Thank you to Mrs. Meyers for her dry wit and her "civilization" project that really got me hooked on this genre of historical creative nonfiction. Thank you to Ms. Dolim for her kind spirit, for teaching me how to think critically, and for always believing in me. Thank you to Ms. Fukawa for her passion and for teaching me such wonderful life lessons of persistence and dedication.

Thank you to all the other professors and teachers who invested their time in me and encouraged me to grow in so many ways.

Thank you to my editors at New Degree Press for their feedback and guidance through the entire editing and publishing process.

Finally, thank you to everyone who supported me and bought this book even while it was still in its baby stages! Thank you to Yannie Lam, Lisa Yang, Shirley Dong, Sandy He, Eric Koester, Amanda Lee, Kaitlan Bui, Mrs. Loecher, Julius Gingles, Professor Glasser, Mikaela Carrillo, Ms. Dolim, Carolyn Lee, Sophia Suh, Josie Butterfiled, Mr. Berke, Kristi Shannon, Ryan Lum, Auntie Fer, Mrs. Edington, Maddie Vavra, Eunsun Choi, Natalie Kwong, Sara Van de Roovaart, Auntie Jean, Auntie Tara, Irene Sung, Claire Lin, Camille Wong, Nicole Park, Lissy Somerville, Suehee Sung, Mr. and Mrs. Olfert, Amienne Spencer-Blume, Naomi Kim, Auntie Sooyoung and Uncle John, Seayoung Yim, Ally McCabe, Carly Hui, Chaelin Jung, Mr. Kwong, Mrs. Park, Haley Seo, Joel and Micah Kim, Isaac and Ava Jones, Ashley Chang, Carolyn Lai, Megan Chen, Jocelyn Salim, Joseph Delamerced, Lucy Tian, Charisa Shin, Karis Ryu, Angel Gonzales, Martin Menz, Mrs. Fukawa, Jasmine Lam, Nana, Halmoni and Harabeoji, and my parents.

NOTES

———

The following sources were used to help the story of *Oil Paper Family*:

CHAPTER ONE

Baker, Don, "A Slippery, Changing Concept: How Korean New Religions Define Religion," p. 59.

Beaver, R. Pierce, "Chondogyo and Korea," p. 116–118. "Ch'ŏndogyo," Encyclopædia Britannica.

Chung, Ah-young, "Chondogyo: From Social Movement to Spiritual Practices." Kang, Jae Chul, "Bridal Palanquin."

Park, Sung Yong, "Arrangement of Marriage."

CHAPTER THREE

Baldwin, Frank Prentiss, Jr, "The March First Movement: Korean Challenge and Japanese Response," p. 70, 82–89.

Kang, Jang-seok, "Spiritual and Practical Assets of Korean Non-violence," p. 33.

Korean Independence Outbreak Collection, Part I. The Deginning [sic] of the Korean Independence Uprising March 1–5, p. 1–32.

Korean Independence Outbreak Collection, Part 8. How the Korean Shops Were Re-Opened, p. T1–T2.

Korean Independence Outbreak Collection, Part 9. Terrible Outrages in Suwon and Neighboring Villages, p. S5–S12.

Lee, Jongsoo, *The Partition of Korea After World War II: A Global History*, p. 4–5.

"3.1운동 대한민국임시정부 100주년 기념사업위원회."

CHAPTER FOUR

Clark, Donald N, *Culture and Customs of Korea*, p. 120–122.

KRPIA database, Korean Folklore Hall: Contents of Folk Songs.

Man-young, Hahn. "Folk Songs of Korean Rural Life and Their Characteristics Based on the Rice Farming Songs," p. 23.

Park, Soon, "Rice Planting Game."

"Rice Paddy Song" Farmers' Song, Timeless Values/ Korean Culture.

CHAPTER FIVE

Kim, Jongdae, "Dano Amulets."

Kim, Sun Poong, "Festival of the Fifth of the Fifth Month."

CHAPTER SIX

KRPIA database, Korean Folklore Hall: Food-Kitchen Utensils: Utensils for Cooking.

CHAPTER SEVEN

Giles, Herbert A, trans., "Elementary Chinese, Three Character Classic."

Lee, Hong Yung, Sorensen, Clark W., Sorensen, Clark W, and Ha, Yong-Chool, eds. *Colonial Rule and Social Change in Korea, 1910–1945*, p. 133.

Seth, Michael J., *Education Fever: Society, Politics, and the Pursuit of Schooling in South Korea.*

Taylor, Insup, and M. Martin Taylor, *Writing and Literacy in Chinese, Korean and Japanese: Revised Edition,* p. 105.

CHAPTER NINE

Caprio, Mark, *Japanese Assimilation Policies in Colonial Korea, 1910-1945,* p. 145–149.

Chang, Iris, *The Rape of Nanking: The Forgotten Holocaust of World War II,* p. 41–53, 89.

Cumings, Bruce, *Korea's Place in the Sun: a Modern History.* p. 177.

Robinson, Michael E., *Korea's Twentieth-Century Odyssey: A Short History,* p. 67, 77, 96.

Ward, Thomas J., and William D. Lay, *Park Statue Politics: World War II Comfort Women Memorials in the United States,* p. 16–17.

CHAPTER TEN

di Schino, June, "Kimchi: Ferment at the Heart of Korean Cuisine, from Local Identity to Global Consumption," p. 78–79.

KRPIA database, Korean Folklore Hall: Daily Life: Weaving, Laundering, Bleaching.

KRPIA database, Korean Folklore Hall: Food-Korean Diet: Reserved Food for Daily Use.

Lee, Eun-yi, "Mosi, Design Using Natural Fibers."

Weaving of Mosi (Fine Ramie) in the Hansan Region.

CHAPTER ELEVEN

Blakemore, Erin, "How Japan Took Control of Korea."

"Korea Under Japanese Rule."

Lee, Min-Jung, and Min-Ja Kim. "Dress and Ideology During the Late 19th and Early 20th Centuries Korea, 1876–1945," p. 23–24.

McClain, James L., *Japan, a Modern History*, p. 464.

Palmer, Brandon, "Imperial Japan's Preparations to Conscript Koreans as Soldiers, 1942—1945," p. 27, 73.

Robinson, Michael E., *Korea's Twentieth-Century Odyssey: A Short History*, p. 96.

Suzuki, Kazuko, "The State and Racialization: The Case of Koreans in Japan," p. 20–21.

CHAPTER TWELVE

Caprio, Mark, *Japanese Assimilation Policies in Colonial Korea, 1910-1945*, p. 134.

Lee, Gilsang, "School Textbooks: An Instance of Modernity Refracted by Colonialism and Tradition," p. 77–78, 81–85.

Suzuki, Kazuko, "The State and Racialization: The Case of Koreans in Japan," p. 24.

CHAPTER THIRTEEN

Cheon, Hye Sook, "Wedding Ceremony."

Choi, In Hak, "Wooden-goose Presenting Ceremony."

Clark, Donald N., *Culture and Customs of Korea*, p. 170.

Hong, Na Young, "Wedding Garments."

Park, Dong Chul, "Mutual Marriage Aid Association."

CHAPTER FOURTEEN

Arcado, Nickii Wantakan, "Visual Puppeteer: Japanese Propaganda During WWII."

Caprio, Mark, *Japanese Assimilation Policies in Colonial Korea, 1910-1945*, p. 67.

Isabella, Jude, "The Untold Story of Japan's First People."

"Japanese Announcement About the Attack at Pearl Harbor, 1941," p. 1.

Navarro, Anthony V., "A Critical Comparison Between Japanese and American Propaganda During World War II."

"Pacific War Timeline," New Zealand History.

Palmer, Brandon, "Imperial Japan's Preparations to Conscript Koreans as Soldiers, 1942–1945," p. 64–68.

"Pearl Harbor," History.com.

Park, Linda Sue, *When My Name Was Keoko*.

Suzuki, Kazuko, "The State and Racialization: The Case of Koreans in Japan," p. 24.

"The Pacific Strategy, 1941–1944."

CHAPTER FIFTEEN

Cumings, Bruce, *Korea's Place in the Sun: a Modern History*, p. 160, 197.

Nahm, Andrew C., and James E. Hoare, "Kim Gu."

Palmer, Brandon, "Imperial Japan's Preparations to Conscript Koreans as Soldiers, 1942–1945," p. 65–66.

Robinson, Michael E., *Korea's Twentieth-Century Odyssey: A Short History*, p. 77, 100.

Vannoy, Allyn, "Korea Under the Rising Sun."

CHAPTER SIXTEEN

Cumings, Bruce, *Origins of the Korean War, Vol. 1: Liberation and the Emergence of Separate Regimes, 1945–1947*, p. 388.

Korean Independence Day, Kyung Ju Korean and Hang Nam, Korea.

Lee, Jongsoo, *The Partition of Korea After World War II: A Global History*, p. 5–9, 37–39.

Revelations from the Russian Archives: The Soviet Union and the United States.

Robinson, Michael E., *Korea's Twentieth-Century Odyssey: A Short History*, p. 100.

Seth, Michael J., *A Concise History of Korea: From Antiquity to the Present*, p. 330–331.

The Voice of Hirohito—1945 Jewel Voice Broadcast.

CHAPTER EIGHTEEN

Glusman, John A., "Darkness Over Kobe."

"Japanese Naval Shipbuilding: 'Know Your Enemy!' "

"[POW Resources, Camplists, Osaka, Kobe, Kobe Bombing, 1945-06-05]."

Selden, Mark, "A Forgotten Holocaust: US Bombing Strategy, the Destruction of Japanese Cities & the American Way of War from World War II to Iraq."

Vannoy, Allyn, "Korea Under the Rising Sun."

CHAPTER NINETEEN

Candy Craftsmanship: Korea's First Family of a Classic Confection.

Cumings, Bruce, *Korea's Place in the Sun: a Modern History*, p. 185, 196.

Cumings, Bruce, *Origins of the Korean War, Vol. 1: Liberation and the Emergence of Separate Regimes, 1945-1947*, p. 388–389, 392–393, 398–401, 407.

Kim, Seong-bo, "The Decision-Making Process and Implementation of the North Korean Land Reform," p. 210, 222–223.

Lee, Chong-Sik, "Land Reform, Collectivisation and the Peasants in North Korea," p. 67–72.

Seth, Michael J., *A Concise History of Korea: From Antiquity to the Present*, p. 331–336.

US Army Area Handbook for Korea, p. 382–384.

CHAPTER TWENTY

Cathcart, Adam, and Charles Kraus, "Peripheral Influence: The Sinŭiju Student Incident of 1945 and the Impact of Soviet Occupation in North Korea," p. 9–10, 14–15.

Haga, Kai Yin Allison, "An Overlooked Dimension of the Korean War: The Role of Christianity and American Missionaries in the Rise of Korean Nationalism, Anti-Colonialism, and Eventual Civil War, 1884-1953," p. 159–162.

Kim, Michael Vince, "The Koreans of Kazakhstan."

Kim, Nam Sik. "The Impact of Japanese Colonial Rule (1910-1945) upon the Witness and Growth of the Korean Presbyterian Church," p. 33, 113–115.

Kim, Victoria, "Lost and Found in Uzbekistan: The Korean Story, Part 1."

Lee, Jongsoo, *The Partition of Korea After World War II: A Global History*, p. 26–27.

Seth, Michael J., *A Concise History of Korea: From Antiquity to the Present,* p. 332.

"Thank You Father Kim Il Sung": Eyewitness Accounts of Severe Violations of Freedom of Thought, Conscience, and Religion in North Korea, p. 64–66.

CHAPTER TWENTY-TWO

"The National Anthem—Aegukga."

CHAPTER TWENTY-FOUR

"A Pioneer of Liver Resection, Called the Korean Schweitzer."

"Trofim Lysenko," Encyclopædia Britannica.

CHAPTER TWENTY-FIVE

Acts 16:25-34.

Cheong, Connie Ockhee. *My Battle for Seoul, Summer, 1950*, p. 50.

Cumings, Bruce. *Korea's Place in the Sun: a Modern History*, p. 241–242.

Haga, Kai Yin Allison, "An Overlooked Dimension of the Korean War: The Role of Christianity and American Missionaries in the Rise of Korean Nationalism, Anti-Colonialism, and Eventual Civil War, 1884-1953," p. 289.

Lee, Jongsoo, *The Partition of Korea After World War II: A Global History*, p. 123.

Mobley, Richard A., "North Korea: How Did It Prepare for the 1950 Attack?", p. 2–3.

Robinson, Michael E., *Korea's Twentieth-Century Odyssey: A Short History*, p. 110.

"Thank You Father Kim Il Sung": Eyewitness Accounts of Severe Violations of Freedom of Thought, Conscience, and Religion in North Korea, p. 66.

CHAPTER TWENTY-SIX

Cheong, Connie Ockhee, *My Battle for Seoul, Summer, 1950*, p. 37.

Cumings, Bruce, *Korea's Place in the Sun: a Modern History*, p. 247–260.

Drain et al., "Incipient and Subclinical Tuberculosis: a Clinical Review of Early Stages and Progression of Infection."

Jager, Sheila Miyoshi, *Brothers at War: the Unending Conflict in Korea*, p. 119–121.

Mobley, Richard A., "North Korea: How Did It Prepare for the 1950 Attack?", p. 6–7.

Yup, Paik Sun, *From Pusan to Panmunjom: Wartime Memoirs of the Republic of Korea's First Four-Star General*, p. 30–37, 78.

CHAPTER TWENTY-SEVEN

Hastings, Max, *The Korean War*, p. 130.

Sides, Hampton. *On Desperate Ground: The Marines at the Reservoir, the Korean War's Greatest Battle*, p. 14, 29, 66.

Yup, Paik Sun, *From Pusan to Panmunjom: Wartime Memoirs of the Republic of Korea's First Four-Star General*, p. 85, 99–100

CHAPTER TWENTY-EIGHT

Digital Horizons database: Korean War Propaganda Leaflets (NDSU).

Sides, Hampton, *On Desperate Ground: The Marines at the Reservoir, the Korean War's Greatest Battle*, p. 39–40.

CHAPTER TWENTY-NINE

Hastings, Max, *The Korean War*, p. 140.

Jager, Sheila Miyoshi, *Brothers at War: the Unending Conflict in Korea*, p. 110, 192, 226–229.

"The Korean War Chronology."

Toland, John, *In Mortal Combat, Korea, 1950-1953*, p. 244–248, 275–280.

Yup, Paik Sun, *From Pusan to Panmunjom: Wartime Memoirs of the Republic of Korea's First Four-Star General*, p. 110.

CHAPTER THIRTY

Choe, Sang-Hun, Charles J. Hanley, and Martha Mendoza, "War's Hidden Chapter: Ex-GIs Tell of Killing Korean Refugees."

Koh, B. C., "The War's Impact on the Korean Peninsula," p. 58.

CHAPTER THIRTY-TWO

Yup, Paik Sun, *From Pusan to Panmunjom: Wartime Memoirs of the Republic of Korea's First Four-Star General*, p. 132.

CHAPTER THIRTY-THREE

Allen, Richard C., *Korea's Syngman Rhee, an Unauthorized Portrait*, p. 138–139.

Choe, Sang-Hun, "Memories of Massacres Were Long Suppressed Here. Tourists Now Retrace the Atrocities."

Jager, Sheila Miyoshi, *Brothers at War: the Unending Conflict in Korea*, p. 231.

Kim, Janice C.H., "'Pusan at War: Refuge, Relief, and Resettlement in the Temporary Capital, 1950–1953,'" p. 103–106, 114–120

Merrill, John, "The Cheju-Do Rebellion," p. 167–169.

"Syngman Rhee," Encyclopædia Britannica.

Yea, Sallie, "Maps of Resistance and Geographies of Dissent in the Chŏlla Region of South Korea," p. 76.

Yup, Paik Sun. *From Pusan to Panmunjom: Wartime Memoirs of the Republic of Korea's First Four-Star General*, p. 14.

CHAPTER THIRTY-FOUR

Kim, Janice C.H., "'Pusan at War: Refuge, Relief, and Resettlement in the Temporary Capital, 1950–1953,'" p. 122–125.

Lankov, Andrei. "January 1951: Life of Korean War Refugees in Busan."

CHAPTER THIRTY-SIX

Hawk, Alan J., "8228th Mobile Army Surgical Hospital, Epidemic Hemorrhagic Fever Center."

LeDuc et al., "Hemorrhagic Fever with Renal Syndrome: Past Accomplishments and Future Challenges."

CHAPTER THIRTY-SEVEN

Jager, Sheila Miyoshi, *Brothers at War: the Unending Conflict in Korea,* p. 306, 416–417, 420–426.

Koh, B. C., "The War's Impact on the Korean Peninsula," p. 57–59.

Korean Currency, p. 10.

Toland, John, *In Mortal Combat, Korea, 1950–1953,* p. 554.

EPILOGUE

Moon, William J., "The Origins of the Great North Korean Famine: Its Dynamics and Normative Implications," p. 106.

APPENDIX

CHAPTER ONE

Baker, Don. "A Slippery, Changing Concept: How Korean New Religions Define Religion." *Journal of Korean Religions*1, no. 1/2 (2010): 57–91. http://www.jstor.org/stable/23943286.

Beaver, R. Pierce. "Chondogyo and Korea." *Journal of Bible and Religion*30, no. 2 (1962): 115–22. http://www.jstor.org/stable/1459740.

"Ch'ŏndogyo." Encyclopædia Britannica. https://www.britannica.com/topic/Chondogyo.

Chung, Ah-young. "Chondogyo: From Social Movement to Spiritual Practices." The Korea Times, February 28, 2011. http://www.koreatimes.co.kr/www/news/culture/2013/08/293_82197.html.

Clark, Donald N. *Culture and Customs of Korea*. Westport, Connecticut: Greenwood Press, 2000.

Hong, Na Young. "Wedding Garments." Encyclopedia of Korean Folk Culture. National Folk Museum of Korea. https://folkency.nfm.go.kr/en/topic/detail/533.

In the Land of the Morning Calm (Im Lande Der Morgenstille). *The National Association for Korean Schools*, 2014. https://

www.naks.org/jml/library-history-culture/776-norbert-
weber-1870-1956.

Kang, Jae Chul. "Bridal Palanquin." Encyclopedia of Korean Folk
Culture. National Folk Museum of Korea. https://folkency.
nfm.go.kr/en/topic/detail/289.

Park, Dong Chul. "Bride's Post-Wedding Journey to the Groom's
Home." Encyclopedia of Korean Folk Culture. National
Folk Museum of Korea. http://folkency.nfm.go.kr/en/topic/
detail/294.

Park, Sung Yong. "Arrangement of Marriage." Encyclopedia
of Korean Folk Culture. National Folk Museum of Korea.
https://folkency.nfm.go.kr/en/topic/detail/353.

CHAPTER THREE

Baldwin, Frank Prentiss, Jr. "The March First Movement:
Korean Challenge and Japanese Response." Order No.
7220026, Columbia University, 1969. https://www.proquest.
com/dissertations-theses/march-first-movement-korean-
challenge-japanese/docview/288040533/se-2?accountid=9758.

"Diary Entry Reveals Japanese Cover-up of Massacre."
Hankyoreh, March 1, 2007. http://english.hani.co.kr/arti/
english_edition/e_international/193609.html.

"Division of Korea." Encyclopædia Britannica. https://www.
britannica.com/place/Korea/Division-of-Korea.

Han, Jeon. "God-Sent Angel for Korea's Independence." Korea.
Korean Culture and Information Service, April 2019. https://
www.kocis.go.kr/eng/webzine/201904/sub05.html.

Kang, Jang-seok. "Spiritual and Practical Assets of Korean
Nonviolence." Essay. In *Nonkilling Korea: Six Culture
Exploration*, edited by Glenn D. Paige and Chung-Si
Ahn, 1st ed., 29–47. Honolulu, Hawaii: Centre for Global
Nonkilling, 2012.

Korean Independence Outbreak Collection. The Burke Library Archives (Columbia University Libraries). http://www.columbia.edu/cgi-bin/cul/resolve?clio7688161.

"Korean Provisional Government." Encyclopædia Britannica. https://www.britannica.com/topic/Korean-Provisional-Government.

"Koreans Protest Japanese Control in the 'March 1st Movement,' 1919." Global Nonviolent Action Database. Swarthmore College. https://nvdatabase.swarthmore.edu/content/koreans-protest-japanese-control-march-1st-movement-1919.

Lee, Jongsoo. *The Partition of Korea After World War II: A Global History.* New York, New York: Palgrave Macmillan, 2006.

"March First Movement." Encyclopædia Britannica. https://www.britannica.com/event/March-First-Movement.

Shin, Gi-Wook and Rennie Moon. "1919 in Korea: National Resistance and Contending Legacies." *The Journal of Asian Studies* 78, no. 2 (05, 2019): 399-408, https://www.proquest.com/scholarly-journals/1919-korea-national-resistance-contending/docview/2222623362/se-2?accountid=9758.

Sihn, Kyu Hwan. "'The 34th National Representative,' Dr. Frank W. Schofield (1889-1970)." Yonsei Medical Journal. Yonsei University College of Medicine, April 2019. https://www.ncbi.nlm.nih.gov/pmc/articles/PMC6433573/.

Weber, Greta. "How an Obsolete Copy Machine Started a Revolution." National Geographic. National Geographic, June 24, 2016. https://www.nationalgeographic.com/adventure/article/mimeo-mimeograph-revolution-literature-beat-poetry-activism#close.

"3.1운동 대한민국임시정부 100주년 기념사업위원회." Ministry of Public Administration and Security: National Presidential Archives. http://19together100.pa.go.kr/lay2/S1T9C38/contents.do.

CHAPTER FOUR

Clark, Donald N. *Culture and Customs of Korea*. Westport, Connecticut: Greenwood Press, 2000.

"Economy of North Korea." Encyclopædia Britannica. https://www.britannica.com/place/North-Korea/Economy.

Foreign Areas Studies Division of The American University. *US Army Area Handbook for Korea*. Washington, DC: US Gov. Printing Office, 1964.

KRPIA database, Korean Folklore Hall: Contents of Folk Songs: https://www-krpia-co-kr.revproxy.brown.edu/viewer/open?plctId=PLCT00004523&nodeId=NODE03999972&medaId=MEDA04105230.

Man-young, Hahn. "Folk Songs of Korean Rural Life and Their Characteristics Based on the Rice Farming Songs." *Asian Music*9, no. 2 (1978): 21–28. https://doi.org/10.2307/833753.

Park, Soon. "Rice Planting Game." Encyclopedia of Korean Folk Culture. National Folk Museum of Korea. Accessed September 27, 2021. https://folkency.nfm.go.kr/en/topic/detail/3794.

"Rice Paddy Song" Farmers' Song, Timeless Values/Korean Culture. YouTube. MBC Chungbuk, 2019. https://www.youtube.com/watch?v=uyywZPtuJpg.

Tudor, Daniel, NK News, and Andrei Lankov. *Ask A North Korean: Defectors Talk About Their Lives Inside the World's Most Secretive Nation*. La Vergne: Tuttle Publishing, 2018.

CHAPTER FIVE

"Aspects of Society in the 1920s." Photo Collection relating to Modern Korea and Contemporary History. http://contents.history.go.kr/photo/1920/1920_period04_01.do?lang=en#.

Kim, Hyokyung. "Ssireum." Encyclopedia of Korean Folk Culture. National Folk Museum of Korea. https://folkency.nfm.go.kr/en/topic/detail/1570.

Kim, Jongdae. "Dano Amulets." Encyclopedia of Korean Folk Culture. National Folk Museum of Korea. https://folkency. nfm.go.kr/en/topic/detail/3533.

Kim, Sun Poong. "Festival of the Fifth of the Fifth Month." Encyclopedia of Korean Folk Culture. National Folk Museum of Korea. https://folkency.nfm.go.kr/en/topic/detail/3529.

Ssireum, Traditional Wrestling in the Republic of Korea. YouTube. The Cultural Heritage Administration, 2018. https://www. youtube.com/watch?v=Vy1PFvDCEoQ.

CHAPTER SIX

KRPIA database, Korean Folklore Hall: Food-Kitchen Utensils: Utensils for Cooking. https://www-krpia-co-kr.revproxy. brown.edu/viewer/open?plctId=PLCT00004523&no-deId=NODE03999972&medaId=MEDA04105230

CHAPTER SEVEN

Caprio, Mark. *Japanese Assimilation Policies in Colonial Korea, 1910-1945.* 1st ed. Seattle: University of Washington Press, 2009.

Giles, Herbert A, trans. "Elementary Chinese, Three Character Classic." Shanghai, 1910.

Hatada, Takashi. *A History of Korea.* Santa Barbara, Calif: ABC-Clio, 1969.

Lee, Hong Yung, Sorensen, Clark W., Sorensen, Clark W, and Ha, Yong-Chool, eds. *Colonial Rule and Social Change in Korea, 1910-1945.* Seattle: University of Washington Press, 2013. Accessed October 5, 2021. ProQuest Ebook Central.

Seth, Michael J. *Education Fever: Society, Politics, and the Pursuit of Schooling in South Korea.* Honolulu: University of Hawai'i Press and Center for Korean Studies, University of Hawai'i, 2002.

Shillony, Ben-Ami. "Universities and Students in Wartime Japan." *The Journal of Asian Studies* 45, no. 4 (1986): 769–87. https://doi.org/10.2307/2056086.

Taylor, Insup, and M. Martin Taylor. *Writing and Literacy in Chinese, Korean and Japanese: Revised Edition.* Amsterdam/Philadelphia: John Benjamins Publishing Company, 2014.

Toby, Ronald. "Education in Korea under the Japanese: Attitudes and Manifestations." *Occasional Papers on Korea*, no. 1 (1974): 55–64. http://www.jstor.org/stable/41490120.

CHAPTER NINE

Blakemore, Erin. "How Japan Took Control of Korea." History.com. A&E Television Networks, February 27, 2018. https://www.history.com/news/japan-colonization-korea.

Blakemore, Erin. "The Brutal History of Japan's 'Comfort Women'." History.com. A&E Television Networks, February 20, 2018. https://www.history.com/news/comfort-women-japan-military-brothels-korea.

Caprio, Mark. *Japanese Assimilation Policies in Colonial Korea, 1910-1945.* 1st ed. Seattle: University of Washington Press, 2009.

Chang, Iris. *The Rape of Nanking: The Forgotten Holocaust of World War II.* Basic Books, 1997.

Clark, Donald N. *Culture and Customs of Korea.* Westport, Connecticut: Greenwood Press, 2000.

Cumings, Bruce. *Korea's Place in the Sun: A Modern History.* New York: W.W. Norton, 2005.

Hatada, Takashi. *A History of Korea.* Santa Barbara, Calif: ABC-Clio, 1969.

Kim, Suzy. *Everyday Life in the North Korean Revolution, 1945-1950.* Ithaca: Cornell University Press, 2013.

"Korea Under Japanese Rule." US Library of Congress. http://countrystudies.us/south-korea/7.htm.

Lee, Hong Yung, Sorensen, Clark W., Sorensen, Clark W, and Ha, Yong-Chool, eds. *Colonial Rule and Social Change in Korea, 1910-1945.* Seattle: University of Washington Press, 2013. Accessed October 5, 2021. ProQuest Ebook Central.

McClain, James L. *Japan, a Modern History* 1st ed. New York: W.W. Norton & Co., 2002.

Robinson, Michael E. *Korea's Twentieth-Century Odyssey: A Short History.* Honolulu: University of Hawaii Press, 2007.

"Second Sino-Japanese War." Encyclopædia Britannica. Encyclopædia Britannica, inc. Accessed September 27, 2021. https://www.britannica.com/event/Second-Sino-Japanese-War.

Ward, Thomas J., and William D. Lay. *Park Statue Politics: World War II Comfort Women Memorials in the United States.* Bristol, England: E-International Relations Publishing, 2019.

CHAPTER TEN

"Aspects of Society in the 1920s." Photo Collection relating to Modern Korea and Contemporary History. http://contents.history.go.kr/photo/1920/1920_period04_01.do?lang=en#.

Cho, Jae-eun. "Weaving Way of Life Faces Extinction." Korea JoongAng Daily, July 22, 2007. https://koreajoongangdaily.joins.com/2007/07/22/features/Weaving-way-of-life-faces-extinction/2878310.html.

Clark, Donald N. *Culture and Customs of Korea.*Westport, Connecticut: Greenwood Press, 2000.

"Contemporary Hemp Weaving in Korea." DigitalCommons@ University of Nebraska—Lincoln, 2006. https://digitalcommons.unl.edu/tsaconf/347.

di Schino, June. "Kimchi: Ferment at the Heart of Korean Cuisine, from Local Identity to Global Consumption." Essay. In *Cured, Smoked, and Fermented: Proceedings of the Oxford Symposium on Food*, edited by Helen Saberi, 76–83. Totnes, Great Britain: Prospect Books, 2011.

Korea Foundation. *Traditional Food: A Taste of Korean Life*. Seoul: Seoul Selection, 2010.

KRPIA database, Korean Folklore Hall: Daily Life: Weaving, Laundering, Bleaching. https://www-krpia-co-kr.revproxy.brown.edu/viewer/open?plctId=PLCT00004523&nodeId=NODE03999972&medaId=MEDA04105230

KRPIA database, Korean Folklore Hall: Food-Korean Diet: Reserved Food for Daily Use. https://www-krpia-co-kr.revproxy.brown.edu/viewer/open?plctId=PLCT00004523&nodeId=NODE03999972&medaId=MEDA04105230.

KRPIA database, Korean Folklore Hall: Food-Special Food: Ceremonial Food. https://www-krpia-co-kr.revproxy.brown.edu/viewer/open?plctId=PLCT00004523&nodeId=NODE03999972&medaId=MEDA04105230.

Lee, Eun-yi. "Mosi, Design Using Natural Fibers." Korea. Korean Culture and Information Service, July 2018. https://www.kocis.go.kr/eng/webzine/201807/sub06.html.

Traditional Korean Food. Socialism on Film: The Cold War and International Propaganda. Adam Matthew. http://www.socialismonfilm.amdigital.co.uk.revproxy.brown.edu/Documents/Details/N_508421_TRADITIONAL_KOREAN_FOOD#MediaSummary.

Weaving of Mosi (Fine Ramie) in the Hansan Region. YouTube. UNESCO, 2011. https://www.youtube.com/watch?v=AUpXye1YjsY.

[100 Icons of Korean Culture] Kimchi (김치). YouTube. Arirang TV, 2013. https://www.youtube.com/watch?v=d_poOs92te8.

CHAPTER ELEVEN

Blakemore, Erin. "How Japan Took Control of Korea." History. com. A&E Television Networks, February 27, 2018. https://www.history.com/news/japan-colonization-korea.

"Korea Under Japanese Rule." US Library of Congress. http://countrystudies.us/south-korea/7.htm.

Lee, Min-Jung, and Min-Ja Kim. "Dress and Ideology During the Late 19th and Early 20th Centuries Korea, 1876–1945." *International Journal of Costume and Fashion*11, no. 1 (June 2011): 15–33. https://doi.org/10.7233/ijcf.2011.11.1.015.

McClain, James L. *Japan, a Modern History* 1st ed. New York: W.W. Norton & Co., 2002.

Palmer, Brandon. "Imperial Japan's Preparations to Conscript Koreans as Soldiers, 1942—1945." *Korean Studies*31 (2007): 63–78. http://www.jstor.org/stable/23720161.

Robinson, Michael E. *Korea's Twentieth-Century Odyssey: A Short History*. Honolulu: University of Hawaii Press, 2007.

Suzuki, Kazuko. "The State and Racialization: The Case of Koreans in Japan." Center for Comparative Immigration Studies, UCSD, February 2003.

CHAPTER TWELVE

Caprio, Mark. *Japanese Assimilation Policies in Colonial Korea, 1910-1945*. 1st ed. Seattle: University of Washington Press, 2009.

Cushman, Stephen, and Roland Greene. *The Princeton Handbook of World Poetries* [Enhanced Credo edition]. Princeton, NJ: Princeton University Press, 2016.

Kim, Soyoung. "Textbook Inspection and Censorship in Korea during the Protectorate Period: A Study of Inspection Copies

of Textbooks Compiled by the Young Korean Academy."
International Journal of Korean History. The Center for
Korean History, August 31, 2016. https://doi.org/10.22372/
ijkh.2016.08.21.2.79.

Lee, Gilsang. "School Textbooks: An Instance of Modernity
Refracted by Colonialism and Tradition." *Korean Studies* 37
(2013): 79–98. http://www.jstor.org/stable/24575277.

Lee, Hong Yung, Sorensen, Clark W., Sorensen, Clark W, and Ha,
Yong-Chool, eds. *Colonial Rule and Social Change in Korea,
1910-1945.* Seattle: University of Washington Press, 2013.
Accessed October 5, 2021. ProQuest Ebook Central.

Seth, Michael J. *Education Fever: Society, Politics, and the Pursuit
of Schooling in South Korea*Honolulu: University of Hawai'i
Press and Center for Korean Studies, University of Hawai'i,
2002.

Suzuki, Kazuko. "The State and Racialization: The Case of Koreans in Japan." Center for Comparative Immigration Studies,
UCSD, February 2003.

Wray, Harold J. "A Study in Contrasts. Japanese School Textbooks of 1903 and 1941-5." *Monumenta Nipponica* 28, no. 1
(1973): 69–86. https://doi.org/10.2307/2383934.

CHAPTER THIRTEEN

Cheon, Hye Sook. "Wedding Ceremony." Encyclopedia of Korean
Folk Culture. National Folk Museum of Korea. https://
folkency.nfm.go.kr/en/topic/detail/101.

Choi, In Hak. "Wooden-goose Presenting Ceremony." Encyclopedia of Korean Folk Culture. National Folk Museum of Korea.
https://folkency.nfm.go.kr/en/topic/detail/384.

Clark, Donald N. *Culture and Customs of Korea.* Westport, Connecticut: Greenwood Press, 2000.

Hong, Na Young. "Wedding Garments." Encyclopedia of Korean Folk Culture. National Folk Museum of Korea. https://folkency.nfm.go.kr/en/topic/detail/533.

Park, Dong Chul. "Bride's Post-Wedding Journey to the Groom's Home." Encyclopedia of Korean Folk Culture. National Folk Museum of Korea. http://folkency.nfm.go.kr/en/topic/detail/294.

Park, Dong Chul. "Mutual Marriage Aid Association." Encyclopedia of Korean Folk Culture. National Folk Museum of Korea. https://folkency.nfm.go.kr/en/topic/detail/538.

CHAPTER FOURTEEN

Arcado, Nickii Wantakan. "Visual Puppeteer: Japanese Propaganda During WWII." Pacific Atrocities Education. Pacific Atrocities Education, January 2019. https://www.pacificatrocities.org/blog/visual-puppeteer-japanese-propaganda-during-world-war-ii.

Caprio, Mark. *Japanese Assimilation Policies in Colonial Korea, 1910-1945.* 1st ed. Seattle: University of Washington Press, 2009.

Cumings, Bruce. *Korea's Place in the Sun: a Modern History.* New York: W.W. Norton, 2005.

Howell, David L. "Making 'Useful Citizens' of Ainu Subjects in Early Twentieth-Century Japan." *The Journal of Asian Studies*63, no. 1 (2004): 5–29. http://www.jstor.org/stable/4133292.

Isabella, Jude. "The Untold Story of Japan's First People." Sapiens. Sapiens, October 25, 2017. https://www.sapiens.org/archaeology/ainu-prejudice-pride/.

"Japanese Announcement About the Attack at Pearl Harbor, 1941." The Gilder Lehrman Institute of American History,

2018. https://www.gilderlehrman.org/sites/default/
files/09552.01_SPS_0.pdf.

"Japanese Propaganda during World War II." World Heritage
Encyclopedia. http://community.worldheritage.org/article/
WHEBN0005934518/Japanese%20propaganda%20during%20
World%20War%20II.

"Kuril Islands." Encyclopædia Britannica. Encyclopædia
Britannica, inc., 2012. https://www.britannica.com/place/
Kuril-Islands.

Kuzmarov, Jeremy. "The Korean War: Barbarism Unleashed."
United States Foreign Policy History and Resource Guide
website, 2016. http://peacehistory-usfp.org/korean-war/.

Navarro, Anthony V. "A Critical Comparison Between Japanese
and American Propaganda During World War II." Michigan
State University. Accessed September 28, 2021. https://www.
msu.edu/~navarro6/srop. html.

"Pacific War Timeline." New Zealand History. New Zealand
Ministry for Culture and Heritage. https://nzhistory.govt.nz/
war/second-world-war/war-in-the-pacific/timeline.

Palmer, Brandon. "Imperial Japan's Preparations to Conscript
Koreans as Soldiers, 1942–1945." *Korean Studies* 31 (2007):
63–78. http://www.jstor.org/stable/23720161.

Park, Linda Sue. *When My Name Was Keoko*. Australia: University of Queensland Press, 2013.

"Pearl Harbor." History.com. A&E Television Networks, October 29, 2009. https://www.history.com/topics/world-war-ii/
pearl-harbor.

Suzuki, Kazuko. "The State and Racialization: The Case of
Koreans in Japan." Center for Comparative Immigration
Studies, UCSD, February 2003.

"The Pacific Strategy, 1941-1944." The National World War
II Museum New Orleans. Accessed September 28, 2021.

https://www.nationalww2museum.org/war/articles/pacific-strategy-1941-1944.

Vannoy, Allyn. "Korea Under the Rising Sun." Warfare History Network. https://warfarehistorynetwork.com/2016/09/29/korea-under-the-rising-sun/.

CHAPTER FIFTEEN

Cumings, Bruce. *Korea's Place in the Sun: a Modern History.* New York: W.W. Norton, 2005.

Hoare, James. "Korean Leaders in 1945." End of Empire. Nordic Institute of Asian Studies. http://www.endofempire.asia/1010-2-korean-leaders-in-1945-3/.

Lankov, Andrei. "What Happened to Kim Ku." The Korea Times. http://www.koreatimes.co.kr/www/nation/2020/07/165_30545.html.

Nahm, Andrew C., and James E. Hoare. "Kim Gu." Modern Korean History Portal. Wilson Center Digital Archive. https://digitalarchive.wilsoncenter.org/resource/modern-korean-history-portal/kim-gu.

Palmer, Brandon. "Imperial Japan's Preparations to Conscript Koreans as Soldiers, 1942–1945." *Korean Studies* 31 (2007): 63–78. http://www.jstor.org/stable/23720161.

Robinson, Michael E. *Korea's Twentieth-Century Odyssey: A Short History.* Honolulu: University of Hawaii Press, 2007.

"Syngman Rhee." Encyclopædia Britannica. Encyclopædia Britannica, inc. https://www.britannica.com/biography/Syngman-Rhee.

Vannoy, Allyn. "Korea Under the Rising Sun." Warfare History Network. https://warfarehistorynetwork.com/2016/09/29/korea-under-the-rising-sun/.

CHAPTER SIXTEEN

"Audio of an Historic Speech Japan's Emperor Gave at the End of World War II Was Just Released in Digital Form." Business Insider. Business Insider, August 1, 2015. https://www.businessinsider.com/audio-of-an-historic-speech-japans-emperor-gave-at-the-end-of-world-war-ii-was-just-released-in-digital-form-2015-8.

Cumings, Bruce. *Origins of the Korean War, Vol. 1: Liberation and the Emergence of Separate Regimes, 1945-1947.* Princeton, New Jersey: Princeton University Press, 1981.

Glantz, David M. *August Storm: The Soviet 1945 Strategic Offensive in Manchuria* Fort Leavenworth, Kan: Combat Studies Institute, US Army Command and General Staff College, 1983.

Korean Independence Day, Kyung Ju Korean and Hang Nam, Korea. National Archives Catalog. National Archives and Records Administration. https://catalog.archives.gov/id/21029.

Lee, Jongsoo. *The Partition of Korea After World War II: A Global History.* New York, New York: Palgrave Macmillan, 2006.

Lee, Soomi. "Portrait of Yi Chae: Curator's Picks." National Museum of Korea. https://www.museum.go.kr/site/eng/archive/united/14949.

Mankoff, Jeff. "The Legacy of the Soviet Offensives of August 1945." Asia Maritime Transparency Initiative, August 13, 2015. https://amti.csis.org/the-legacy-of-the-soviet-offensives-of-august-1945/.

Park, Lalien Guillen. "The Day of the Restoration of Light." Korea.net. Korean Culture and Information Service, August 15, 2017. https://www.korea.net/NewsFocus/Society/view?articleId=148499.

Prefer, Nathan N. "The Soviet Invasion of Manchuria Led to Japan's Greatest Defeat." Warfare History Network. https://warfarehistorynetwork.com/2020/01/07/the-soviet-invasion-of-manchuria-led-to-japans-greatest-defeat/.

Revelations from the Russian Archives: The Soviet Union and the United States. Exhibitions. From the Library of Congress, https://www.loc.gov/exhibits/archives/sovi.html.

Robinson, Michael E. *Korea's Twentieth-Century Odyssey: A Short History.* Honolulu: University of Hawaii Press, 2007.

Seth, Michael J. *A Concise History of Korea: From Antiquity to the Present.* 2nd ed. Lanham, Maryland: Rowman & Littlefield, 2016.

The Voice of Hirohito—1945 Jewel Voice Broadcast. Historical Recordings, 2019. https://www.youtube.com/watch?v=Fn-Mk1Vhg10M.

CHAPTER EIGHTEEN

"Deadly WWII Firebombings of Japanese Cities Largely Ignored." Tampa Bay Times. Tampa Bay Times, March 9, 2015. https://www.tampabay.com/news/military/war/deadly-wwii-firebombings-of-japanese-cities-largely-ignored/2220606/.

Glusman, John A. "Darkness Over Kobe." HistoryNet. HistoryNet. https://www.historynet.com/darkness-over-kobe.htm.

"Japanese Naval Shipbuilding: 'Know Your Enemy!'" Naval History and Heritage Command. Naval History and Heritage Command, April 8, 2020. https://www.history.navy.mil/research/library/online-reading-room/title-list-alphabetically/j/japanese-naval-shipbuilding.html.

"[POW Resources, Camplists, Osaka, Kobe, Kobe Bombing, 1945-06-05]." Photographs. From the Center for Research Allied POWS Under the Japanese. Sponsored by Roger Mansell, Palo

Alto, California, http://www.mansell.com/pow_resources/
camplists/osaka/kobe/Kobe_bombing_1945-06-05.pdf.

Robinson, Michael E. *Korea's Twentieth-Century Odyssey: A Short
History*. Honolulu: University of Hawaii Press, 2007.

Selden, Mark. "A Forgotten Holocaust: US Bombing Strategy,
the Destruction of Japanese Cities & the American Way of
War from World War II to Iraq." *The Asia-Pacific Journal:
Japan Focus*, no. 5 (May 2, 2007). https://apjjf.org/-Mark-
Selden/2414/article.html.

Vannoy, Allyn. "Korea Under the Rising Sun." Warfare History
Network. https://warfarehistorynetwork.com/2016/09/29/
korea-under-the-rising-sun/.

CHAPTER NINETEEN

Candy Craftsmanship: Korea's First Family of a Classic Confection.
YouTube. Great Big Story, 2017. https://www.youtube.com/
watch?v=KB4RXPOuMik.

Cumings, Bruce. *Korea's Place in the Sun: a Modern History*. New
York: W.W. Norton, 2005.

Cumings, Bruce. *Origins of the Korean War, Vol. 1: Liberation and
the Emergence of Separate Regimes, 1945-1947*. Princeton, New
Jersey: Princeton University Press, 1981.

Foreign Areas Studies Division of The American University. *US
Army Area Handbook for Korea*. Washington, DC: US Gov.
Printing Office, 1964.

Kim, Seong-bo. "The Decision-Making Process and Implementa-
tion of the North Korean Land Reform." Essay. In *Landlords,
Peasants and Intellectuals in Modern Korea*, edited by Kie-
Chung Pang and Michael D. Shin, 207–41. Ithaca, New York:
Cornell University East Asia Program, 2005.

Kim, Suzy. *Everyday Life in the North Korean Revolution, 1945-1950*. Ithaca: Cornell University Press, 2013.

KRPIA database, Korean Folklore Hall: Food-Substitute Food in Time of Famine. https://www-krpia-co-kr.revproxy. brown.edu/viewer/open?plctId=PLCT00004523&nodeId=NODE03999972&medaId=MEDA04105230.

Lee, Chong-Sik. "Land Reform, Collectivisation and the Peasants in North Korea." *The China Quarterly*, no. 14 (1963): 65–81. http://www.jstor.org/stable/651343.

Seth, Michael J. *A Concise History of Korea: From Antiquity to the Present*. 2nd ed. Lanham, Maryland: Rowman & Littlefield, 2016.

"Soviet Report on Communists in Korea, 1945." Wilson Center Digital Archive. https://digitalarchive.wilsoncenter.org/ document/114890.

Stueck, William. "The United States, the Soviet Union, and the Division of Korea: A Comparative Approach." *The Journal of American-East Asian Relations* 4, no. 1 (1995): 1–27. http:// www.jstor.org/stable/23612581.

Tudor, Daniel. *Ask a North Korean: Defectors Talk About Their Lives Inside the World's Most Secretive Nation*. Tuttle Publishing, 2017.

US Army Area Handbook for Korea. Foreign Areas Studies Division of The American University. Washington, DC: US Gov. Printing Office, 1964.

CHAPTER TWENTY

Cathcart, Adam, and Charles Kraus. "Peripheral Influence: The Sinaŭiju Student Incident of 1945 and the Impact of Soviet Occupation in North Korea." *The Journal of Korean Studies* 13, no. 1 (2008): 1–27. http://www.jstor.org/stable/41490245.

Cumings, Bruce. *Korea's Place in the Sun: A Modern History*. New York: W.W. Norton, 2005.

Garon, Sheldon M. "State and Religion in Imperial Japan, 1912-1945." *Journal of Japanese Studies*12, no. 2 (1986): 273–302. https://doi.org/10.2307/132389.

Haga, Kai Yin Allison. "An Overlooked Dimension of the Korean War: The Role of Christianity and American Missionaries in the Rise of Korean Nationalism, Anti-Colonialism, and Eventual Civil War, 1884-1953." *Dissertations, Theses, and Masters Projects*. Paper 1539623326. W&M ScholarWorks. College of William and Mary, 2007. https://dx.doi.org/doi:10.21220/s2-q887-wf52.

Kim, Michael Vince. "The Koreans of Kazakhstan." LensCulture. https://www.lensculture.com/projects/106511-the-koreans-of-kazakhstan.

Kim, Nam Sik. "The Impact of Japanese Colonial Rule (1910-1945) upon the Witness and Growth of the Korean Presbyterian Church." ThD diss., University of Stellenbosh, 2000.

Kim, Sung-Gun. "The Shinto Shrine Issue in Korean Christianity Under Japanese Colonialism." *Journal of Church and State*39, no. 3 (1997): 503–21. http://www.jstor.org/stable/23921260.

Kim, Victoria. "Lost and Found in Uzbekistan: The Korean Story, Part 1." The Diplomat, June 8, 2016. https://thediplomat.com/2016/06/lost-and-found-in-uzbekistan-the-korean-story-part-1/.

Lee, Jongsoo. *The Partition of Korea After World War II: A Global History*. New York, New York: Palgrave Macmillan, 2006.

Ryu, Dae Young. "Fresh Wineskins for New Wine: A New Perspective on North Korean Christianity." *Journal of Church and State* 48, no. 3 (2006): 659–75. http://www.jstor.org/stable/23921666.

Seth, Michael J. *A Concise History of Korea: From Antiquity to the Present.* 2nd ed. Lanham, Maryland: Rowman & Littlefield, 2016.

Suzuki, Kazuko. "The State and Racialization: The Case of Koreans in Japan." Center for Comparative Immigration Studies, UCSD, February 2003.

"Thank You Father Kim Il Sung": Eyewitness Accounts of Severe Violations of Freedom of Thought, Conscience, and Religion in North Korea. Washington, DC: US Commission on International Religious Freedom, 2005.

CHAPTER TWENTY-ONE

Clark, Donald N. *Culture and Customs of Korea.* Westport, Connecticut: Greenwood Press, 2000.

CHAPTER TWENTY-TWO

"The National Anthem—Aegukga." National Administration. Korean Ministry of the Interior and Safety. Accessed September 30, 2021. https://mois.go.kr/eng/sub/a03/nationalSymbol_2/screen.do.

CHAPTER TWENTY-FOUR

"A Pioneer of Liver Resection, Called the Korean Schweitzer." Persons of Distinguished Service to Science and Technology. http://www.iassf.or.kr/eng/merit/merit-list/?boardId=bbs_0000000000000051&mode=view&cntId=45&category=2018&pageIdx=.

Borinskaya, Svetlana A, Andrei I Ermolaev, and Eduard I Kolchinsky. "Lysenkoism Against Genetics: The Meeting of the Lenin All-Union Academy of Agricultural Sciences of August 1948, Its Background, Causes, and Aftermath." *Genetics*

212, no. 1 (May 1, 2019): 1–12. https://doi.org/10.1534/genet-ics.118.301413.

Grafting Apple Trees Onto Root Stock. YouTube. YouTube, 2018. https://www.youtube.com/watch?v=AEWciboGN_w.

Heo, Yun Jung, and Young Soo Cho. "Formation of Medical Education in North Korea: 1945-1948." *Korean Journal of Medical History* 23, no. 2 (August 31, 2014): 239–68. https://doi.org/10.13081/kjmh.2014.23.239.

"Trofim Lysenko." Encyclopædia Britannica. Encyclopædia Britannica, inc. Accessed September 30, 2021. https://www.britannica.com/biography/Trofim-Lysenko.

CHAPTER TWENTY-FIVE

Cheong, Connie Ockhee. *My Battle for Seoul, Summer, 1950.* Seoul, Korea, Seoul, Korea: Geulnurim, 2011.

Cumings, Bruce. *Korea's Place in the Sun: A Modern History.* New York: W.W. Norton, 2005.

Haga, Kai Yin Allison. "An Overlooked Dimension of the Korean War: The Role of Christianity and American Missionaries in the Rise of Korean Nationalism, Anti-Colonialism, and Eventual Civil War, 1884-1953." W&M ScholarWorks. College of William and Mary, 2007. https://dx.doi.org/doi:10.21220/s2-q887-wf52.

Lee, Jongsoo. *The Partition of Korea After World War II: A Global History.* New York, New York: Palgrave Macmillan, 2006.

Mobley, Richard A. "North Korea: How Did It Prepare for the 1950 Attack?" *Army History,* no. 49 (2000): 1–15. http://www.jstor.org/stable/26304870.

Robinson, Michael E. *Korea's Twentieth-Century Odyssey: A Short History.* Honolulu: University of Hawaii Press, 2007.

"Thank You Father Kim Il Sung": *Eyewitness Accounts of Severe Violations of Freedom of Thought, Conscience, and Religion in North Korea*. Washington, DC: US Commission on International Religious Freedom, 2005.

CHAPTER TWENTY-SIX

Cheong, Connie Ockhee. *My Battle for Seoul, Summer, 1950*. Seoul, Korea, Seoul, Korea: Geulnurim, 2011.

Cumings, Bruce. *Korea's Place in the Sun: a Modern History*. New York: W.W. Norton, 2005.

Drain, Paul K., Kristina L. Bajema, David Dowdy, Keertan Dheda, Kogieleum Naidoo, Samuel G. Schumacher, Shuyi Ma, Erin Meermeier, David M. Lewinsohn, and David R. Sherman. "Incipient and Subclinical Tuberculosis: a Clinical Review of Early Stages and Progression of Infection." *Clinical Microbiology Reviews* 31, no. 4 (July 18, 2018). https://doi.org/10.1128/cmr.00021-18.

Jager, Sheila Miyoshi. *Brothers at War: The Unending Conflict in Korea*. New York: W. W. Norton & Company, 2013.

Mobley, Richard A. "North Korea: How Did It Prepare for the 1950 Attack?" *Army History*, no. 49 (2000): 1–15. http://www.jstor.org/stable/26304870.

"The Ambassador in Korea (Muccio) to the Secretary of State (Seoul, June 25, 1950)." *Foreign Relations of the United States, 1950, Korea*, Volume VII (United States Government Printing Office, Washington, 1976), Document 68, 795.00/6–2550: Telegram. From Office of Historian, Department of State, https://history.state.gov/historical-documents/frus1950v07/d68.

Yup, Paik Sun. *From Pusan to Panmunjom: Wartime Memoirs of the Republic of Korea's First Four-Star General*. Dulles: Potomac Books Inc, 1999.

CHAPTER TWENTY-SEVEN

Cumings, Bruce. *Korea's Place in the Sun: A Modern History*. New York: W.W. Norton, 2005.

Hastings, Max. *The Korean War*. New York, New York: Simon & Schuster Paperbacks, 1987.

Sides, Hampton. *On Desperate Ground: The Marines at the Reservoir, the Korean War's Greatest Battle*. New York, New York: Doubleday, 2018.

"The Korean War Chronology." The Korean War Chronology. US Army Center of Military History. Accessed October 2, 2021. https://history.army.mil/reference/Korea/kw-chrono.htm.

Yup, Paik Sun. *From Pusan to Panmunjom: Wartime Memoirs of the Republic of Korea's First Four-Star General*. Dulles: Potomac Books Inc, 1999.

CHAPTER TWENTY-EIGHT

Digital Horizons database: Korean War Propaganda Leaflets (NDSU).

http://www.digitalhorizonsonline.org/digital/collection/ndsu-korea/search/page/2.

Sides, Hampton. *On Desperate Ground: The Marines at the Reservoir, the Korean War's Greatest Battle*. New York, New York: Doubleday, 2018.

Yup, Paik Sun. *From Pusan to Panmunjom: Wartime Memoirs of the Republic of Korea's First Four-Star General*. Dulles: Potomac Books Inc, 1999.

CHAPTER TWENTY-NINE

Hastings, Max. *The Korean War*. New York, New York: Simon & Schuster Paperbacks, 1987.

Jager, Sheila Miyoshi. *Brothers at War: the Unending Conflict in Korea*. New York: W. W. Norton & Company, 2013.

Kim, Janice C.H. "Pusan at War: Refuge, Relief, and Resettlement in the Temporary Capital, 1950–1953." *The Journal of American-East Asian Relations* 24, no. 2/3 (2017): 103–27. https://www.jstor.org/stable/26549202.

Mossman, Billy C. *Ebb and Flow: November 1950-July 1951*. Washington, DC: Center of Military History, US Army, 1990.

Sides, Hampton. *On Desperate Ground: The Marines at the Reservoir, the Korean War's Greatest Battle*. New York, New York: Doubleday, 2018.

"The Korean War Chronology." The Korean War Chronology. US Army Center of Military History. Accessed October 2, 2021. https://history.army.mil/reference/Korea/kw-chrono.htm.

Toland, John. *In Mortal Combat, Korea, 1950-1953*. Norwalk, Connecticut: Easton Press, 2002.

United Press. "U.N. Troops Slaughtered at Unsan By Chinese Reds in Surprise Attack; Americans and South Koreans Massacred in Indian-Style Assault—Civilians Are Killed as They Try to Escape." *The New York Times*, November 3, 1950, Page 4, https://www.nytimes.com/1950/11/03/archives/un-troops-slaughtered-at-unsan-by-chinese-reds-in-surprise-attack.html.

Yup, Paik Sun. *From Pusan to Panmunjom: Wartime Memoirs of the Republic of Korea's First Four-Star General*. Dulles: Potomac Books Inc, 1999.

CHAPTER THIRTY

Choe, Sang-Hun, Charles J. Hanley, and Martha Mendoza. "War's Hidden Chapter: Ex-GIs Tell of Killing Korean Refugees." The Pulitzer Prizes. Associated Press, September 29, 1999. https://www.pulitzer.org/winners/sang-hun-choe-charles-j-hanley-and-martha-mendoza.

Cumings, Bruce. *Korea's Place in the Sun: a Modern History*. New York: W.W. Norton, 2005.

Cumings, Bruce. *Origins of the Korean War, Vol. 1: Liberation and the Emergence of Separate Regimes, 1945-1947*. Princeton, New Jersey: Princeton University Press, 1981.

Halberstam, David. *The Coldest Winter: America and the Korean War*. New York, New York: Hachette Books, 2015.

Koh, B. C. "The War's Impact on the Korean Peninsula." *The Journal of American-East Asian Relations* 2, no. 1 (1993): 57–76. http://www.jstor.org/stable/23612666.

Kuzmarov, Jeremy. "The Korean War: Barbarism Unleashed." United States Foreign Policy History and Resource Guide website, 2016. http://peacehistory-usfp.org/korean-war/.

Lee, Jung Ha. "Armistice and Aid." Encyclopædia Britannica. Encyclopædia Britannica, inc. https://www.britannica.com/place/Korea/Armistice-and-aid.

Yup, Paik Sun. *From Pusan to Panmunjom: Wartime Memoirs of the Republic of Korea's First Four-Star General*. Dulles: Potomac Books Inc, 1999.

CHAPTER THIRTY-TWO

Halberstam, David. *The Coldest Winter: America and the Korean War*. New York, New York: Hachette Books, 2015.

Mossman, Billy C. *Ebb and Flow: November 1950-July 1951*. Washington, DC: Center of Military History, US Army, 1990.

Yup, Paik Sun. *From Pusan to Panmunjom: Wartime Memoirs of the Republic of Korea's First Four-Star General*. Dulles: Potomac Books Inc, 1999.

CHAPTER THIRTY-THREE

Allen, Richard C. *Korea's Syngman Rhee, an Unauthorized Portrait*. Rutland, Vermont: Charles E. Tuttle Company, 1960.

Cassel, Christopher and Scott Miller. *Korean War in Color*, 2001.

Choe, Sang-Hun. "Memories of Massacres Were Long Suppressed Here. Tourists Now Retrace the Atrocities." The New York Times. The New York Times, May 28, 2019. https://www.nytimes.com/2019/05/28/world/asia/south-korea-jeju-massacres.html.

Jager, Sheila Miyoshi. *Brothers at War: the Unending Conflict in Korea*. New York: W. W. Norton & Company, 2013.

Kim, Janice C.H. "'Pusan at War: Refuge, Relief, and Resettlement in the Temporary Capital, 1950–1953.'" *The Journal of American-East Asian Relations*24, no. 2/3 (2017): 103–27. https://www.jstor.org/stable/26549202.

Lankov, Andrei. "January 1951: Life of Korean War Refugees in Busan." The Korea Times. https://www.koreatimes.co.kr/www/news/special/2010/02/113_60003.html.

Merrill, John. "The Cheju-Do Rebellion." *The Journal of Korean Studies*2 (1980): 139–97. http://www.jstor.org/stable/41490155.

Mossman, Billy C. *Ebb and Flow: November 1950-July 1951*. Washington, DC: Center of Military History, US Army, 1990.

"Syngman Rhee." Encyclopædia Britannica. Encyclopædia Britannica, inc. https://www.britannica.com/biography/Syngman-Rhee.

Yea, Sallie. "Maps of Resistance and Geographies of Dissent in the Chŏlla Region of South Korea." *Korean Studies*24 (2000): 69–93. http://www.jstor.org/stable/23719705.

Yup, Paik Sun. *From Pusan to Panmunjom: Wartime Memoirs of the Republic of Korea's First Four-Star General*. Dulles: Potomac Books Inc, 1999.

CHAPTER THIRTY-FOUR

Kim, Janice C.H. "'Pusan at War: Refuge, Relief, and Resettlement in the Temporary Capital, 1950–1953.'" *The Journal of American-East Asian Relations*24, no. 2/3 (2017): 103–27. https://www.jstor.org/stable/26549202.

Lankov, Andrei. "January 1951: Life of Korean War Refugees in Busan." The Korea Times. https://www.koreatimes.co.kr/www/news/special/2010/02/113_60003.html.

Lee, Jongsoo. *The Partition of Korea After World War II: A Global History*. New York, New York: Palgrave Macmillan, 2006.

Stueck, William. "The United States, the Soviet Union, and the Division of Korea: A Comparative Approach." *The Journal of American-East Asian Relations*4, no. 1 (1995): 1–27. http://www.jstor.org/stable/23612581.

CHAPTER THIRTY-FIVE

"Republic of Korea Naval Academy History." Republic of Korea Naval Academy. https://www.navy.ac.kr:10001/intro/intro_gaegwan.jsp.

CHAPTER THIRTY-SIX

"Directory and Station List of the United States Army—Korea." Korean War Educator. http://www.koreanwar-educator.org/topics/directory_and_station_list.htm.

Ginn, Richard V. N. *The History of the US Army Medical Service Corps*. Washington, DC: United States Government Printing, 1996.

Hawk, Alan J. "8228th Mobile Army Surgical Hospital, Epidemic Hemorrhagic Fever Center." Academia. Military Healthcare System Research Symposium, 2019. https://www.academia. edu/40299589/8228th_Mobile_Army_Surgical_Hospital_Epidemic_Hemorrhagic_Fever_Center.

LeDuc, James W., James E. Childs, Greg E. Glass, and A.J. Watson. "Hemorrhagic Fever with Renal Syndrome: Past Accomplishments and Future Challenges." In *Epidemiology in Military and Veteran Populations*, 35–48. National Academies Press, 2017.

"Seoul National University Hospital: History." Seoul National University Hospital. http://www.snuh.org/global/en/about/ EN05002.do.

Yup, Paik Sun. *From Pusan to Panmunjom: Wartime Memoirs of the Republic of Korea's First Four-Star General.* Dulles: Potomac Books Inc, 1999.

CHAPTER THIRTY-SEVEN

Jager, Sheila Miyoshi. *Brothers at War: the Unending Conflict in Korea.* New York: W. W. Norton & Company, 2013.

Koh, B. C. "The War's Impact on the Korean Peninsula." *The Journal of American-East Asian Relations* 2, no. 1 (1993): 57–76. http://www.jstor.org/stable/23612666.

Korean Currency. Seoul, Korea: Bank of Korea, 2010.

"Seoul National University Hospital: History." Seoul National University Hospital. http://www.snuh.org/global/en/about/ EN05002.do.

Toland, John. *In Mortal Combat, Korea, 1950-1953.* Norwalk, Connecticut: Easton Press, 2002.

EPILOGUE

Moon, William J. "The Origins of the Great North Korean Famine: Its Dynamics and Normative Implications." *North Korean Review* 5, no. 1 (2009): 105-22. http://www.jstor.org/stable/43910265.